THE NORTON SCORES

An Anthology for Listening

Expanded Edition

Volume 1

THE NORTON SCORES

An Anthology for Listening

EXPANDED EDITION IN TWO VOLUMES

VOLUME I:
MACHAUT TO BEETHOVEN

EDITED BY

ROGER KAMIEN

ASSISTANT PROFESSOR OF MUSIC, QUEENS COLLEGE
OF THE CITY UNIVERSITY OF NEW YORK

W · W · NORTON & COMPANY · INC ·
New York

Acknowledgments

The scores for items 1, 2, 3, 4, 6, 7, 8, 12, and 28 are reprinted from *Masterpieces of Music Before 1750,* edited by Carl Parrish and John F. Ohl, New York: W. W. Norton & Company, 1951.

The scores for items 10 and 11 are reprinted from *A Treasury of Early Music,* edited by Carl Parrish, New York: W. W. Norton & Company, 1958.

The scores for items 18, 20 (Overture), 23, 25, 26, 30, 31, 32, 33, 35, 37, and 38 are reprinted, with the kind permission of Ernst Eulenburg Ltd., from the complete scores published in the Eulenburg miniature score series.

The scores for items 20 (vocal excerpts), 27, 29, and 34 are reprinted by kind permission of G. Schirmer, Inc.

FIRST EDITION

Library of Congress Catalog Card No. 78–95537

SBN 393 02143 2 (cloth edition)

SBN 393 09909 1 (paper edition)

PRINTED IN THE UNITED STATES OF AMERICA

1 2 3 4 5 6 7 8 9 0

Contents

Preface

This anthology is designed for use in introductory music courses, where the ability to read music is not a prerequisite. The unique system of highlighting employed in this book enables students to follow full orchestral scores after about one hour of instruction. This system also has the advantage of permitting students who *can* read music to perceive every aspect of the score. It is felt that our system of highlighting will be of greater pedagogical value than artificially condensed scores, which restrict the student's vision to pre-selected elements of the music. The use of scores in introductory courses makes the student's listening experience more intense and meaningful, and permits the instructor to discuss music in greater depth.

The works included in this Expanded Edition have been chosen from among those most frequently studied in introductory courses. The selections range from the fourteenth century up to the middle of the twentieth, and represent a wide variety of forms, genres, and performing media. More than half of the pieces are given in their entirety, while the others are represented by complete movements or sections that are particularly suitable for classroom study. Scenes from operas and some choral works are presented in vocal score, while all others are reprinted in their full original form. This anthology may be used independently, or along with any introductory text.

A few words about the highlighting system employed in the full scores: Each system of score is covered with a light gray screen, and the most prominent line in the music at any given point is spotlighted by a white band (see No. 1 in sample on page x). In cases where two or more simultaneous lines are equally prominent, they are each highlighted. When a musical line continues from one system or page to the next, the white highlighting band ends with a wedge shape at the right-hand margin, and its continuation begins with a reverse wedge shape (see No. 2 in sample). By following these white bands in sequence through the score, the listener will perceive the notes corresponding to the most audible lines. Naturally, the highlighting will not *always* correspond with the most prominent instruments in a specific recording, for performances differ in their emphasis of particular lines. In such cases, we have highlighted those parts that, in our opinion, *should* emerge most clearly. To facilitate the following of highlighted scores, a narrow white band running the full width of the page has been placed between systems when there is more than one on a page.

It must be emphasized that we do not seek here to *analyze* melodic structure, contrapuntal texture, or any other aspect of the music. The highlighting may break off before the end of a phrase when the entrance of another part is more audible, and during long-held notes the attention will usually be drawn to more rhythmically active parts. The highlighting technique has been used primarily for instrumental music; in vocal works, the text printed under the music provides a firm guideline for the novice score-reader.

A few suggestions for the use of this anthology may be found useful:

1. The rudiments of musical notation should be introduced with a view to preparing the student to associate audible melodic contours with their written equivalents. It is more important for the beginning student to recognize rising and falling lines, and long and short notes, than to identify specific pitches or rhythms. It is helpful to explain the function of a tie, and the layout of a full score.

2. Before listening to a work, it is best for the student to familiarize himself with the names and abbreviations for instruments used in that particular score (a glossary of instrumental names and abbreviations will be found at the conclusion of the book). We have retained the Italian, German, French, and English names used in the scores reproduced in this anthology. This exposure to a wide range of terminology will prepare the student for later encounters with scores.

3. The student should be careful to notice whether there is more than one system on a page of score. He should be alerted for tempo changes, repeat signs, and *da capo* indications. Since performances often differ, it is helpful for the instructor to forewarn the class about the specific repeats made or not made in the recordings used for listening.

4. When a piece is very fast or difficult, it is helpful to listen once without a score.

5. It is best to begin with music that is relatively simple to follow: e.g. (in approximate order of difficulty) Dowland, *My Thoughts Are Wing'd With Hope;* the respective second movements of Vivaldi's Concerto Grosso in D minor, Opus 3, No. 11, and Haydn's String Quartet in C major, Opus 76, No. 3; the first and third movements of Mozart's *Eine*

kleine Nachtmusik; the Air from Bach's Suite No. 3 in D major; and the second movement of Haydn's Symphony No. 94 in G major ("Surprise").

6. Important thematic material and passages that are difficult to follow should be pointed out in advance and played either on the recording or at the piano. (We have found that rapid sections featuring two simultaneously highlighted instruments sometimes present difficulties for the students—e.g. Beethoven, Symphony No. 5, first movement, m. 65 ff., and Mozart, Symphony No. 40, first movement, m. 72 ff.)

We have attempted to keep the highlighted bands simple in shape while showing as much of the essential slurs and dynamic indication as possible. Occasionally, because of the layout of the original score, stray stems and slurs will intrude upon the white area and instrumental directions will be excluded from the highlighting. (Naturally, the beginning of a highlighted area will not always carry a dynamic or similar indication, as the indication may have occurred measures earlier when the instrument in question was not the most prominent.) As the student becomes more experienced in following the scores, he can be encouraged to direct his attention outside the highlighted areas, and with practice should eventually develop the skill to read conventional scores.

I should like to record here my great debt to the late Nathan Broder, who originated the system of highlighting employed here and whose advice and counsel were invaluable. My thanks go also to Mr. David Hamilton, for many helpful suggestions. I am most grateful to my wife, Anita, who worked with me on every aspect of the book. She is truly the co-editor of this anthology.

R.K.

60
Fl.
Ob.
Cl.
Fg.
Cor. (Es)
zu 2
ff
sf
sf
sf
p
Tr. (C)
Timp.
Vl.
p dolce
p
Vla.
p
Vc. Cb.
70
Fl.
1.
Cl.
1.
p
Fg.
p
Cor. (Es)
Vl.
p
Vla.
Vc. Cb.
p

How to Follow the Highlighted Scores

1. The most prominent line in the music at any given time is highlighted by a white band.

2. When a musical line continues from one system (group of staffs) or page to the next, the white highlighted band ends with a wedge shape, and its continuation begins with a reverse wedge shape.

3. By following the highlighted bands in sequence through the score, the listener will perceive the notes corresponding to the most audible lines.

4. A narrow white band running the full width of the page separates one system from another when there is more than one on a page. It is very important to be alert for these separating bands.

5. When two or more lines are equally prominent, they are each highlighted. When encountering such passages for the first time, it is sometimes best to focus on only one of the lines.

THE NORTON SCORES

An Anthology for Listening

Expanded Edition

Volume 1

1. GUILLAUME DE MACHAUT (1304?-1377), Agnus Dei I from the Mass

Translation

O Lamb of God, that takest away the sins of the world, have mercy upon us.

2. GUILLAUME DUFAY, (c. 1400-1474), Kyrie I from the Mass *Se la face ay pale*

son,
e—lei—son,
—son,

Ky— ri— e—
Ky - ri—

e - lei—son,
Ky - ri - e,— e - lei—
e— e - lei—

e—
son,
Ky—
son.

Translation

Lord, have mercy upon us.

The tune "Se la face ay pale" (Tenor of Dufay's chanson on the tune)

[Note values halved]

Se la face ay pa——le, la cause est a-
If my face is pal——lid, know the cause is

mer, C'est la prin - ci - pa——le,
love, It a - lone doth cause—— it,

et tant m'est a - mer a - mer—— qu'en la mer me
and so sharp to me is love—— that I fain in

vol - dray - e vo——ir, or scet bien de voir
deep sea would drown—— me, for o, she knows well

la belle a qui suis——— que nul bien a - voir
she whose slave I am——— that with - out her love

sans el - le ne——— puis.
no good can I——— have.

3. GILLES BINCHOIS, (c. 1400-1460), *Adieu m'amour et ma maistresse*

15
A - dieu mon con - fort
Fare - well my so - lace
Pen - sant a vo bel -
Doth think up - on your
et li - es se.
and my heart's joy.
le jou - nes se.
love - ly beau ty.

4. JOSQUIN DES PRÉS (c. 1450-1521), *Ave Maria*

be ne - di cta tu,
be - ne - di cta tu in
cta tu,
cta tu, in mu - li - e - ri-
in mu - li - e - ri - bus in mu
mu - li - e - ri - bus, in mu li-
in mu - li-
bus,
li - e - ri - bus, et be - ne - di -
e - ri - bus, et be - ne - di - ctus fru-
e - ri - bus, et be - ne-
et be - ne - di - ctus fru - ctus ven - tris tu-
ctus fru - ctus ven - tris tu - i, Je - sus Chri
ctus ven - tris tu - i Je - sus Chri - stus Fi-
di - ctus fru - ctus ven - tris tu - i, Je - sus
i, Je - sus Chri - stus, Fi li -
stus Fi - li - us De - i vi
li - us De - i Fi li - us De
Chri - stus Fi- li - us De - i
us De - i vi - vi, De

[Note values quartered]
vi. Et be - ne - di - cta sint
i vi - vi. Et be-
vi vi. Et be - ne - di - cta sint
i vi - vi. Et be-
be - a - ta u - be - ra tu - a quae lac - ta-
ne - dic - ta sint be - a - ta u - be - ra tu - a
be - a - ta u - be - ra tu - a
ne - di - cta sint be - a - ta u - be - ra tu-
ve runt re - gem re
quae lac - ta - ve - runt re gem re
quae lac - ta - ve runt re - gem re-
a, quae lac - ta - ve - runt re gem re-
gum, et Do mi - num
gum, et Do mi - num De - um no
gum, et Do
gum, et Do mi - num De - um no
De - um no strum.
strum, no strum.
mi - num De - um no strum.
strum, no strum.

[Original a perfect fourth lower]
A - ve Ma - ri___a, gra - ti - a ple__na, Do - mi - nus te - cum,
be - ne - di - cta tu in__ mu - li___e - ri___bus,
[etc.]

Translation

Ave Maria, gratia plena,	Hail, Mary, full of grace
Dominus tecum;	the Lord is with thee;
benedicta tu in mulieribus,	blessed art thou among women,
et benedictus fructus ventris tui,	and blessed the fruit of thy womb,
Jesus Christus Filius Dei vivi.	Jesus Christ, Son of the living God.
Et benedicta sint beata ubera tua	And blessed be thy breasts,
quae lactaverunt regem regum,	that have suckled the King of Kings
et Dominum Deum nostrum.	and the Lord our God.

5. GIOVANNI PIERLUIGI DA PALESTRINA (c. 1525-1594), Kyrie from the *Pope Marcellus Mass* (PUBL. 1567)

- *lei* - - - - - *son.*

- son, Ky - rie e - lei - - - - - - son.

- *son,* e - lei - son, Ky - rie e - lei - - - - son.

- - - - - - *son,* Ky - ri - e e - lei - - son.

Ky - rie e - lei - son, *Ky - rie* *e - lei - - son.*

- *son,* Ky - rie e - lei - son, e - lei - - - son.

Chri - ste e - lei - son, *Chri - - ste e - - lei* -

Chri - ste e - lei - - - son, *Chri - ste e - lei - son,*

Chri - ste e - - - lei - - - son, *Chri-*

Chri - ste e - - - lei - -

Chri - ste e - - lei - son, *Chri - ste e* - -

Chri - ste e - lei - - - son, *Chri - ste e - lei - - son,*

- *son,* *Chri - ste e - lei - son,* *Chri - ste e - - lei-*

Chri - ste e - lei - son, Chri - ste e - lei - son, *Chri* -

- *ste e - lei - son,* *Chri - ste - lei* - - - *son, e* -

- son, *Chri - ste e - lei - son,* *Chri - ste e - lei - - son,* *Chri - ste e* -

- *lei - son,* *Chri - ste e - lei - - son,*

Chri - ste e - lei - - son, *Chri - ste e* -

-son, e-le - - son, Chri - ste e-lei - son, Chri - -
-ste e - lei - - son, Chri - ste e - lei - son, e - lei - son,
-lei - son, Chri-ste e-lei-son, Chri - ste e -
-lei - - son, Chri-ste e-lei - son, Chri-ste e - lei - son, Chri-
Chri - - ste e-lei - - son, Chri - ste e -
-lei - - - - son, Chri - ste e - lei - - son,
-ste - e - lei - - - son. Ky - rie e - lei - - son,
Chri-ste e - lei - - son. Ky - rie e - lei - - -
-lei - - - - - son. Ky - - rie e - lei - -
-ste e - lei - - son, Ky -
-lei - son, e - - lei - - son. Ky - - rie e - lei -
Chri - ste e-lei - - - - son.
-rie e - lei - - - - - - son, Ky - rie e -
-son, Ky - - rie e - lei - - - son, Ky - rie
-son, Ky - rie e-lei-son, Ky - - rie e - lei - - son,
- rie e - lei - - - - son, Ky - rie e-lei - -
-son, Ky - rie e-lei - son, Ky - - rie e - lei - -
Ky - rie e - lei - - - - son, e - lei - - son, Ky -

Translation

Lord, have mercy upon us.
Christ, have mercy upon us.
Lord, have mercy upon us.

6. ORLANDUS LASSUS (1532-1594), *Tristis est anima mea*

[Note values halved]

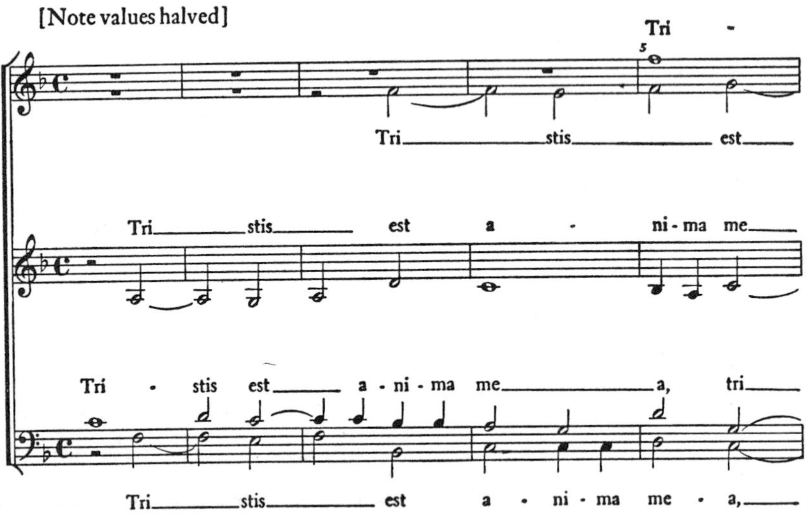

tri - stis est a___ni - ma me - a___ us - que ad
est a___ni - ma me___a us -
ma me___a us - que ad mor - tem, us - que___
me - a us - que ad mor - tem, us - que
est a - ni - ma me - a us___que ad
mor - tem: su___
que ad mor - tem: su___sti - ne - te hic,
___ad mor - tem: su___sti - ne - te hic,
ad mor - tem: su - sti - ne te___hic, et
mor - tem: su___sti - ne - te hic,
___sti - ne - te hic, et vi - gi -
su - sti - ne - te hic et
su - sti - ne___te hic, et vi - gi -
vi___gi - la - te me - cum,
et vi - gi - la___

la - te me - cum, et vi - gi - la_____ te
vi - gi - la_____ te me - cum, et vi - gi-
la - te me_____ cum, et vi_____ gi-
et vi - gi - la_____ te me_____ cum,_____
_____ te me_____ cum, et vi_____

me_____
la - te me_____ cum, et vi - gi - la - te
la - te me - cum, et vi - gi - la - te me_____
_____ et vi - gi - la - te me_____
_____ gi - la_____ te me -

_____ cum:_____ nunc vi - de - bi - tis, nunc_____
me - cum: nunc vi - de - bi - tis, nunc vi - de - bi - tis, nunc_____
_____ cum: nunc vi - de - bi - tis, nunc vi - de - bi - tis, nunc_____
_____ cum: nunc vi - de - bi - tis, nunc vi - de - bi - tis,
cum: nunc vi - de - bi - tis nunc_____

vi - de - bi - tis tur bam,
35
vi - de - bi - tis tur bam, quae cir - cum -
vi - de - bi - tis tur - bam,
nunc vi - de - bi - tis tur - bam, quae
vi - de - bi - tis tur - bam, quae cir - cum -
quae cir - cum - da - bit me, quae cir - cum - da - bit
da bit me, quae
quae cir - cum - da - bit me, quae cir - cum -
cir - cum - da - bit me, quae cir - cum - da - bit me,
da - bit me, quae cir - cum - da - bit me, quae cir - cum -
me;
vos
40
cir - cum - da - bit me:
da - bit me, quae cir cum - da bit
quae cir - cum - da - bit me, quae cir - cum - da - bit
da - bit me, quae cir - cum da - bit me:

fu - gam ca - pi - e- tis vos fu - gam
vos fu - gam ca - pi - e -
me: vos fu - gam ca - pi - e -
me: vos fu - gam ca - pi-
vos fu - gam ca - pi - e - tis,

45
ca - pi - e - tis, vos fu - gam ca - pi-
tis, vos fu - gam
tis, vos fu - gam ca - pi - e
e - tis, vos fu - gam ca - pi - e
vos fu - gam ca - pi - e tis,

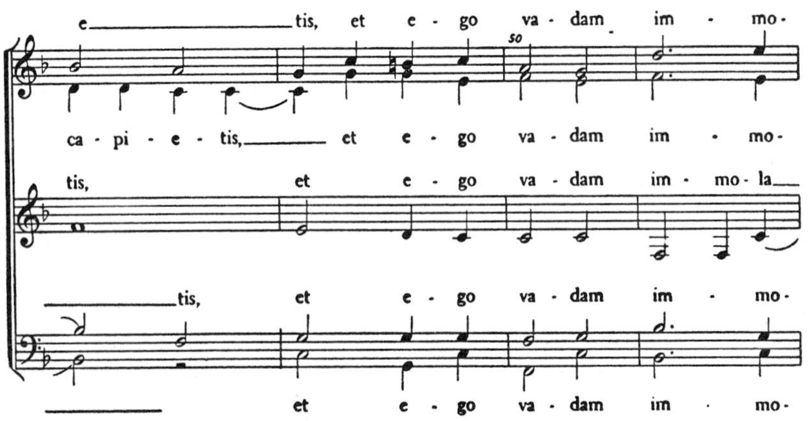
e tis, et e - go va - dam im - mo-
50
ca - pi - e - tis, et e - go va - dam im - mo-
tis, et e - go va - dam im - mo - la
tis, et e - go va - dam im - mo-
et e - go va - dam im - mo-

la - ri, et e - go va - dam im mo - la
la - ri, et e - go va - dam im mo - la-
ri, et e - go va - dam, im - mo la
la - ri, et e - go va - dam im mo - la-
la - ri,
55
ri, et e - go va - dam im mo - la -
ri, et e go va - dam im mo - la -
ri, et e - go va - dam im - mo - la
ri et e - go va - dam im mo - la -
et e - go va - dam im mo - la -
60
ri pro vo - bis.
ri pro vo - bis.
ri pro vo - bis.
ri pro vo - bis.
ri pro vo - bis.

Translation

Tristis est anima mea usque ad mortem:
sustinete hic, et vigilate mecum:
nunc videbitis turbam,
   quae circumdabit me:
vos fugam capietis,
et ego vadam immolari pro vobis.

My soul is very sorrowful, even unto death;
remain here, and watch with me:
Now ye will see the multitude
   that will surround me:
Ye will take flight,
and I shall go to be sacrificed for you.

RESPOND FOR MAUNDY THURSDAY

7. WILLIAM BYRD (1543-1623), *Ego sum panis vivus* (PUBL. 1607)

Note: The value of the quarter note remains constant in bars of varying lengths.

qui de coe - lo de - scen di.
de - scen di, de - scen di.
lo de - scen - di, de coe lo de - scen
scen di, de - scen di. Si
15
Si quis man - du - ca - ve -
Si quis man - du - ca - ve - rit,
di. Man - du - ca ve - rit, si
quis man - du - ca - ve - rit, si
rit, si quis man-du - ca - ve - rit ex hoc pa
20
si quis man-du - ca - ve - rit ex hoc pa
quis man - du - ca - ve - rit ex hoc pa
quis man-du-ca - ve - rit ex hoc pa
ne, vi vet in ae - ter -
ne, vi vet in ae - ter
ne, vi - vet in ae - ter -
ne,

num, vi—vet in ae - ter - num.
num, vi—vet in ae - ter—
num, vi - vet in— ae - ter -
vi - vet in ae - ter -

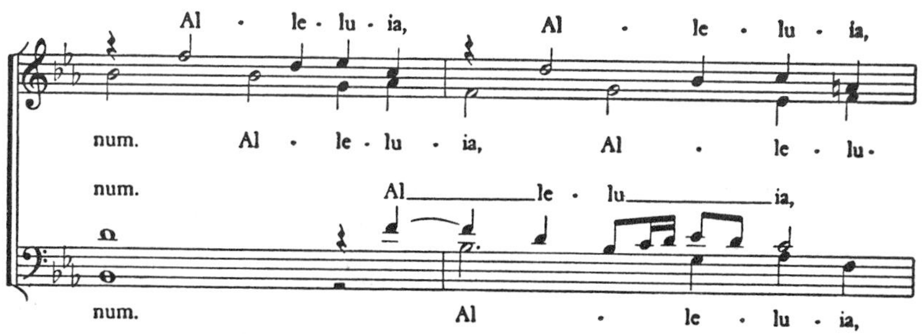
Al - le - lu - ia, Al - le - lu - ia,
num. Al - le - lu - ia, Al - le - lu-
num. Al— le - lu— ia,
num. Al - le - lu - ia,

Al - le - lu - ia, Al - le - lu— ia,
ia, Al - le - lu - ia, Al - le - lu—
Al - le - lu— ia, Al - le-
Al - le - lu - ia, Al - le - lu - ia,

Al - le - lu— ia, Al - le - lu— ia, Al - le - lu—
— ia. Al - le - lu— ia,
lu— ia, Al - le-
Al - le - lu— ia. Al - le - lu— ia.

Translation

Ego sum panis vivus,
qui de coelo descendi.
Si quis manducaverit ex hoc pane,
vivet in aeturnum.
Alleluia.

I am the living bread
which came down from heaven.
If any man eat of this bread,
he shall live forever.
Alleluia.

ST. JOHN 6 (KING JAMES VERSION), VERSE 51

8. LUCA MARENZIO (1553-1599), *S'io parto, i' moro* (PUBL. 1594)

Note: The value of the quarter note remains constant in bars of varying lengths.

dunque il mio be - ne, E que sta mia par-
die then, my dear - est, And this my sad de-
que il mio be - ne, E que - sta mia par-
then, my dear - est, and this my sad de-
que il mio be - ne, E que sta mia par-
then, my dear - est, and this my sad de-
E que - sta mia par-
And this my sad de-
E que - sta mia par-
And this my sad de-

ti - ta Che mi ti to - glie mi tor-
part - ing that takes me from thee, takes from
ti - ta Che mi ti to - glie mi tor-
part - ing that takes me from thee, takes from
ti - ta, mi tor - rà la
part - ing, takes from me my
ti - ta Che mi ti to - glie, mi tor-
part - ing That takes me from thee, takes from
ti - ta Che mi ti to - glie, mi tor - rà la
part - ing, That takes me from thee, takes from me my

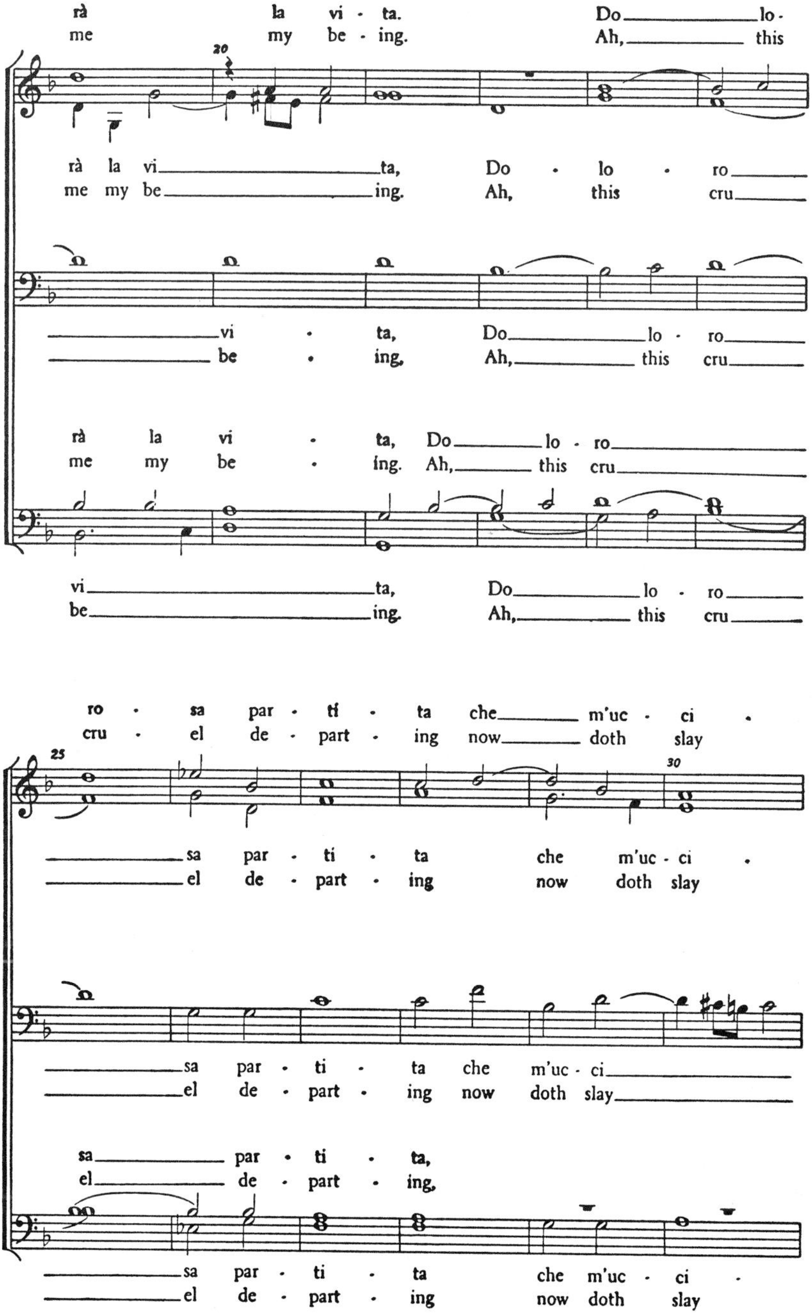

rà la vi - ta. Do lo -
me my be - ing. Ah, this

20

rà la vi ta, Do - lo - ro
me my be ing. Ah, this cru

vi - ta, Do lo - ro
be - ing, Ah, this cru

rà la vi - ta, Do lo - ro
me my be - ing. Ah, this cru

vi ta, Do lo - ro
be ing. Ah, this cru

ro - sa par - ti - ta che m'uc - ci -
cru - el de - part - ing now doth slay

25 30

sa par - ti - ta che m'uc - ci -
el de - part - ing now doth slay

sa par - ti - ta che m'uc - ci
el de - part - ing now doth slay

sa par - ti - ta,
el de - part - ing,

sa par - ti - ta che m'uc - ci -
el de - part - ing now doth slay

di, Quei che con giuns' A - mor
me, For those whom love hath joined,
di, Quei che con - giuns' A - mor per -
me, For those whom love hath joined, Ah
di, Per - che,
me, Ah how,
di,
me,

35
per - che di - vi - di?
Ah, how di - vide them?
che, per - che di vi di? Do
how, ah how di vide them? Ah,
per - che, Do lo -
ah how, Ah this
Per - che di - vi di? Do
Ah how di - vide them? Ah
Do
Ah

Do lo - ro - sa par - ti - ta che
Ah, this cru - el de - part - ing now
lo - ro sa par - ti ta che
this cru el de - part ing now
ro sa par - ti - ta,
cru el de - part - ing,
lo - ro sa par - ti - ta che m'uc-ci
this cru el de - part - ing now doth slay
lo - ro sa par - ti - ta che m'uc-
this cru el de - part - ing now doth

m'uc - ci - di,
doth slay me,
m'uc - ci - di,
doth slay me,
Quei che con giuns' A -
For those whom love hath
di, Quei che
me, For those
ci - di, Quei che con - giuns' A -
slay me, For those whom love hath

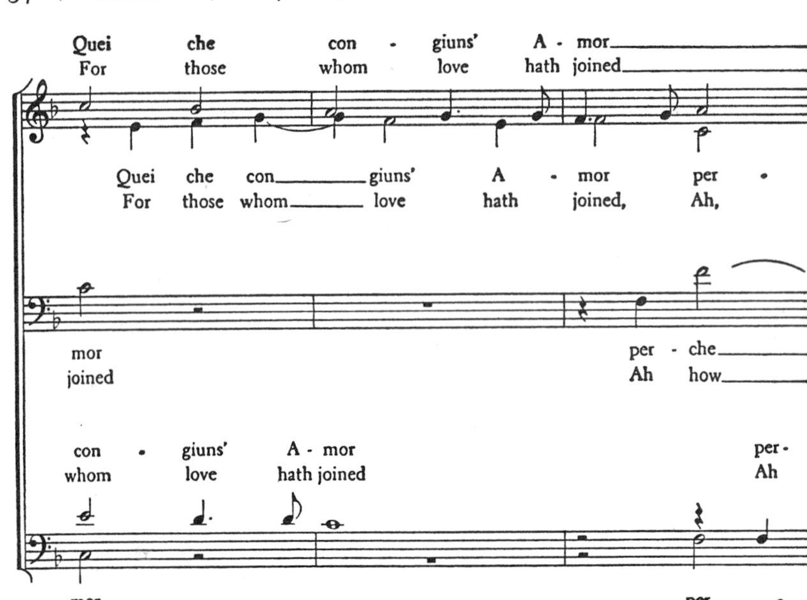
Quei che con - giuns' A - mor
For those whom love hath joined
Quei che con giuns' A - mor per -
For those whom love hath joined, Ah,
mor per - che
joined Ah how
con - giuns' A - mor per -
whom love hath joined Ah
mor per -
joined Ah

per - che,
ah how,
55
che di - vi di? per -
how di - vide them? ah
di - vi - di? per - che,
di - vide them? Ah how,
che di vi di? per -
how di vide them? ah
che di - vi - di?
how di - vide them?

per - che di - vi - di?
ah how, di - vide them?
60
che, per - che di vi di?
how, ah how di vide them?
per - che, per - che di - vi - di?
ah how, ah how di - vide them?
che, per - che, di - vi - di?
how, ah how, di - vide them?
per - che di - vi - di?
ah how di - vide them?

9. THOMAS MORLEY (1557-1602), *Sing We and Chant It* (PUBL. 1595)

hast - eth, Now is best lei - sure, To take our pleas - ure.
lack - ing, Let spare no treas - ure, To live in pleas - ure.
hast - eth, Now is best lei - sure, To take our pleas - ure.
lack - ing, Let spare no treas - ure, To live in pleas - ure.
Fa la
hast - eth, Now is best lei - sure, To take our pleas - ure.
lack - ing, Let spare no treas - ure, To live in pleas - ure.
Fa la la
hast - eth, Now is best lei - sure, To take our pleas - ure.
lack - ing, Let spare no treas - ure, To live in pleas - ure.
Fa la
hast - eth, Now is best lei - sure, To take our pleas - ure.
lack - ing, Let spare no treas - ure, To live in pleas - ure.
Fa la

1.
2.
Fa la la la la la. Fa la la la la. la.
la la la la la la. Fa la la la. Fa la la la. la.
la. Fa la la la la la la la. Fa la la la la. la.
la la la la. Fa la la la la la la. Fa la la la la. la.
la la la la la la. Fa la la la la la la la la la. la.

10. CARLO GESUALDO (c. 1560-1613), *Moro lasso* (PUBL. 1611)

ahi, che m'an - ci - de e non vuol
15
ahi, che m'an - ci - de e non vuol
ahi, che m'an - ci - - - de e non vuol
ta, ahi, che m'an - ci - de e non
ahi, che m'an - ci - de e non vuol
dar - mi vi - - ta, e non vuol dar- mi vi - - ta.
20
dar - mi vi - - ta, e non vuol dar-mi vi - - ta.
dar - mi vi - ta, e non vuol dar - mi vi - ta.
vuol dar - mi vi - ta, e non vuol dar - mi vi - ta.
dar - mi vi - ta, e non vuol dar - mi vi - ta.
Mo - - ro las - so al mio duo - lo,
25
Mo - - ro las - so al mio duo - - lo,
Mo - - ro las - so al mio duo - - lo, e chi mi
Mo - - ro las - so al mio duo - lo, e
e chi

e chi mi può dar vi - - - -
30
e chi mi può dar vi - - - - - - ta,
può dar vi - - - - ta, e chi mi
chi mi può dar vi - - - - ta, e
mi può dar vi - - ta, e chi
- ta, e chi mi può dar vi - - - - ta,
e chi mi può dar vi - - - - - ta,
può dar vi - - - - ta,
chi mi può dar vi - - - - - ta,
mi può dar vi - - - - - - - ta,
Ahi, che m'an- ci - de e non vuol
35
Ahi, che m'an-ci - de e non vuol
ahi, che m'an - ci - - - - de e non vuol
Ahi, che m'an - ci - de e non vuol
Ahi, che m'an - ci - - de e non vuol

dar mi ai - ta, e non vuol dar mi ai - ta.
dar mi ai - ta, e non vuol dar mi ai - ta.
dar mi ai - ta, e non vuol dar mi ai - ta.
dar mi ai - - - ta, e non vuol dar mi ai - - ta.
dar mi ai - ta, e non vuol dar mi ai - ta.
45
O
O dolorosa forte,
O dolorosa forte, O
O dolorosa forte, O dolo-
O dolorosa forte,
50
dolorosa forte, chi dar vi - ta mi
O dolorosa forte, chi dar vi - ta mi
dolorosa forte, chi dar vi - ta mi
ro - - sa for - - te, chi dar vi - ta mi
chi dar vi - ta mi

può, ahi, mi da mor - te,
può, ahi, mi da mor - te, ahi,
può, ahi, mi da mor - te,
può, ahi, mi da mor - - te, ahi,
può, ahi,
ahi, mi da mor - - te,
mi da mor - te, ahi, mi da mor -
ahi, mi da mor - te, ahi, mi da
mi da mor - - te, ahi, mi da
mi da mor - te,
ahi, ahi, mi da mor - te.
te, ahi, mi da mor - - - - te.
mor - te, ahi, mi da mor - - - - te.
mor - te, ahi, mi da mor - te.
ahi, mi da mor - - - - te.

Translation

Moro lasso al mio duolo, e chi mi può dar vita, ahi, che m'ancide e non vuol darmi vita.	I die, alas! from my pain, And who can give me life, Alas, kills me and will not give me life.
Moro lasso al mio duolo, e chi mi può dar vita, , ahi, che m'ancide e non vuol darmi aita.	I die, alas! from my pain, And who can give me life, Alas, kills me and will not give me succour.
O dolorosa forte, chi dar vita mi può, ahi, mi da morte.	Oh painful lot, Who can give me life, Alas, gives me death.

11. JOHN DOWLAND (1562-1626),
My Thoughts Are Wing'd With Hope (PUBL. 1597)

My thoughts are wing'd with hopes, my hopes with love,
mount love, un - to the moon in clear - est night,
And say as she doth in the hea - vens move,

in earth so wanes and wax - eth my de - light,

And whis - per this but soft - ly in her__ ears,

hope oft doth hang the head, and trust___ shed tears.

12. CLAUDIO MONTEVERDI (1567-1643), *Tu se' morta* from *L'Orfeo* (1ST PERF. 1607)

Note: The value of the quarter note remains constant in bars of varying lengths.

fon - di a - bis - si, e in te - ne - ri - to il cor del rè del-
found a : bys - ses, and with my song en - treat the king of
20
l'om - bre, me - co tra - rot - ti a ri - ver - der le
sha - dows, to let me bring thee to see a - gain the
25
stel - le, o se ciò ne - ghe - ram - mi em
hea - vens, or if this cru - el for - tune
pio de - sti - no, ri - mar - rò te - co in com - pa - gnia
still de - nies me, I shall stay with thee with - in the realm
30
di mor - te! ad - dio ter - ra, ad - dio
of sha - dows! fare - well earth, then, fare - well
35

cie - lo, e so - le, ad - di - o.
hea - vens, and sun - light, for - e - ver.

13. MONTEVERDI, *Zefiro torna* (PUBL. 1632)

na e di___ so - a - vi ac - cen - ti
na l'a - - - - -
e di___ so - a - vi ac - cen - ti
er l'a - er fa gra - to e di___ so - a - vi ac - cen - ti
l'a - - - er l'a - er fa gra - to___ e'l piè di - sciol -
l'a - - - - er l'a - er fa gra - -
- - - - glie di - scio - glie a l'on - - - - - -
to e'l piè di - scio - -
- - - - - - - - de di - scio - glie a l'on - -
- - - - glie di - scio - glie a l'on - - - - - -

- - - - - (♯) - - - - - - - - - - - -

- - - - - - - - - - - - - - -

de e mor - mo - ran - - - - - - -

de e mor - mo - ran - - -

- - - - - do tra le ver - di fron - -

- - - - - - do tra le ver - di fron -

de fa dan - zar al___ bel___

de al___ bel___ suon

suon al___ bel___ suon fa dan -

fa dan - zar al___ bel___ suon

zar al___ bel___ suon su'l pra - to i fio - ri in - ghir - lan - da - to il

al___ bel___ suon su'l pra - to i fio - ri

crin Fil - li - de e Clo - ri in - ghir - lan - da - to il crin Fil - li - de e Clo -

in - ghir - lan - da - to il crin Fil - li - de e Clo - ri

ri no - te

no - te no - te

no - te no - te tem - pran - do a

no - te no - te tem - pran - do a

mor ca - re ca - re ca - re e gio - con -

mor ca - re ca - re ca - re e gio - con -

de
e da mon - ti da mon -
de
ti
i - me
e da val - li da val - li
e pro - fon -
forte
forte
rad - dop - pian l'ar - mo - nia
rad - dop - - -
piano
de
rad - dop - pian l'ar - mo - nia
forte
- pian
rad - dop - - - - - -
piano
piano
rad - dop - - - pian
rad - dop - - -
forte
- - - - pian
rad - do - pian l'ar - mo -
- - - - - - - - pian

forte
nia gli an - - - - tri
piano
piano
rad - dop - pian l'ar - mo - nia gli an - - -
(piano)
gli an - tri ca - no - ri sor - ge più va - ga in
piano
tri gli an - tri ca - no - ri
Ciel l'au - ro - ra sor - ge più va - ga in Ciel l'au - ro -
sor - ge più va - ga in Ciel l'au - ro -
ra el So - le el So - le el So - le el So -
ra el So - le el So - le el So -
le spar - ge spar - - - - - - -
le spar - ge spar - - - - - - -

ge— più lu - ci d'or più pu - ro ar - gen -
ge— più lu - ci d'or
to fre - gia di Te - ti il bel ce - ru - leo man -
più pu - ro ar - gen to fre - gia di Te -
to fre - gia di Te - ti più pu - - ro ar - gen -
ti il bel ce - ru - leo man - to fre - gia di Te -
to fre - gia di Te - ti il bel ce - ru - leo man -
ti il bel ce - ru - leo man - to il
to il bel ce - ru - leo man -
bel ce - ru - leo man - to il bel ce - ru - leo man -

to Sol
to Sol i - o per sel - ve ab-ban-do-na - te e - so - le l'ar -
i - o per sel - ve ab-ban-do-na - te e so - le l'ar -
dor di due be - gli oc - chi el mio tor - men - to
dor di due be - gli oc - chi el mio tor - men - to sol
sol
i - o per sel - ve ab - ban - do - na - te e so - le l'ar dor
i - o per sel - ve ab - ban - do - na - te e so - le l'ar dor
de due be-gl'oc - chi el mio tor-men - to
de due be-gl'oc - chi el mio tor-men - to co - me vuol mia ven-tu-ra hor pian - -

co - me vuol mia ven-tu-ra hor pian - - - - - go

- - - - go co - me vuol mia ven-tu-ra hor pian - -

hor can - - - -

go hor can - - - - - to hor

- to hor can - - - - to

can - - - - to

Co-me vuol mia ven-tu-ra hor pian - - - - - go hor

Co-me vuol mia ven-tu-ra hor pian - - - - - - -

can - - - - to hor can - - - -

go hor can - - - - to

Translation

Zefiro torna e di soavi accenti
L'aer fa grato e'l piè discioglie a l'onde,
E mormorando tra le verdi fronde,
Fa danzar al bel suon su'l prato i fiori;

The West Wind returns and with gentle accents
Makes the air pleasant and quickens one's step,
And, murmuring among the green branches,
Makes the meadow flowers dance to its lovely sound.

Inghirlandato il crin Fillide e Clori,
Note temprando amor care e gioconde;
E da monti e da valli ime e profonde,
Raddoppian l'armonia gli antri canori.

With garlands in their hair Phyllis and Clorinda
Are sweet and joyous while Love makes music,
And from the mountains and valleys hidden deep,
The echoing caves redouble the harmony.

Sorge più vaga in ciel l'aurora el Sole,
Sparge più luci d'or più puro argento,
Fregia di Teti più il bel ceruleo manto.

At dawn the sun rises in the sky more gracefully,
Spreads abroad more golden rays, a purer silver,
Adorns the sea with an even lovelier blue mantle.

Sol io per selve abbandonate e sole,
L'ardor di due begli occhi el mio tormento,
Come vuol mia ventura hor piango, hor canto.

Only I am abandoned and alone in the forest,
The ardor of two beautiful eyes is my torment:
As my fate may decree, now I weep, now I sing.

14. ORLANDO GIBBONS (1583-1625), *The Silver Swan* (PUBL. 1612)

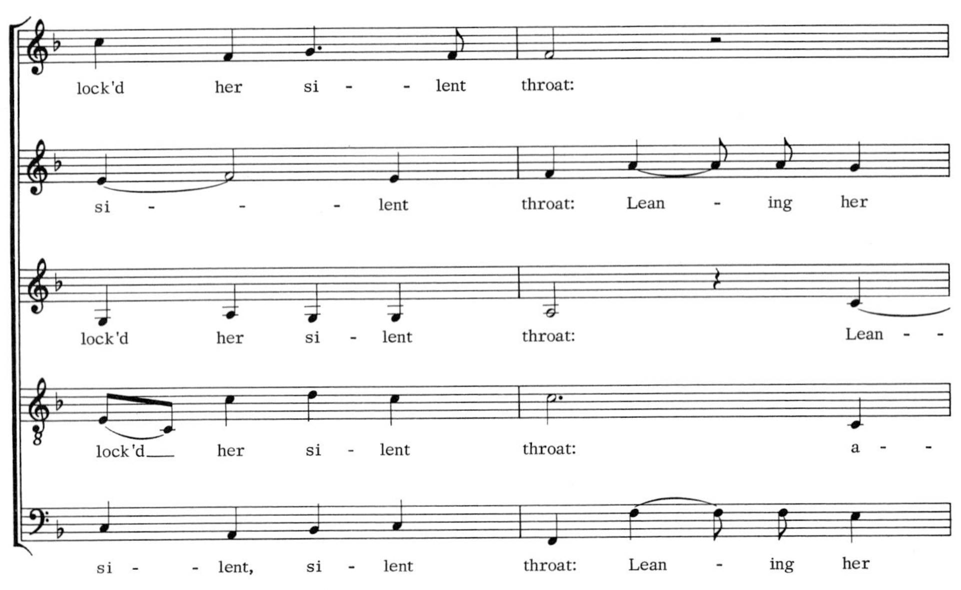
lock'd her si - - lent throat:
si - - - lent throat: Lean - ing her
lock'd her si - lent throat: Lean - -
lock'd___ her si - lent throat: a - -
si - - lent, si - lent throat: Lean - ing her

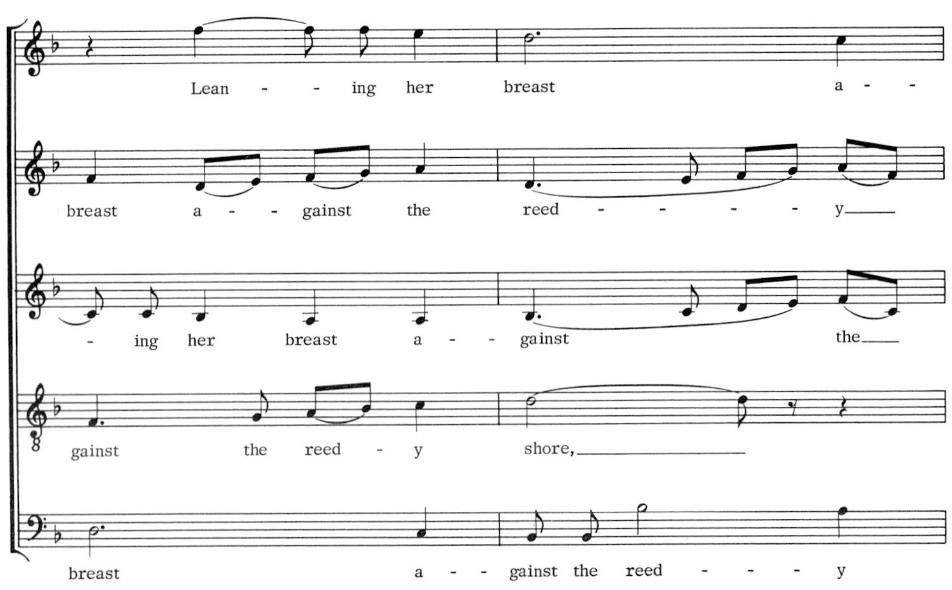
Lean - - ing her breast a - -
breast a - - gainst the reed - - - - y___
- ing her breast a - - gainst the___
gainst the reed - y shore,___
breast a - - gainst the reed - - - y

gainst the reed - y shore, Thus sang her first and
shore, Thus sang her first and last, and sang, and
reed - y shore, Thus sang her first and last, and
Thus sang her first and last, and sang no more, and sang
shore, Thus sang her first and last, and

last, and sang no more. Fare - well all
sang no more. Fare - well, all joys, O death, come
sang no more. Fare - well, all joys, O
no more. Fare - well, all joys, O
sang no more. Fare - well, all joys, O

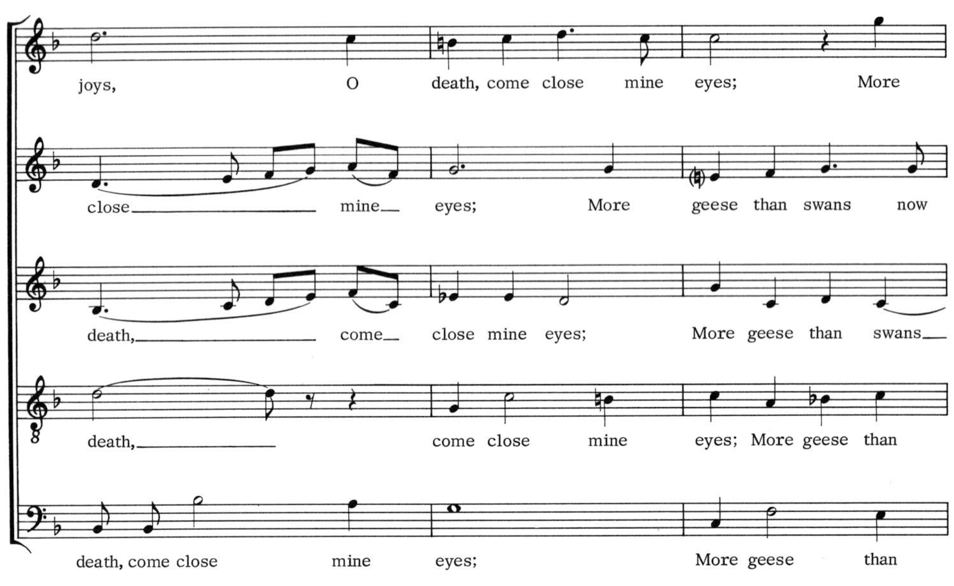
joys, O death, come close mine eyes; More
close mine eyes; More geese than swans now
death, come close mine eyes; More geese than swans
death, come close mine eyes; More geese than
death, come close mine eyes; More geese than

geese than swans now live, more fools than wise.
live, more fools, more fools than wise.
now live, more fools than wise.
swans now live, more fools than wise.
swans now live, more fools than wise.

15. HEINRICH SCHÜTZ (1585-1672), *Saul, Saul* (PUBL. 1650)

Sop. I
Saul, Saul, Saul, Saul, was ver-folgst du mich?
Sop. II
Saul, Saul, Saul, Saul, was ver - folgst du mich?
Solo Voices
Ten. I
Saul, was ver-folgst du mich?
Ten. II
Saul, was ver - folgst du mich?
Bass I
Bass II
Chorus I
Sop.
Alto
Ten.
Bass
Chorus II
Sop.
Alto
Ten.
Bass
Violins
I
II
Cont.

Solo Voices
Sop. I
f
Saul, Saul, Saul, Saul, was ver-folgst du
Sop. II
f
Saul, Saul, Saul, Saul, was ver-folgst du
Ten. I
f
Saul, Saul, Saul, Saul, was ver - folgst du
Ten. II
f
Saul, Saul, Saul, Saul, was ver-folgst du
Bass I
f
Saul, Saul, Saul, Saul, was ver-folgst du
Bass II
f
Saul, Saul, Saul, Saul, was ver - folgst du
Chorus I
Sop.
f
Saul, Saul, Saul, Saul, was ver - folgst du
Alto
f
Saul, Saul, Saul, Saul, was ver - folgst du
Ten.
f
Saul, Saul, Saul, Saul, was ver - folgst du
Bass
f
Saul, Saul, Saul, Saul, was ver - folgst du
Chorus II
Sop.
f
Saul, Saul, Saul, Saul, Saul, was ver-folgst du
Alto
f
Saul, Saul, Saul, Saul, Saul, was ver-folgst du
Ten.
f
Saul, Saul, Saul, Saul, Saul, was ver-folgst du
Bass
f
Saul, Saul, Saul, Saul, Saul, was ver-folgst du
Violins
I
f
II
f
Cont.
4
f

Solo Voices
Sop. I
mp
pp
mich, was ver - folgst du mich, was ver - folgst du mich?
Sop. II
mich, was ver - folgst du mich, was ver - folgst du mich?
Ten. I
mich, was ver - folgst du mich, was ver - folgst du mich?
Ten. II
f
mich, was ver - folgst du mich, was ver - folgst du mich? Es wird dir
Bass I
mich, was ver - folgst du mich, was ver - folgst du mich?
Bass II
mich, was ver - folgst du mich, was ver - folgst du mich?
Chorus I
Sop.
mich?
Alto
mich?
Ten.
mich?
Bass
mich?
Chorus II
Sop.
mich?
Alto
mich?
Ten.
mich?
Bass
mich?
Violins
I
II
Cont.

Sop. I
Sop. II
Ten. I
Ten. II
Bass I
Bass II
Cont.
Solo Voices
schwer wer - den, wi - der den Sta - chel zu lö - - cken.
6 ♯ 4 4 ♯

Sop. I
Sop. II
Ten. I
Ten. II
Bass I
Bass II
Cont.
Solo Voices
Es wird dir schwer wer - den, wi-der den Sta - chel zu lö - - cken.
♭ 6 ♯ 4 ♯

Sop. I
Sop. II
Ten. I
Ten. II
Bass I
Bass II
Solo Voices
Sop.
Alto
Ten.
Bass
Chorus I
Sop.
Alto
Ten.
Bass
Chorus II
Violins
I
II
Cont.
Saul, Saul, Saul, Saul, was ver - folgst du mich, was ver -
Saul, Saul, Saul, was ver - folgst du mich?
Saul, Saul, Saul, was ver - folgst du mich?

Solo Voices

Sop. I — pp — folgst du mich, was ver-folgst du mich? Es wird dir schwer wer - den,

Sop. II — pp — folgst du mich, was ver-folgst du mich?

Ten. I — pp — folgst du mich, was ver-folgst du mich?

Ten. II — pp — folgst du mich, was ver-folgst du mich?

Bass I — pp — folgst du mich, was ver-folgst du mich? Es wird dir schwer wer - den, wi-der den

Bass II — pp — folgst du mich, was ver-folgst du mich?

Violins I — pp

Violins II — pp

Cont. — ♯ (♮) ♭ ♯ — p

Sop. I
es wird dir schwer wer - - -
Sop. II
wer - den, es wird dir schwer wer -
Solo Voices
Ten. I
schwer wer - den, es wird dir schwer
Ten. II
schwer wer - den, es wird dir schwer
Bass I
wer - den, es wird dir schwer, schwer
Bass II
es wird dir schwer wer - - den,
Violins I II
♭6 5 ♮ ♭
Cont.

Sop. I
- - - den,
Sop. II
- - - den,
Solo Voices
Ten. I
wer - - den,
Ten. II
wer - - den,
Bass I
wer - - den,
Bass II
wi-der den Sta - chel zu lö - - - - -
Chorus I
Sop.
Alto
Ten.
Bass
Chorus II
Sop.
Alto
Ten.
Bass
Violins
I
II
Cont.

Solo Voices
Sop. I
wi-der den Sta - chel zu lö - - - - - cken. Saul, Saul,
Sop. II
Saul, Saul, Saul, Saul, Saul,
Ten. I
wi-der den Sta - chel zu lö - - - cken. Saul, Saul,
Ten. II
Saul, Saul, Saul, Saul, Saul,
Bass I
wi-der den Sta - chel zu lö - - - - - cken. Saul, Saul,
Bass II
cken. Saul, Saul, Saul, Saul, Saul,
Chorus I
Sop.
Saul, Saul, Saul, Saul, Saul,
Alto
Saul, Saul, Saul, Saul, Saul,
Ten.
Saul, Saul, Saul, Saul, Saul,
Bass
Saul, Saul, Saul, Saul, Saul,
Chorus II
Sop.
Saul, Saul, Saul, Saul, Saul,
Alto
Saul, Saul, Saul, Saul, Saul,
Ten.
Saul, Saul, Saul, Saul, Saul,
Bass
Saul, Saul, Saul, Saul, Saul,
Violins
I
II
Cont.

Sop. I
Saul, Saul, was ver - folgst du mich, was ver - folgst du mich, was ver - folgst du mich, was ver -
Sop. II
Saul, Saul, was ver - folgst du mich, was ver - folgst du mich, was ver - folgst du mich, was ver -
Solo Voices
Ten. I
Saul, Saul, was ver - folgst du mich, was ver - folgst du mich, was ver - folgst du mich, was ver -
Ten. II
Saul, Saul, was ver - folgst du mich, Saul, Saul, Saul,
Bass I
Saul, Saul, was ver - folgst du mich, was ver - folgst du mich, was ver - folgst du mich, was ver -
Bass II
Saul, Saul, was ver - folgst du mich, was ver - folgst du mich, was ver - folgst du mich, was ver -
Chorus I
Sop.
Saul, Saul, was ver - folgst du mich, was ver -
Alto
Saul, Saul, was ver - folgst du mich, was ver -
Ten.
Saul, Saul, was ver - folgst du mich, was ver -
Bass
Saul, Saul, was ver - folgst du mich, was ver -
Chorus II
Sop.
Saul, was ver - folgst du mich, was ver -
Alto
Saul, was ver- folgst du mich, was ver -
Ten.
Saul, was ver - folgst du mich, was ver -
Bass
Saul, was ver - folgst du mich, was ver -
Violins
I
II
Cont.
mp
pp
f

Solo Voices
Sop. I
folgst du mich, was ver - folgst du mich, was ver - folgst du mich, was ver - folgst du mich, was ver -
Sop. II
folgst du mich, was ver - folgst du mich, was ver - folgst du mich, was ver - folgst du mich, was ver -
Ten. I
folgst du mich, was ver - folgst du mich, was ver - folgst du mich, was ver - folgst du mich, was ver -
Ten. II
Saul, Saul, Saul, Saul, Saul, Saul, Saul,
Bass I
folgst du mich, was ver - folgst du mich, was ver - folgst du mich, was ver - folgst du mich, was ver -
Bass II
folgst du mich, was ver - folgst du mich, was ver - folgst du mich, was ver - folgst du mich, was ver -
Chorus I
Sop.
folgst du mich, was ver - folgst du mich,
Alto
folgst du mich, was ver - folgst du mich,
Ten.
folgst du mich, was ver - folgst du mich,
Bass
folgst du mich, was ver - folgst du mich,
Chorus II
Sop.
folgst du mich, was ver - folgst du mich,
Alto
folgst du mich, was ver - folgst du mich,
Ten.
folgst du mich, was ver - folgst du mich,
Bass
folgst du mich, was ver - folgst du mich,
Violins
I
II
Cont.
mp pp f mp

Sop. I
folgst du mich, was ver - folgst du mich, was ver -
Sop. II
folgst du mich, was ver - folgst du mich, was ver -
Ten. I
folgst du mich, was ver - folgst du mich, was ver -
Ten. II
Saul, was ver - folgst du mich, Saul, Saul,
Bass I
folgst du mich, was ver - folgst du mich, was ver -
Bass II
folgst du mich, was ver - folgst du mich, was ver - folgst du mich, was ver -
Solo Voices
Sop.
was ver -
Alto
was ver -
Ten.
was ver -
Bass
was ver -
Chorus I
Sop.
was ver -
Alto
was ver -
Ten.
was ver -
Bass
was ver -
Chorus II
I
Violins
II
Cont.
pp
f

Solo Voices

Sop. I — *mp* … *pp*
folgst du mich, was ver - folgst du mich, was ver - folgst du mich?

Sop. II — *mp* … *pp*
folgst du mich, was ver - folgst du mich, was ver - folgst du mich?

Ten. I — *mp* … *pp*
folgst du mich, was ver - folgst du mich, was ver - folgst du mich, was ver - folgst du mich?

Ten. II
Saul, Saul, Saul, was ver - folgst du mich?

Bass I — *mp* … *pp*
folgst du mich, was ver - folgst du mich, was ver - folgst du mich?

Bass II — *mp* … *pp*
folgst du mich, was ver - folgst du mich was ver - folgst du mich?

Chorus I

Sop.
folgst du mich?

Alto
folgst du mich?

Ten.
folgst du mich?

Bass
folgst du mich?

Chorus II

Sop.
folgst du mich?

Alto
folgst du mich?

Ten.
folgst du mich?

Bass
folgst du mich?

Violins I — *mp* … *pp*

Violins II — *mp* … *pp*

Cont. — *mp* … *pp*

Translation

Saul, Saul, who dost thou persecute me? It will be hard for thee to kick against the traces.

ACTS 9:4–5

16. ARCANGELO CORELLI (1653-1713), Sonata da chiesa, Opus 3, No. 7 (PUBL. 1689)

Org
Adagio.

Adagio.

Allegro.

17. HENRY PURCELL (c. 1659-1695), *Dido's Lament* from *Dido and Aeneas* (1ST PERF. 1689)

DIDO
Thy hand, Bel - in - da! dark - - - - ness shades me, On thy

bos - om let me rest, More I would, but death in -

vades me Death is now a wel - come guest!
pp

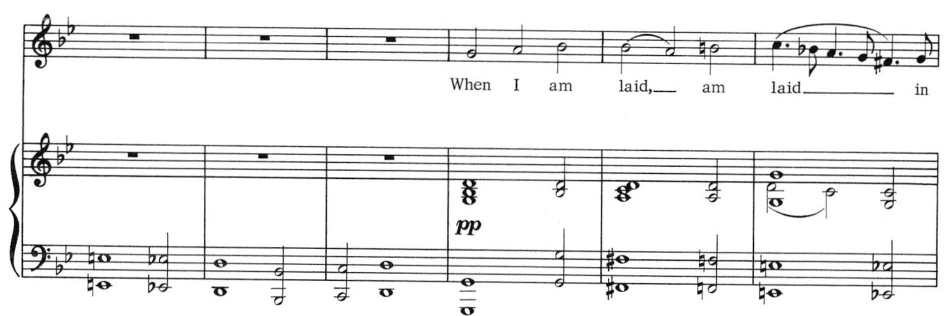
When I am laid, am laid in
pp

earth, may my wrongs cre - ate no trou - ble, no trou - ble in___ thy breast.

When I am laid,_ am laid_______ in earth, may my wrongs cre-

ate no trou - ble, no trou - ble in___ thy breast. Re - mem - ber me,

re - mem - ber me, But ah!__________ for - get my fate, Re -

mem-ber me, but ah!______ for - get my__ fate. Re-mem-ber me,

re-mem-ber me, But ah!______ for-get my fate, Re-

mem-ber me, but ah!______ for - get my__ fate.

p *cresc.* ***f***

dim. sempre ***pp***

18. ANTONIO VIVALDI (c. 1678-1741), Concerto Grosso in D minor, Opus 3, No. 11 (PUBL. 1712)

Reprinted with permission of Ernst Eulenburg Ltd., London-Zürich, from the Eulenburg miniature score.

15
Vl. I Solo
Vl. II Solo
20
Vc. Solo
Cont.
ff
25
5 6
30

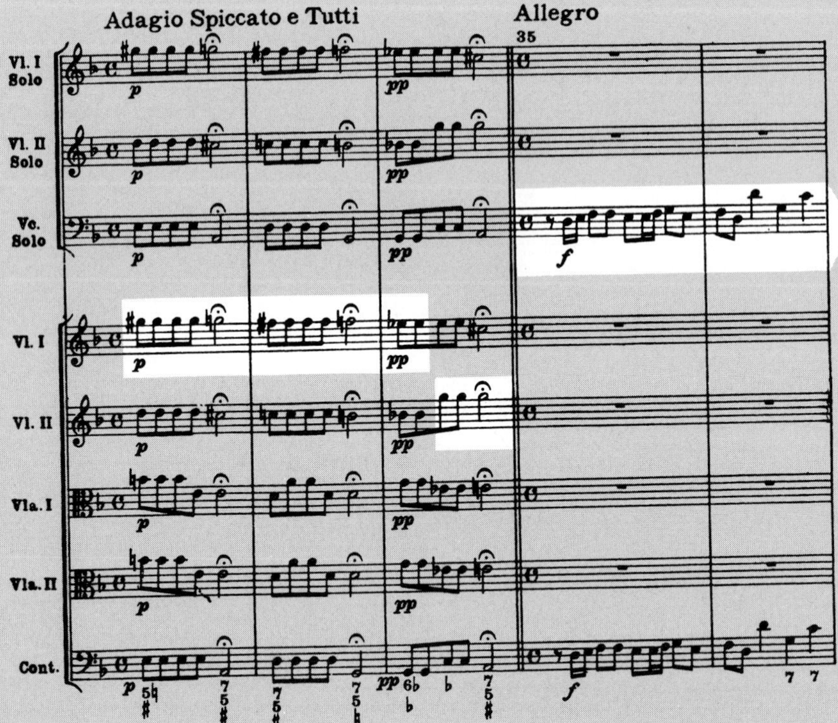

Adagio Spiccato e Tutti
Allegro
35
Vl. I Solo
Vl. II Solo
Vc. Solo
Vl. I
Vl. II
Vla. I
Vla. II
Cont.
p
pp
f

40
Vc. Solo
Vla. I
Vla. II
Cont.
f

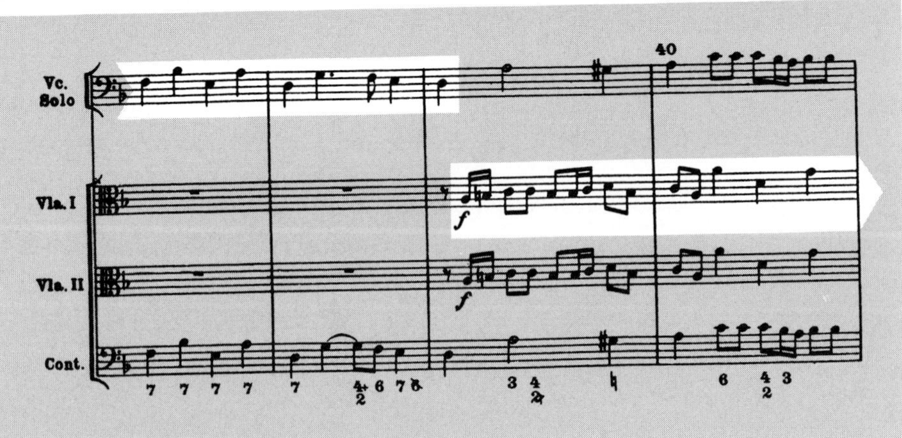

Vl. II Solo
Vc. Solo
Vl. II
Vla. I
Vla. II
Cont.

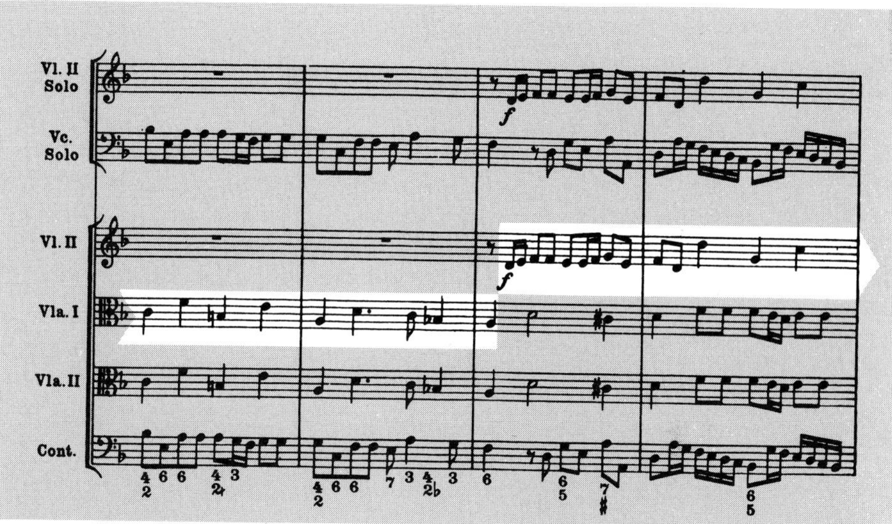

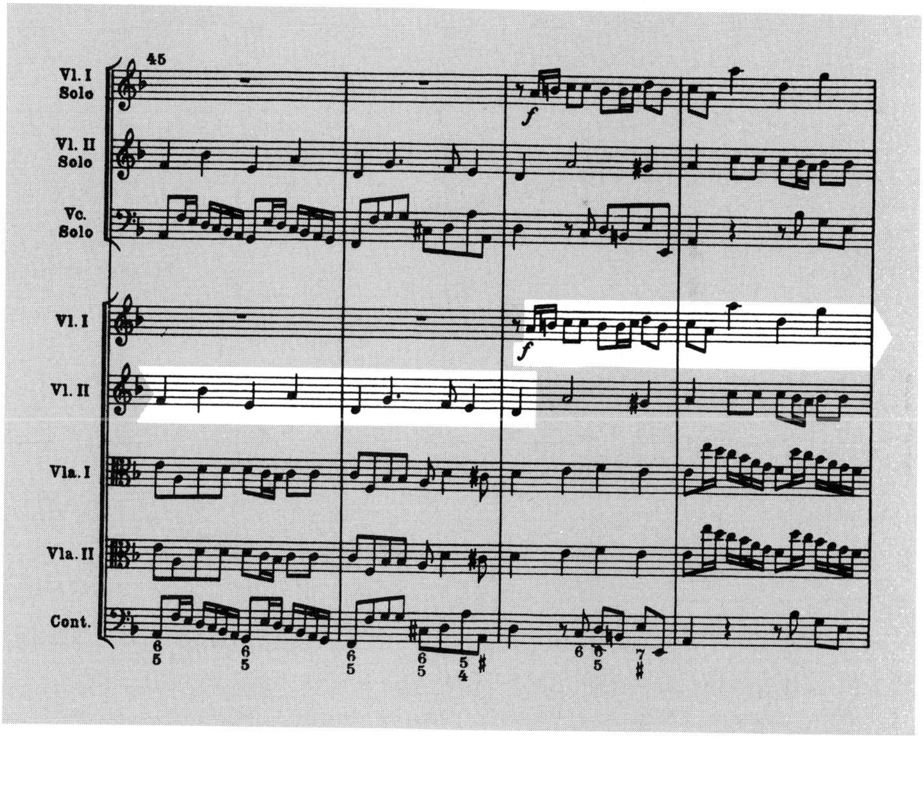

45
Vl. I Solo
Vl. II Solo
Vc. Solo
Vl. I
Vl. II
Vla. I
Vla. II
Cont.

50
Vl. I Solo
Vl. II Solo
Vc. Solo
Vl. I
Vl. II
Vla. I
Vla. II
Cont.
9 8
6
5
5
4
7
7

Soli
Vl. I Solo
p
Soli
Vl. II Solo
p
Solo
Vc. Solo
p
Vl. I
Vl. II
Vla. I
Vla. II
Cont.
7
7
7
7
7
7
7 6
5
4

55
Vl. I Solo
Vl. II Solo
Vc. Solo
Cont.
p

60
Vl. I Solo
Vl. II Solo
Vc. Solo
Cont.

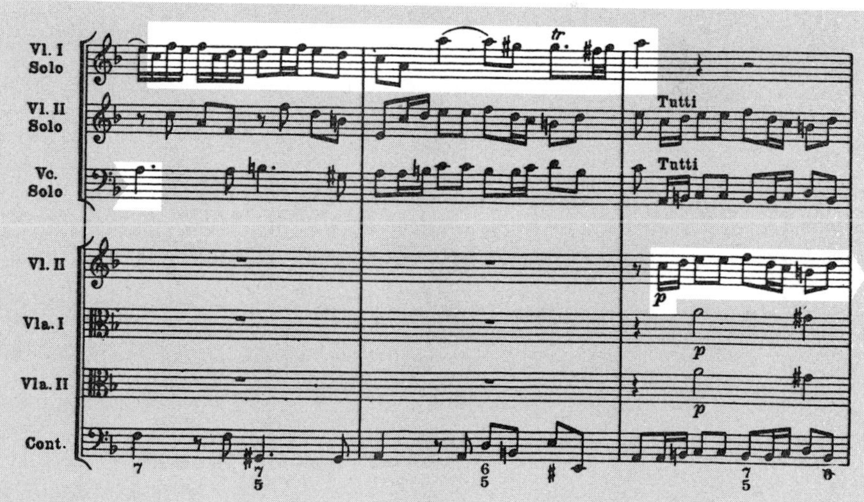
Vl. I Solo
Vl. II Solo
Vc. Solo
Tutti
Tutti
Vl. II
Vla. I
Vla. II
Cont.
tr
p
p
p

Tutti
65
Fl. I Solo
Vl. II Solo
Vc. Solo
Vl. I
p
Vl. II
Vla. I
Vla. II
Cont.

Vl. I Solo
Vl. II Solo
Vc. Solo
Vl. I
Vl. II
Vla. I
Vla. II
Cont.

70
Vl. I Solo
Vl. II Solo
Vc. Solo
Vl. I
Vl. II
Vla. I
Vla. II
Cont.

75
Vl. I Solo
Vl. II Solo
Vc. Solo
Vl. I
Vl. II
Vla. I
Vla. II
Cont.

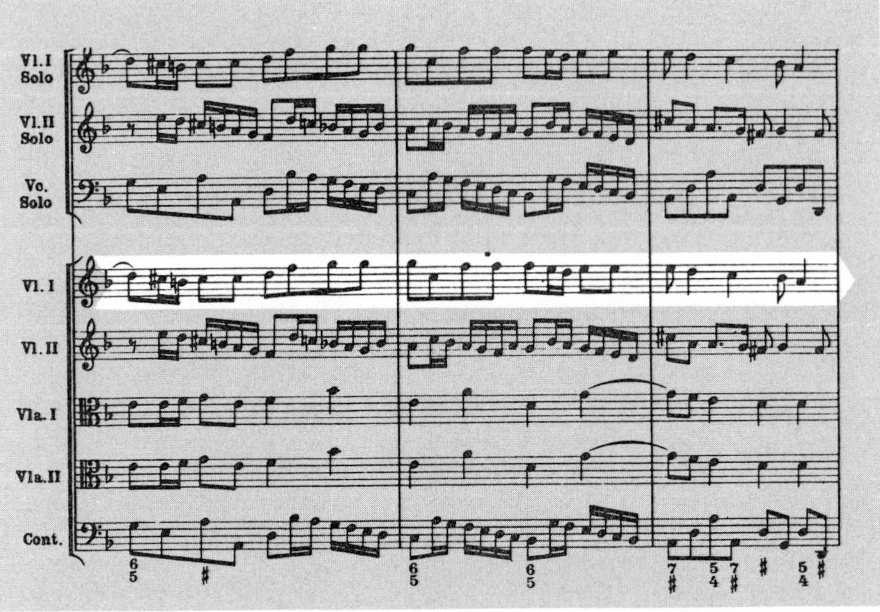

Vl. I Solo
Vl. II Solo
Vc. Solo
Vl. I
Vl. II
Vla. I
Vla. II
Cont.

Soli
80
Solo
Vl. I Solo
Vl. II Solo
Vc. Solo
Vl. I
Vl. II
Vla. I
Vla. II
Cont.

Vl. I Solo
Vl. II Solo
[sic]
Vc. Solo

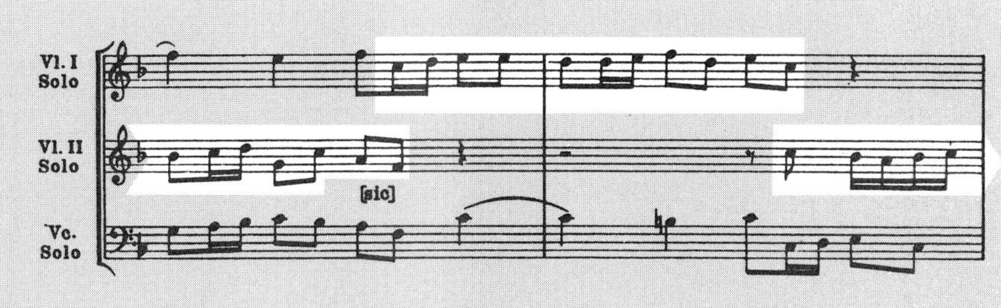

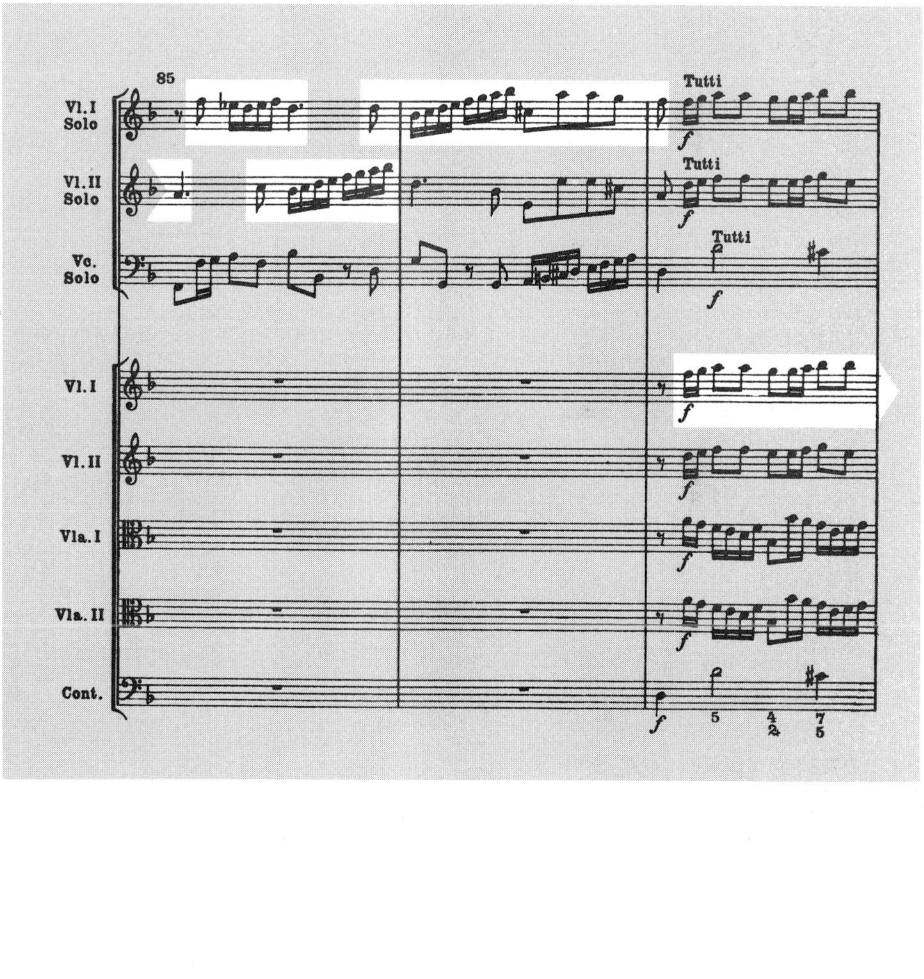

85
Vl. I Solo
Tutti
f
Vl. II Solo
Tutti
f
Vc. Solo
Tutti
f
Vl. I
f
Vl. II
f
Vla. I
f
Vla. II
f
Cont.
f
5
4
2
7
5

Vl. I Solo
Vl. II Solo
Vc Solo
Vl. I
Vl. II
Vla. I
Vla. II
Cont.
6
5
4
Tasto Solo

90
Vl. I Solo
Vl. II Solo
Vc Solo
Vl. I
Vl. II
Vla. I
Vla. II
Cont.
piano
forte

Vl. I Solo
piano
forte
Vl. II Solo
piano
forte
Vc. Solo
Vl. I
piano
forte
Vl. II
piano
forte
Vla. I
piano
Vla. II
piano
Cont.

95
Vl. I Solo
Vl. II Solo
Vc. Solo
Vl. I
Vl. II
Vla. I
forte
Vla. II
forte
Cont.

100
Vl. I Solo
Vl. II Solo
Vc. Solo
Vl. I
Vl. II
Vla. I
Vla. II
Cont.

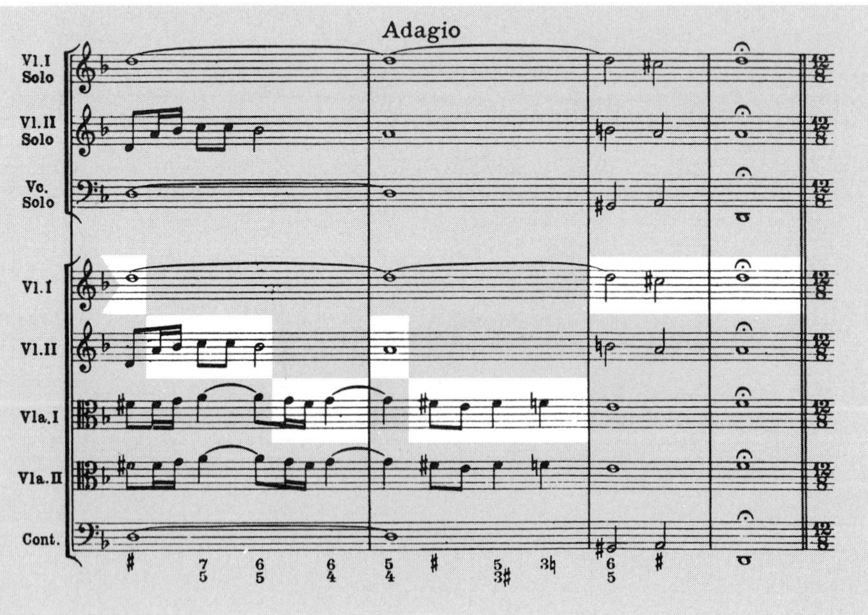
Adagio
Vl. I Solo
Vl. II Solo
Vc. Solo
Vl. I
Vl. II
Vla. I
Vla. II
Cont.

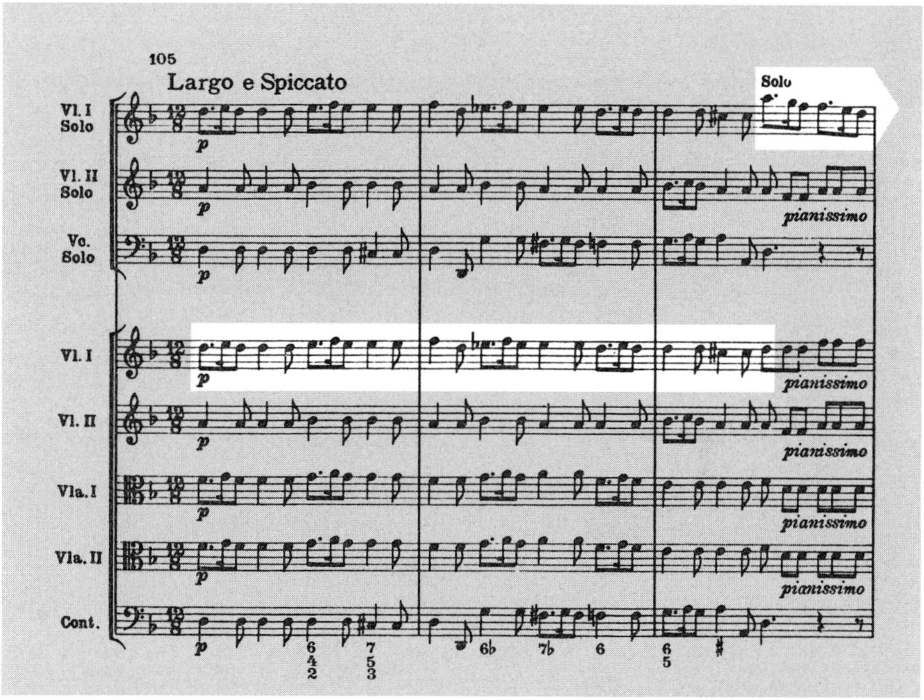

105
Largo e Spiccato
Solo
Vl. I Solo
Vl. II Solo
Vc. Solo
Vl. I
Vl. II
Vla. I
Vla. II
Cont.
p
pianissimo

110
tr
Vl. I Solo
Vl. II Solo
Vl. I
Vl. II
Vla. I
Vla. II

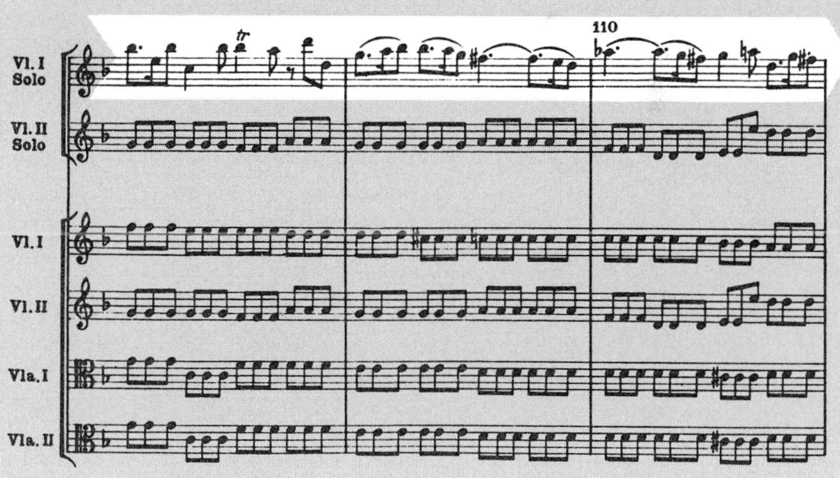

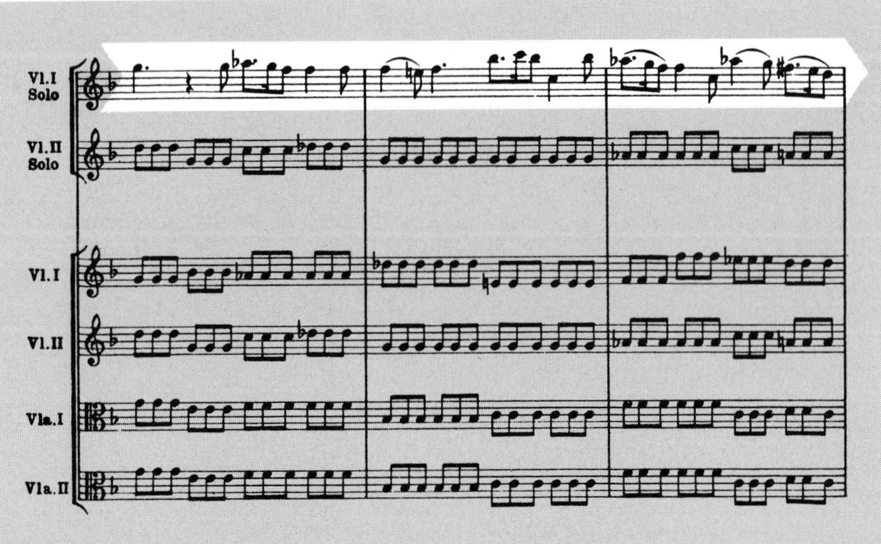
Vl. I
Solo
Vl. II
Solo
Vl. I
Vl. II
Vla. I
Vla. II

115
tr
Vl. I
Solo
Vl. II
Solo
Vl. I
Vl. II
Vla. I
Vla. II

Vl. I Solo
Vl. II Solo
Vl. I
Vl. II
Vla. I
Vla. II
tr
120

Vl. I Solo
Vl. II Solo
Vc. Solo
Vl. I
Vl. II
Vla. I
Vla. II
Cont.
tr
Tutti
f
forte

125
Allegro
Soli
tr
Vl. I Solo
Vl. II Solo
130
Solo
Vc. Solo
Tutti
Vl. I
Vl. II
Vla. I
Vla. II
Cont.
f
7

135
Vl. I Solo
Vl. II Solo
Vc. Solo
Tutti
Vl. I
Vl. II
Vla. I
Vla. II
Cont.
7
7
6
♯
6
7
6
7
6

Vl. I Solo
Vl. II Solo
Soli
Vc. Solo
Solo
Vl. I
Vl. II
Vla. I
Vla. II
Cont.
7
♯
6
5
♯

140
Vl. I Solo
Vl. II Solo
Vc. Solo

145
Vl. I Solo
Vl. II Solo
Vc. Solo

Vl. I Solo
Vl. II Solo
Tutti
Vc. Solo
Tutti
Vl. I
Vl. II
Vla. I
Vla. II
Cont.

150
Tutti
Vl. I Solo
Vl. II Solo
Vc. Solo
Vl. I
Vl. II
Vla. I
Vla. II
Cont.
7
7
7
7
6
6
6

Vl. I Solo
Vl. II Solo
Vc. Solo
Vl. I
Vl. II
Vla. I
Vla. II
Cont.
Solo
p
piano

155
Vl. I Solo
Vl. II Solo
Vc. Solo
Vl. I
Vl. II
Vla. I
Vla. II
Cont.
7
7
7
7
7
7
#

160
Vl. I Solo
pp
Vl. II Solo
pianissimo
Vc. Solo
Vl. I
pianissimo
Vl. II
pianissimo
Vla. I
pianissimo
Vla. II
pianissimo
Cont

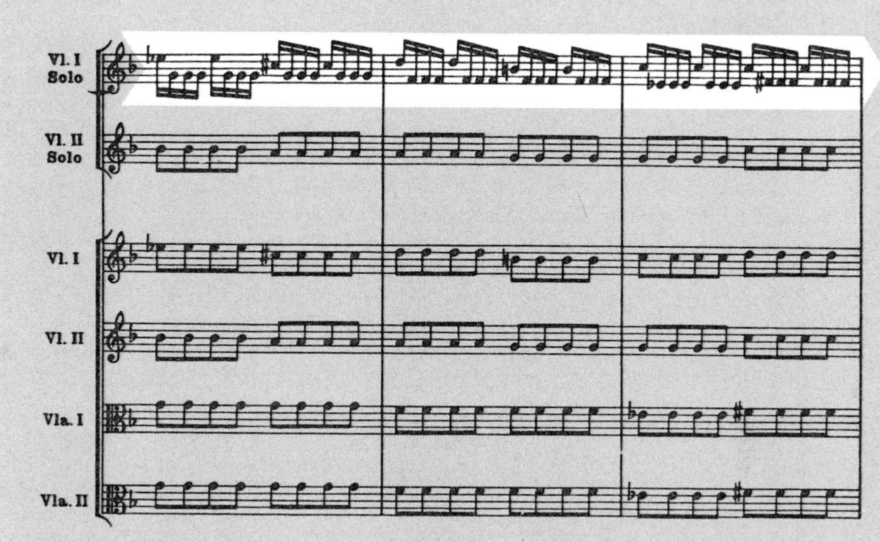
Vl. I Solo
Vl. II Solo
Vl. I
Vl. II
Vla. I
Vla. II

165
Vl. I Solo
Vl. II Solo
Vl. I
Vl. II
Vla. I
Vla. II

Tutti
Vl. I Solo
Vl. II Solo
Vc. Solo
Vl. I
Vl. II
Vla. I
Vla. II
Cont.
f
forte

170
Soli
Solo
Vl. I Solo
Vl. II Solo
Vc. Solo
Vl. I
Vl. II
Vla. I
Vla. II
Cont.

Vl. I Solo
Vl. II Solo
Vc. Solo
Vl. I
Vl. II
Vla. I
Vla. II
Cont.
Tutti
Tutti
Tutti
175
Soli
Soli
Soli
tr

Vl. I Solo
Vl. II Solo
Vc. Solo
Vl. I
Vl. II
Vla. I
Vla. II
Cont.
Tutti
Tutti
Tutti
Soli
Soli
Solo
tr

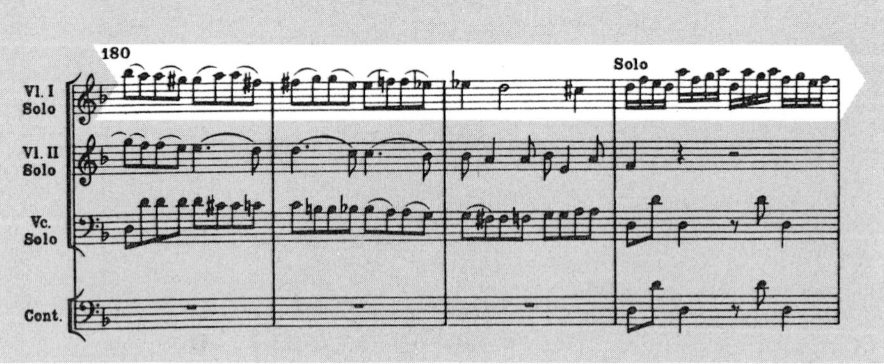
180
Solo
Vl. I Solo
Vl. II Solo
Vc. Solo
Cont.

185
Vl. I Solo
Vc. Solo
Cont.
6
5
#

Vl. I Solo
Vc. Solo
Cont.

190
Vl. I Solo
Vc. Solo
Cont.
#

Tutti
Vl. I Solo
Tutti
Vl. II Solo
Vc. Solo
Vl. I
Vl. II
Vla. I
Vla. II
Cont.
piano
piano
piano
piano
piano
piano
piano
piano
6 7 7 6 7 ♯ 6 5 ♯ 6

195
197
Vl. I Solo
Vl. II Solo
Vc. Solo
Vl. I
Vl. II
Vla. I
Vla. II
Cont.
forte
forte
forte
forte
forte
forte
forte
7 6 7 6 7 ♯ 6 5 ♯

19. GEORGE FRIDERIC HANDEL (1685-1759), *Piangerò* from *Giulio Cesare* (1ST PERF. 1724)

Allegro.
Viol. I. II.
Mà poi mor - ta d'ogn' in - tor - no il ti - ran - no e not - te e gior - no
Violoncello.
fatta spet - tro a - gi - te - rò,
fatta spet - - - tro, fatta spet - tro a - gi - te - rò;
mà poi mor - ta d'ogn'in - tor - no il ti - ran - no e not - te e gior - no fatta
spet - tro a - gi - te - rò, fatta spet - tro a - gi - te - rò.
Da Capo.

Translation

Piangerò la sorte mia,
sì crudelo e tanto ria,
finchè vita in petto avrò.

Mà poi morte d'ogn'intorno
il tiranno e notte e giorno
fatta spettro agiterò.

I shall lament my fate,
so cruel and so wicked,
as long as there is life in my breast.

But when I am dead, from every side,
both night and day,
I, become a specter, will torment the tyrant.

20. HANDEL, Excerpts from *Messiah* (1741)

No. 1, Overture

21
Ob. I
II
Fag.
[tr]
[f]
21
Viol. I
II
Viola
[f]
[tr]
Vc.
Basso cont.
[f]
29
Ob. I
II
Fag.
[tr]
29
Viol. I
II
Viola
Basso cont.
[tr]
88
Ob. I
II
Fag.
88
Viol. I
II
Viola
Basso cont.

46
I
Ob.
II
Fag.
46
I
Viol.
II
Viola
Basso cont.
[tr]
[tr]
55
I
Ob.
II
Fag.
55
I
Viol.
II
Viola
Basso cont.
63
I
Ob.
II
Fag.
63
I
Viol.
II
Viola
Basso cont.

71
Ob. I
II
Fag.
71
Viol. I
II
Viola
Basso cont.
81
Ob. I
II
Fag.
[tr]
81
Viol. I
II
Viola
Basso cont.
[tr]
89
Ob. I
II
Fag.
[tr]
89
Viol. I
II
Viola
Basso cont.
[tr]

No. 2, *Comfort Ye*

saith your God, saith your God;
fp
mf
speak ye com-fort-a-bly to Je - ru - sa-lem, speak ye
p simile
com - fort-a - bly to Je - ru - sa-lem, and cry un - to her that her
mf
war - fare, her war - fare is ac-complished, that her in -
p

i - qui - ty is par-don'd, that her in - i - qui - ty is par - - don'd.
mf
The voice of him that crieth in the wilderness, Pre-pare ye the way of the
f
Lord, make straight in the desert a high-way for our God.

No.3, *Ev'ry valley*

ex-alt
ed, shall be ex - alt - ed,
shall be ex-alt
ed, and ev-'ry moun - tain and hill made low;
f
p
p

the crook-ed straight,
and the rough plac-es
plain,
the crook-ed
straight, the crook - ed straight, and rough plac-es
plain,
cresc.
p
simile

— and the rough plac-es plain.
Ev-'ry val-ley,
ev-'ry val-ley —
— shall be ex-alt - - - - - - - - - - - - -
- ed,
p
mf
f

ev - 'ry val-ley,
ev - 'ry val - ley shall be ex-alt -
- ed,
and ev-'ry moun-tain and
hill made low;
the crook-ed straight,
the
crook-ed straight, the crook-ed straight, and the rough plac-es plain,
p
f
p
p
tr

and the rough plac-es plain, and the rough plac-es
plain,
the crook-ed straight,
ad lib.
and the rough plac - es plain.
colla voce
senza Ped.
f a tempo
p
f
p
cresc.
f

No. 12, *For unto us a Child is born*

us a Child is born:
un-to us a Son is giv-en, un-to
us a Son is giv-en:
For un-to us a Child is born,
For un-to
un-to us a Son is giv-en, un-to
us a Child is born,

us a Son is giv-en, un-to us a Son is

un-to us a Son is giv-en:

mf and the gov-ern-ment shall

giv-en:

mf and the gov-ern-ment shall be up-on His shoul - - - - - - - - - -

mf

be up-on His shoul - - - - - - - - - der, up-on His shoul-der; and His *cresc.*

mf and the gov-ern-ment shall be up-on His shoul-der; and His *cresc.*

der; and His *cresc.*

mf and the gov-ern-ment shall be up-on His shoul-der; and His *cresc.*

cresc.

Name shall be call-ed Won - der-ful, Coun - sel-lor,
Name shall be call-ed Won - der-ful, Coun - sel-lor,
Name shall be call-ed Won - der-ful, Coun - sel-lor,
Name shall be call-ed Won - der-ful, Coun - sel-lor,
The might-y God, The ev - er - last-ing Fa-ther, The Prince of Peace.
The might-y God, The ev - er - last-ing Fa-ther, The Prince of Peace. Un-to
The might-y God, The ev - er - last-ing Fa-ther, The Prince of Peace.
The might-y God, The ev - er - last-ing Fa-ther, The Prince of Peace.
us a Child is born, un-to us a Son is
For un-to us a Child is born,

p
Un-to us a Child is born,
giv-en:
mf
and the gov-ern-ment shall
p
un-to us a Son is giv-en:
be up-on His shoul -
mf
and the gov-ern-ment shall be up on His shoul -
cresc.
and His Name shall be call-ed
ff
Won - der-ful,
- der; and His Name shall be call - ed
cresc.
ff
Won - der-ful,
cresc.
and His Name shall be call - ed
ff
Won - der-ful,
- der; and His Name shall be call - ed
cresc.
ff
Won - der-ful,
cresc.
ff

Coun - sel-lor, The might - y God, The
Coun - sel-lor, The might - y God, The
Coun - sel-lor, The might - y God, The
Coun - sel-lor, The might - y God, The
ev - er-last-ing Fa-ther, The Prince of Peace. For un-to
ev - er-last-ing Fa-ther, The Prince of Peace.
ev - er-last-ing Fa-ther, The Prince of Peace. Un-to us a Child is born,
ev - er-last-ing Fa-ther, The Prince of Peace.
us a Child is born,
For un-to us a Child is born,
For un-to us a Child is born, un-to

p
un-to us a Son is
p
un-to us a Son is
us a Son is giv-en:
giv-en:
mf
and the gov-ern-ment shall
mf
giv-en: and the gov-ern-ment shall be up-on His shoul - - - der;
mf
be up-on His shoul - - - der;
cresc.
and His
mf
cresc.
and the gov-ern-ment shall be up-on His shoul-der; and His
cresc.
and His
mf
cresc.
and the gov-ern-ment shall be up-on His shoul-der; and His

Name shall be call - ed Won - - der - ful,
Name shall be call - ed Won - - der - ful,
Name shall be call - ed Won - - der - ful,
Name shall be call - ed Won - - der - ful,
Coun - - sel - lor, The might - y God, The
Coun - - sel - lor, The might - y God, The
Coun - - sel - lor, The might - y God, The
Coun - - sel - lor, The might - y God, The
ev - er - last - ing Fa - - ther, Prince of Peace. For un - to
ev - er - last - ing Fa - - ther, Prince of Peace. For un - to
ev - er - last - ing Fa - - ther, Prince of Peace. For un - to
ev - er - last - ing Fa - - ther, Prince of Peace. Un - to us a Child is born, un - to

us a Child is born,
us a Child is born,
us a Child is born, un - to us a Son is
us a Child is born, un - to us a Son is
giv - en, un - to us a Son is
giv - en, un - to us a Son is
un-to us a Son is giv-en: and the gov-ern-ment, the gov-ern-ment shall
un-to us a Son is giv-en: and the gov-ern-ment shall
giv-en, un-to us a Son is giv-en:
giv-en, un-to us a Son is giv-en:

be up - on His shoul - - - - - der, and the gov - ern - ment shall
be up - on His shoul - der, and the gov - ern - ment shall
and the gov - ern - ment, the gov - ern - ment shall
and the gov - ern - ment, the gov - ern - ment shall
be up - on His shoul - der; and His Name shall be call - ed
be up - on His shoul - der; and His Name shall be call - ed
be up - on His shoul - der; and His Name shall be call - ed
be up - on His shoul - der; and His Name shall be call - ed
ff
Won - der - ful, Coun - sel - lor,
Won - der - ful, Coun - sel - lor,
Won - der - ful, Coun - sel - lor,
Won - der - ful, Coun - sel - lor,

The might-y God, The ev-er-last-ing Fa-ther, The Prince of Peace, The
The might-y God, The ev-er-last-ing Fa-ther, The Prince of Peace, The
The might-y God, The ev-er-last-ing Fa-ther, The Prince of Peace, The
The might-y God, The ev-er-last-ing Fa-ther, The Prince of Peace, The
ev-er-last-ing Fa-ther, The Prince of Peace.
ev-er-last-ing Fa-ther, The Prince of Peace.
ev-er-last-ing Fa-ther, The Prince of Peace.
ev-er-last-ing Fa-ther, The Prince of Peace.
f

No. 23, *He was despised*

a man of sor - - rows, and ac - quainted with grief, ——

—— a man of sor-rows, and ac-quainted with grief.

pp *p*

f

He

was des-pis-ed, re-ject-ed, He was des-

pp *p* *pp* *p* *fp*

pis-ed and re-ject-ed of men; a man of sorrows, and acquainted with
grief, a man of sor-rows, and ac-quaint-ed with grief.
He was despis-ed, re-ject-ed; a man of
pp
fp
sorrows, and acquainted with grief, and acquainted with grief,
p
a man of sorrows, and ac-quainted with grief.
f

Fine

He gave His back to the

Un poco piano

Fine

smit-ers, He gave His back to the

smit-ers, and His cheeks to them that plucked off the

hair, and His cheeks to them that plucked off the

hair, and his cheeks to them that plucked off the
hair: He hid not His face from shame and
spit-ting, He hid not His face from shame,
from shame,
He hid not His
face from shame,
from shame and spitting.
D. C.
p
D. C.

No. 44. *Hallelujah*

lu-jah! Hal-le-lu-jah! Hal - le - lu - jah! for the Lord
lu-jah! Hal-le-lu-jah! Hal - le - - lu-jah! for the Lord
lu-jah! Hal-le-lu-jah! Hal - le- - lu-jah! for the Lord
lu-jah! Hal-le-lu-jah! Hal - le - lu - jah! for the Lord
God Om - ni - po-tent reign-eth. Hal-le - lu-jah! Hal-le-lu-jah! Hal-le-
God Om - ni - po-tent reign-eth. Hal-le - lu-jah! Hal-le-lu-jah! Hal-le-
God Om - ni - po-tent reign-eth. Hal-le - lu-jah! Hal-le-lu-jah! Hal-le-
God Om - ni - po-tent reign-eth. Hal-le - lu-jah! Hal-le-lu-jah! Hal-le-
lu-jah! Hal-le-lu-jah! Hal-le-
lu-jah! Hal-le-lu-jah! for the Lord God Om-ni - po-tent reign-eth. Hal-le-
lu-jah! Hal-le-lu-jah! for the Lord God Om-ni - po-tent reign-eth. Hal-le-
lu-jah! Hal-le-lu-jah! for the Lord God Om-ni - po-tent reign-eth. Hal-le-

lu - jah! Hal - le - lu - jah! Hal - le - lu - jah! Hal - le - lu - jah!
lu - jah! Hal - le - lu - jah! Hal - le - lu - jah! Hal - le - lu - jah!
lu - jah! Hal - le - lu - jah! Hal - le - lu - jah! Hal - le - lu - jah!
lu - jah! Hal - le - lu - jah! Hal - le - lu - jah! Hal - le - lu - jah!
for the Lord God Om - ni - - - po - tent
Hal - le -
Hal - le - lu - jah! Hal - le - lu - jah! Hal - le - lu - jah! Hal -
reign - - - eth. Hal - le - lu - jah! Hal - le - lu - jah! Hal - le - lu -
lu-jah! Hal - le - lu - jah! Hal - le - lu - jah! Hal - le - lu - jah! Hal - le - lu - -
le - - lu - - jah! Hal - le - lu - jah! for the Lord
Hal - le - lu - jah! for the Lord

jah! Hal-le-lu-jah! Hal- -le- -lu- -jah! Hal-le-lu-jah!
jah! Hal-le-lu-jah! Hal - -le- -lu- -jah! Hal-le-
God Om - ni- - -po - tent reign - - -eth. Hal-le-lu-jah!
God Om - ni- - -po - tent reign - - -eth. Hal-le-
Hal-le-lu-jah! Hal-le-lu-jah! Hal-le-lu-jah! Hal-le-lu-jah!
lu-jah! Hal-le-lu-jah! for the Lord
Hal-le-lu-jah! Hal-le-lu-jah! for the Lord
lu-jah! Hal-le-lu-jah! Hal-le-lu-jah! Hal-le-
Hal-le-lu-jah! Hal-le-lu-jah! Hal - le- - lu - jah! Hal-
God Om - ni- - po - tent reign - - eth. Hal-le-lu-jah!
God Om - ni - - po - tent reign - - - eth. Hal -
*)
lu-jah! Hal-le-lu-jah! Hal-le - lu-jah! Hal-le - lu-jah! Hal-le-

(p)
le - - lu - -jah! The king-dom of this—
Hal - le - lu - jah! The king-dom of this
le - - - lu - jah! The king-dom of this
lu - jah! Hal-le - lu - jah! The king-dom of this—
mf
f
world is be - come the King - dom of our
world is be - - come the King - dom of our—
world is be - - come the King - dom of our
world is be - - come the King - dom of our—
Lord and of His Christ, and of His Christ;
Lord and of His Christ, and of His Christ;
Lord and of His Christ, and of His Christ;
Lord and of His Christ, and of His Christ; and He shall reign for ev - er and

and He shall reign for ev- - er and ev- - -
ev - er, for ev - er and ev- - er, and He shall
and He shall reign for ev- - er and
er, and He shall reign for ev- - er and
reign, and He shall reign for ev- er, for
and He shall reign for ev - er and ev- -
ev- - er, for ev-er and ev-er, for ev - er and
ev- - er. and He shall reign for ev-er and
ev-er, for ev-er, for ev-er and ev-er, for ev - er, for ev-er and

er. King of Kings,
ev - er. King of Kings,
ev - er, for ev - er and ev - er. Hal-le-lu-jah! Hal-le-
ev - er, for ev - er and ev - er. Hal-le-lu-jah! Hal-le-
and Lord of Lords.
and Lord of Lords.
lu-jah! For ev - er and ev - er. Hal-le-lu-jah! Hal-le-
lu-jah! For ev - er and ev - er. Hal-le-lu-jah! Hal-le-
King of Kings,
For ev - er and ev - er. Hal-le-lu-jah! Hal-le-
lu-jah! For ev - er and ev - er. Hal-le-lu-jah! Hal-le-
lu-jah! For ev - er and ev - er. Hal-le-lu-jah! Hal-le-

and Lord of Lords,
lu-jah! For ev-er and ev-er. Hal-le-lu-jah! Hal-le-
lu-jah! For ev-er and ev-er. Hal-le-lu-jah! Hal-le-
lu-jah! For ev-er and ev-er. Hal-le-lu-jah! Hal-le-
King of Kings,
lu-jah! For ev-er and ev-er. Hal-le-lu-jah! Hal-le-
lu-jah! For ev-er and ev-er. Hal-le-lu-jah! Hal-le-
lu-jah! For ev-er and ev-er. Hal-le-lu-jah! Hal-le-
ff
and Lord of Lords, and Lord of Lords, and He shall
lu-jah! King of Kings, and Lord of Lords,
lu-jah! King of Kings, and Lord of Lords,
lu-jah! King of Kings, and Lord of Lords, and He shall
f

reign, and
and He shall reign, and He shall
and He shall reign, and He shall reign,
reign for ev - er and ev - er,
He shall reign for ev - er and ev - er,
reign for ev - er and ev - er, King of
and He shall reign for ev - er and ev - er, King of
and He shall reign for ev - er and ev - er, King of
for ev - er and ev - er. Hal - le - lu - jah! Hal - le -
Kings, for ev - er and ev - er, and Lord of Lords. Hal - le - lu - jah! Hal - le -
Kings, and Lord of Lords,
Kings, for ev - er and ev - er, and Lord of Lords. Hal - le - lu - jah! Hal - le -

lu - jah! and He shall reign for ev - - er, for
lu - jah! and He shall reign for
and He shall reign for ev - - er, for
lu - jah! and He shall reign for ev - - er, for
ev - er and ev - - er, King of Kings, and Lord of
ev - er and ev - - er, King of Kings, and Lord of
ev - er and ev - - er, King of Kings, and Lord of
ev - er and ev - - er, King of Kings, and Lord of
Lords, King of Kings, and Lord of Lords, and
Lords, King of Kings, and Lord of Lords, and
Lords, King of Kings, and Lord of Lords, and
Lords, King of Kings, and Lord of Lords, and He shall

He shall reign for ev-er and ev - - er, King of

He shall reign for ev-er and ev - - er, for ev-er and

He shall reign for ev-er and ev - - er, for ev-er and

reign for ev - - er, for ev-er and ev - - er, for ev-er and

Kings, and Lord of Lords. Hal-le-lu-jah! Hal-le-

ev - er, for ev - er and ev - er. Hal-le-lu-jah! Hal-le-

ev - er, for ev - er and ev - er. Hal-le-lu-jah! Hal-le-

ev - er, for ev - er and ev - er. Hal-le-lu-jah! Hal-le-

lu-jah! Hal-le-lu-jah! Hal-le - lu-jah! Hal - le - lu - jah!

lu-jah! Hal-le-lu-jah! Hal-le - lu-jah! Hal - le - lu - jah!

lu-jah! Hal-le-lu-jah! Hal-le - lu-jah! Hal - le - lu - jah!

lu-jah! Hal-le-lu-jah! Hal-le - lu-jah! Hal - le - lu - jah!

21. JOHANN SEBASTIAN BACH (1685-1750),
Organ Fugue in G minor ("Little") (1709?)

tr
tr
(tr)
tr
(tr)

tr

tr
tr
tr

(tr)

22. BACH, Organ Passacaglia and Fugue in C minor (1717?)

3
3
3
3

Thema fugatum.

Adagio

23. BACH, Brandenburg Concerto No. 2 in F major (1721?)

Tr. (F)
Fl.
Ob.
Vl.
Vl.
Vla.
V.
Vcl. Cont.
tr
10

Tr. (F)
Fl.
Ob.
tr
Vl.
Vl.
Vla.
V.
Vcl. Cont.

Tr. (F)
Fl.
tr
Ob.
Vl.
Vl.
Vla.
V.
Vcl. Cont.

20
Tr.
Fl.
Ob.
Vl.
Vl.
Vla.
V.
Vcl.
Cont.

Tr.
tr.
Fl.
Ob.
Vl.
Vl.
Vla.
V.
Vcl.
Cont.

Tr. (F)
Fl.
Ob.
Vl.
Vl.
Vla.
V.
Vcl. Cont.

Tr. (F)
tr
Fl.
Ob.
Vl.
Vl.
Vla.
V.
Vcl. Cont.

30

Tr. (F)
Fl.
Ob.
Vl.
Vl.
Vla.
V.
Vcl. Cont.

Tr. (F)
Fl.
Ob.
Vl.
Vl.
Vla.
V.
Vcl. Cont.

Tr. (F)
Fl.
Ob.
Vl.
Vl.
Vla.
V.
Vcl. Cont.

40
Tr. (F)
Fl.
Ob.
Vl.
Vl.
Vla.
V.
Vcl. Cont.
p
piu Piano
pp

Tr.
(F)
Fl.
Ob.
Vl.
Vl.
Vla.
V.
Vcl.
Cont.
pp
p

Tr.
(F)
Fl.
Ob.
Vl.
Vl.
Vla.
V.
Vcl.
Cont.
p
pp
f

Tr.
(F)
Fl.
Ob.
Vl.
Vl.
Vla.
V.
Vcl.
Cont.

Tr. (F)
Fl.
Ob.
Vl.
Vl.
Vla.
V.
Vcl. Cont.

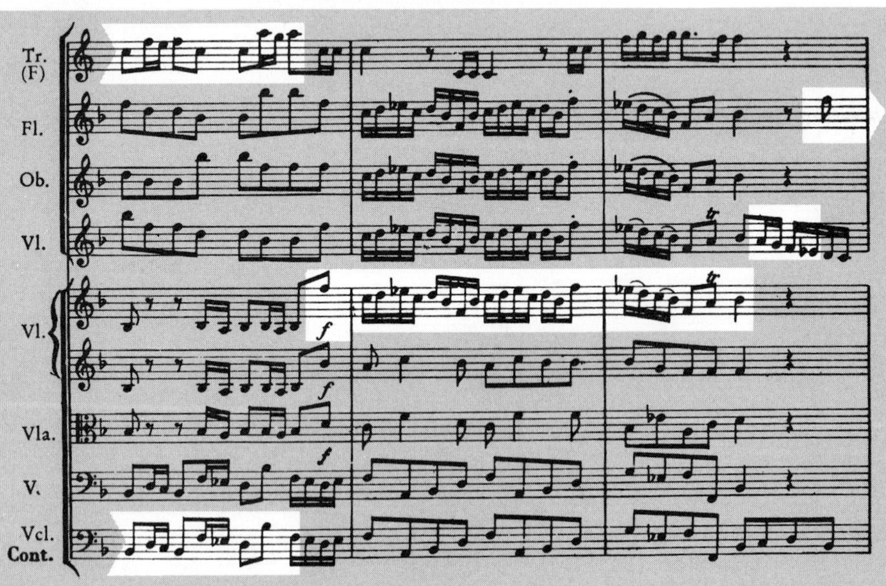
Tr. (F)
Fl.
Ob.
Vl.
Vl.
Vla.
V.
Vcl. Cont.

60
Tr. (F)
Fl.
Ob.
Vl.
Vl.
Vla.
V.
Vcl. Cont.

Tr. (F)
Fl.
Ob.
Vl.
Vl.
Vla.
V.
Vcl. Cont.

Tr. (F)
tr
Fl.
Ob.
Vl.
Vl.
p
p
Vla.
p
V.
Vcl. Cont.

70

Tr. (F)
Fl.
Ob.
Vl.
Vl.
f
f
Vla.
V.
Vcl. Cont.

Tr.
(F)
Fl.
Ob.
Vl.
Vl.
Vla.
V.
Vcl.
Cont.

Tr.
(F)
Fl.
Ob.
Vl.
Vl.
Vla.
V.
Vcl.
Cont.

80
Tr. (F)
Fl.
Ob.
Vl.
Vl.
Vla.
Vl.
Vcl. Cont.

Tr. (F)
Fl.
Ob.
Vl.
Vl.
Vla.
Vl.
Vcl. Cont.

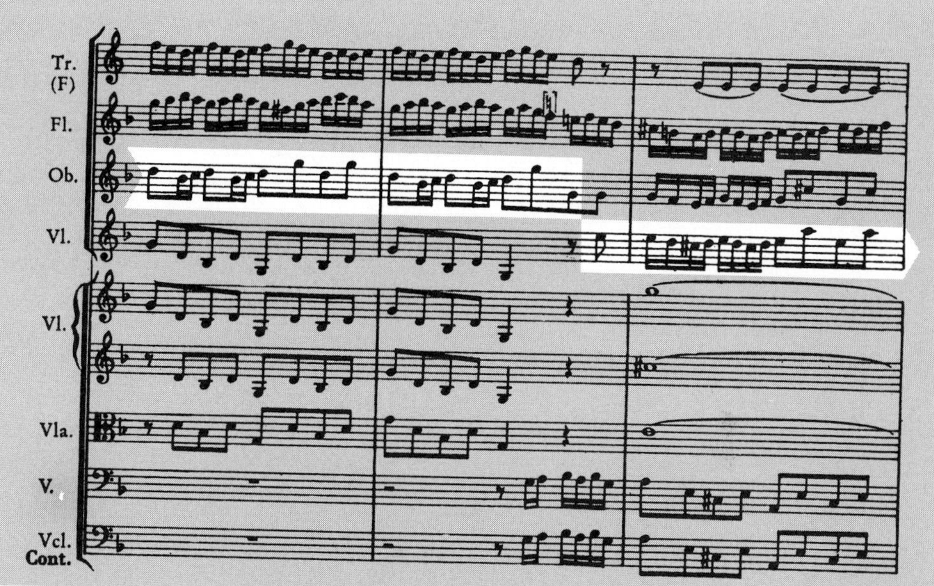
Tr.
(F)
Fl.
Ob.
Vl.
Vl.
Vla.
V.
Vcl.
Cont.

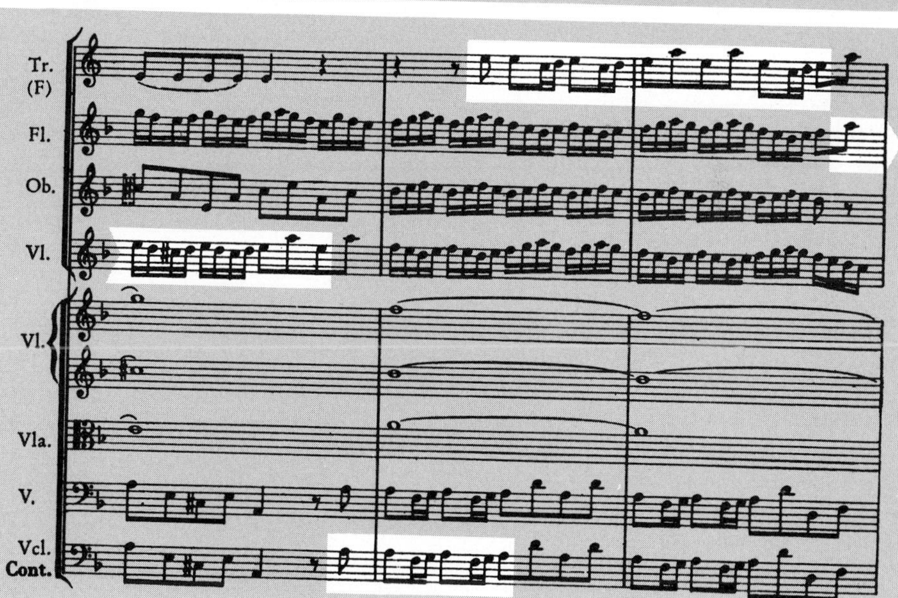
Tr.
(F)
Fl.
Ob.
Vl.
Vl.
Vla.
V.
Vcl.
Cont.

90
Tr. (F)
Fl.
Ob.
Vl.
Vl.
Vla.
V.
Vcl. Cont.
p
p
Tr. (F)
Fl.
Ob.
Vl.
Vl.
Vla.
V.
Vcl. Cont.
f
f
p
p
p
p
f
f
f

Tr.
(F)
Fl.
Ob.
Vl.
Vl.
Vla.
V.
Vcl.
Cont.

100
Tr.
(F)
Fl.
Ob.
Vl.
Vl.
Vla.
V.
Vcl.
Cont.

Tr.
(F)
Fl.
Ob.
Vl.
Vl.
Vla.
V.
Vcl.
Cont.
tasto solo
accomp.

Tr.
(F)
Fl.
Ob.
Vl.
Vl.
Vla.
V.
Vcl.
Cont.

110
Tr. (F)
Fl.
Ob.
Vl.
Vl.
Vla.
V.
Vcl. Cont.
f
p
7
6
4
7
Tr. (F)
Fl.
Ob.
Vl.
Vl.
Vla.
V.
Vcl. Cont.
f
p
6
4+
2

Tr. (F)
Fl.
Ob.
Vl.
Vl.
Vla.
V.
Vcl. Cont.
f

2.
Andante.
Flauto.
Oboe.
Violino.
Violoncello e Cembalo.
tr
10
Fl.
Ob.
Vl.
Vcl. Cont.
20

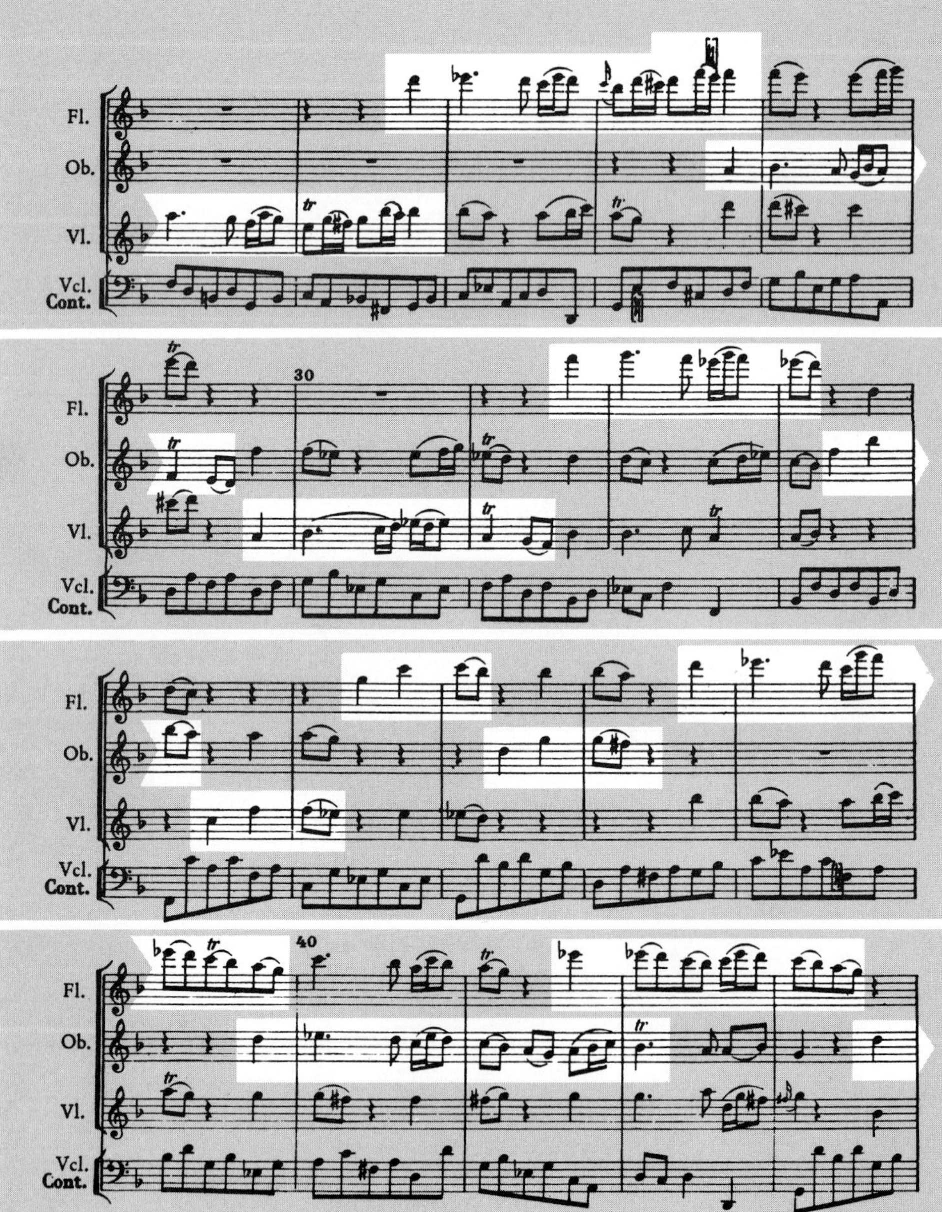
Fl.
Ob.
Vl.
Vcl.
Cont.
tr
30
40

Fl.
Ob.
Vl.
Vcl.
Cont.
50
60
tr

3. Allegro assai.
Tromba (in F)
Flauto.
Oboe.
Violino.
Violino I rip.
Violino II rip.
Viola rip.
Violone rip
Violoncello e Cembalo.

Tr. (F)
Fl.
Ob.
Vl.
Vl.
Vla.
V.
Vcl. Cont.
10

Tr.
(F)
Fl.
Ob.
Vl.
Vl.
Vla.
V.
Vcl.
Cont.

20
Tr.
(F)
Fl.
Ob.
Vl.
Vl.
Vla.
V.
Vcl.
Cont.

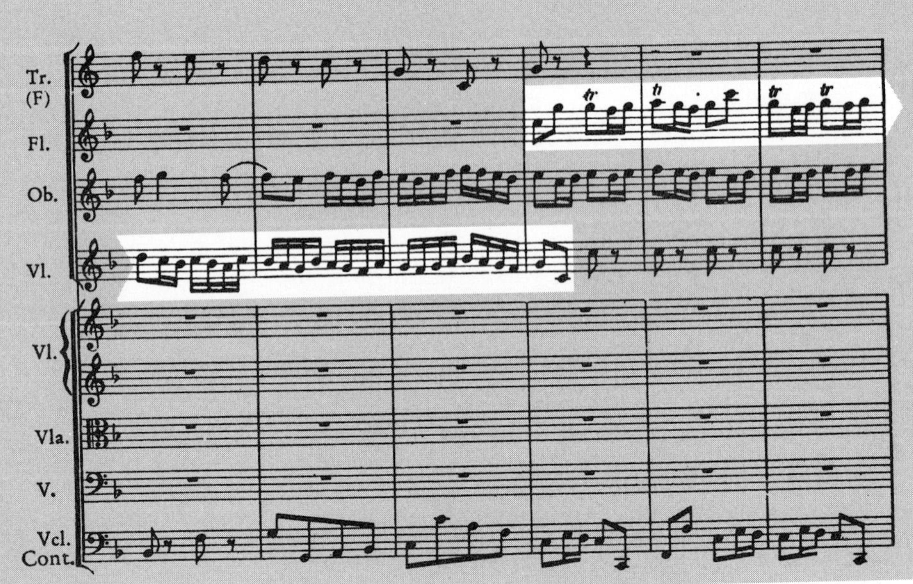
Tr. (F)
tr
Fl.
Ob.
Vl.
Vl.
Vla.
V.
Vcl. Cont.

30
Tr. (F)
tr
Fl.
Ob.
Vl.
Vl.
Vla.
V.
Vcl. Cont.

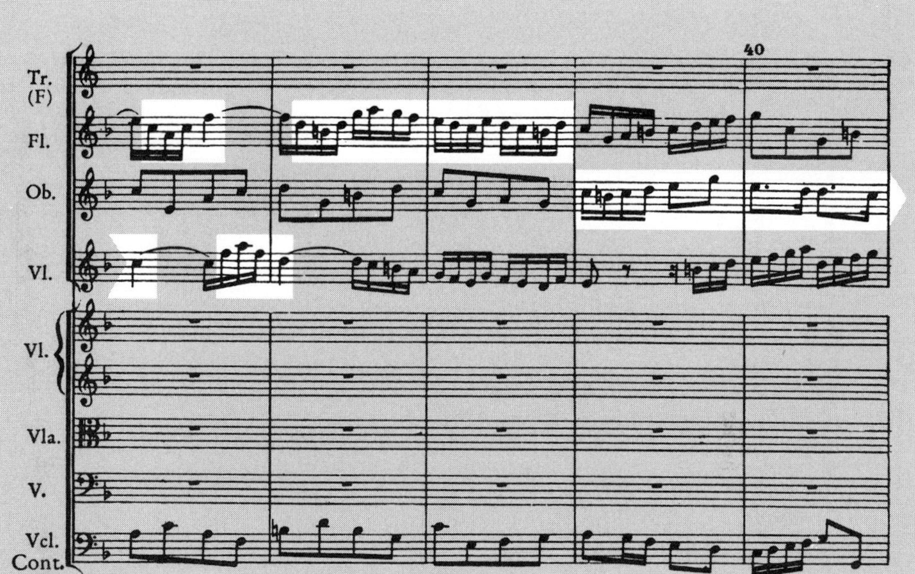
40
Tr.
(F)
Fl.
Ob.
Vl.
Vl.
Vla.
V.
Vcl.
Cont.

Tr.
(F)
Fl.
Ob.
Vl.
Vl.
Vla.
V.
Vcl.
Cont.

50
Tr. (F)
Fl.
Ob.
Vl.
Vl.
Vla.
V.
Vcl. Cont.

Tr. (F)
Fl.
Ob.
Vl.
Vl.
Vla.
V.
Vcl. Cont.

60
Tr. (F)
Fl.
Ob.
Vl.
Vl.
Vla.
V.
Vcl. Cont.

Tr. (F)
Fl.
Ob.
Vl.
Vl.
Vla.
V.
Vcl. Cont.

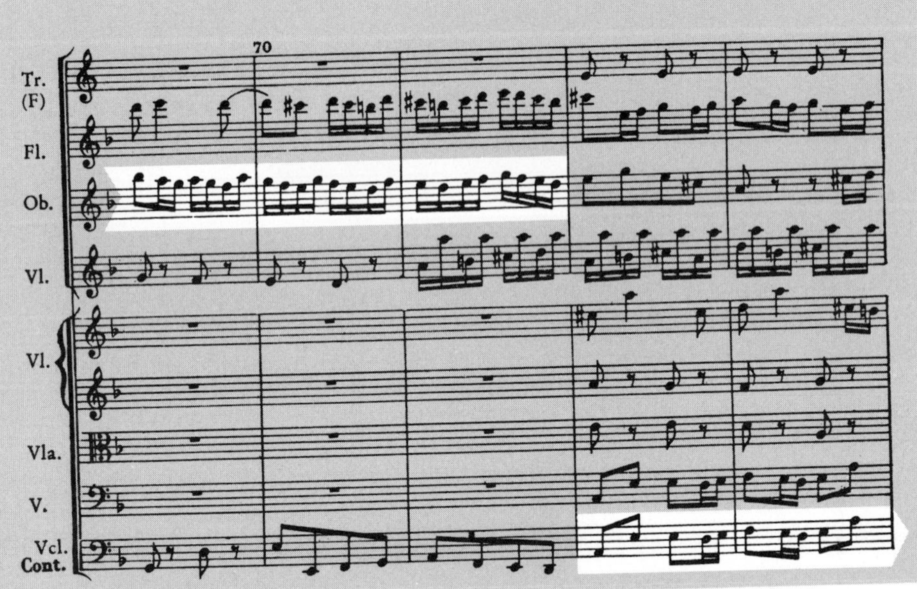
70
Tr.
(F)
Fl.
Ob.
Vl.
Vl.
Vla.
V.
Vcl.
Cont.

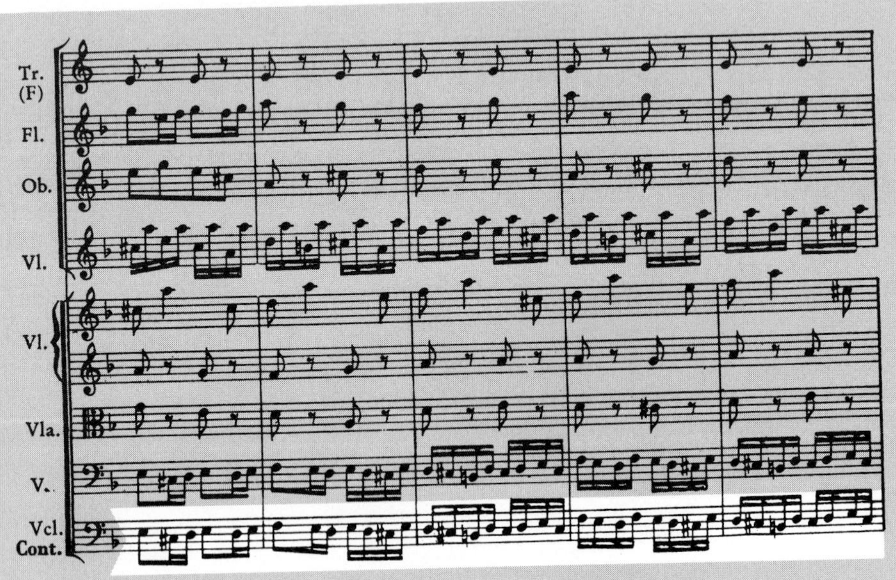
Tr.
(F)
Fl.
Ob.
Vl.
Vl.
Vla.
V.
Vcl.
Cont.

80
Tr. (F)
Fl.
Ob.
Vl.
Vl.
Vla.
V.
Vcl. Cont.

tr
Tr. (F)
Fl.
Ob.
Vl.
Vl.
Vla.
V.
Vcl. Cont.

90
Tr. (F)
Fl.
Ob.
Vl.
Vl.
Vla.
V.
Vcl. Cont.

Tr. (F)
Fl.
Ob.
Vl.
Vl.
Vla.
V.
Vcl. Cont.

100
Tr.
(F)
Fl.
Ob.
Vl.
Vl.
Vla.
V.
Vcl.
Cont.

Tr.
(F)
Fl.
Ob.
Vl.
Vl.
Vla.
V.
Vcl.
Cont.

110

Tr. (F)
Fl.
Ob.
Vl.
Vl.
Vla.
V.
Vcl. Cont.

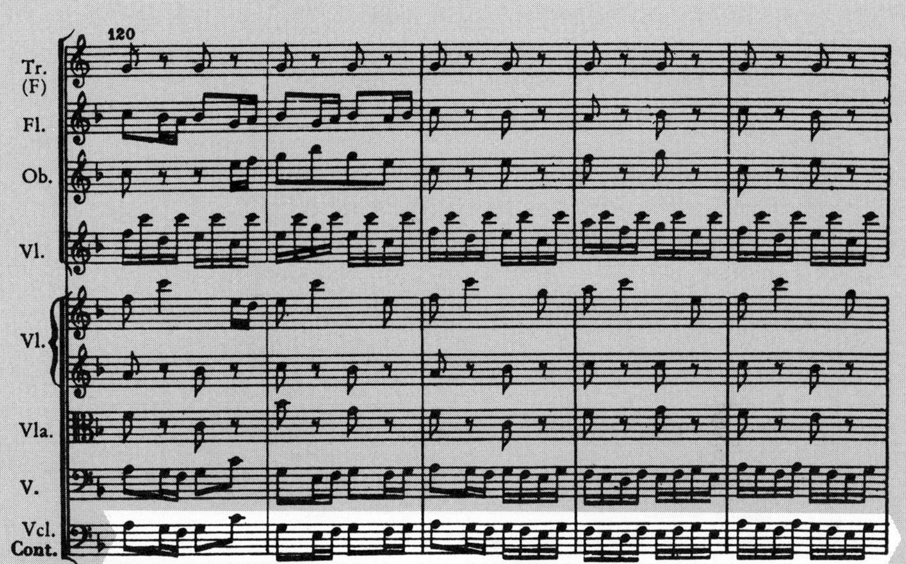
120
Tr. (F)
Fl.
Ob.
Vl.
Vl.
Vla.
V.
Vcl. Cont.

Tr. (F)
Fl.
Ob.
Vl.
Vl.
Vla.
V.
Vcl. Cont.

130
Tr. (F)
Fl.
Ob.
Vl.
Vl.
Vla.
V.
Vcl. Cont.
Tr. (F)
Fl.
Ob.
Vl.
Vl.
Vla.
V.
Vcl. Cont.

24. BACH, Prelude and Fugue in C minor from *The Well-Tempered Clavier*, Book I (PUBL. 1722)

Presto.
Adagio.
Allegro.

25. BACH, Air and Gigue from Suite No. 3 in D major (1723?)

10
Vl.
Vla.
C.

Vl.
Vla.
C.

[tr]
Vl.
tr
Vla.
C.

Oboe I
Oboe II
Tromba I (in D)
Tromba II (in D)
Tromba III (in D)
Timpani
tr
Violino I
Violino II
Viola
Continuo

10
Ob.
Tr. (D)
I
II
Vl.
Vla.
C.

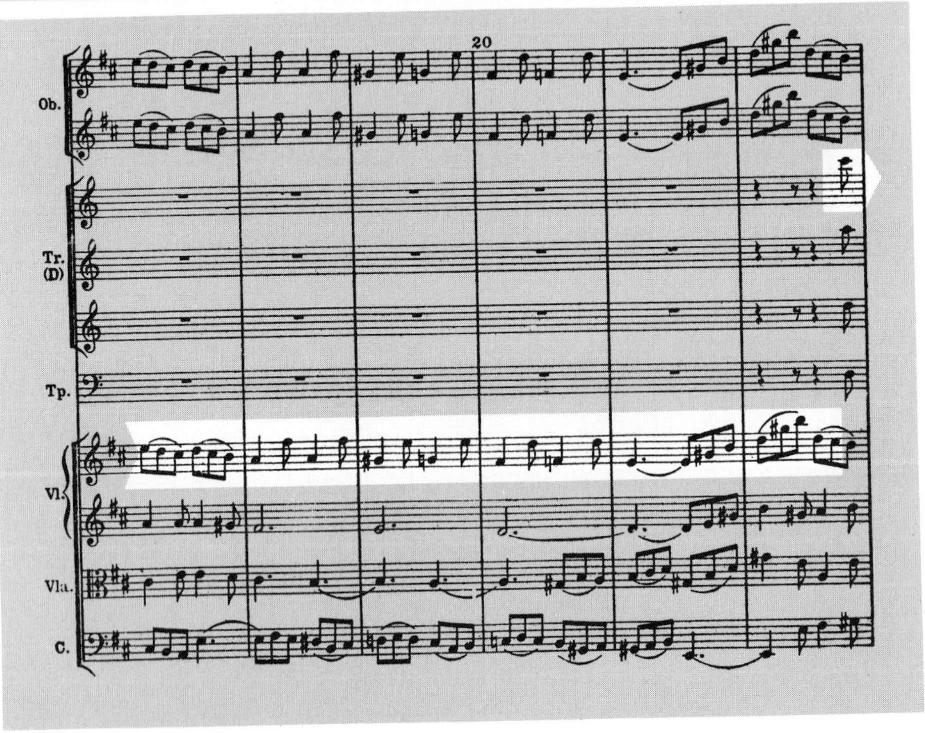

20
Ob.
Tr.
(D)
Tp.
Vl.
Vla.
C.

Ob.
Tr.
(D)
Tp.
[tr]
tr
[tr]
Vl.
Vla.
C.

30
Ob.
Tr.
(D)
Tp.
[tr]
Vl.
Vla.
C.

Ob.
Tr.
(D)
Tp.
Vl.
Vla.
C.

40
Ob.
Tr.
(D)
Tp.
Vl.
Vla.
C.

50
Ob.
Tr.
(D)
tr
[tr]
Tp.
Vl.
Vla.
C.

Ob.
Tr.
(D)
Vl.
Vla.
C.

60
Ob.
Tr.
(D)
Tp.
Vl.
Vla.
C.

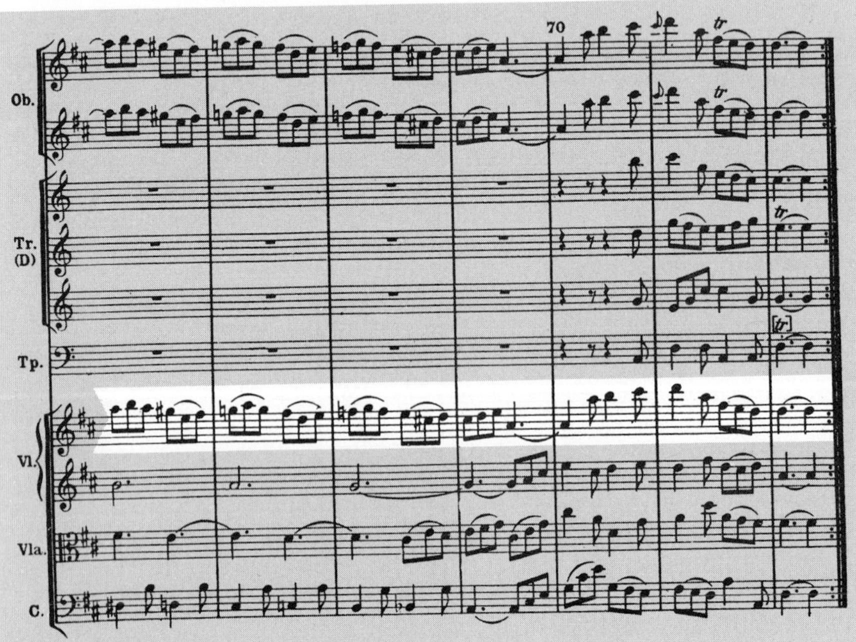
70
tr
Ob.
Tr.
(D)
Tp.
Vl.
Vla.
C.

26. BACH, Cantata No. 140, *Wachet auf* (1731)

10
Ob.
Tail.
Vl.
Vla.
Cont.
6 6 9 5 6 5 9 5♭

Ob.
Tail.
tr
Vl.
Vla.
Cont.
6 5 6 4 2 6 5 6 4 2 6 6 5 6 4 5 3

20

1.

Ob. — piano — forte

Tail.

Vl. — piano — (forte)

Vla.

S. Wa - - - chet auf, ruft uns

A. Wa - chet auf, wa - chet auf, ruft

T. Wa - chet auf, wa - chet

B. Wa - chet

Cont.

Ob.

Tail.

Vl. I

S. die Stim - - - - - - - me

A. uns die Stim - me, ruft uns die Stim - me

T. auf, ruft uns die Stim - - me, die Stim - me

B. auf, wa - chet auf, ruft uns die Stim - me

Cont.

30

Ob.
Tail.
Vl.
Vla.
S.
T.
Cont.

der Wäch - - -

der Wächter sehr

5 6 4 2 6 5 — 7 7 ♮ 6 5 7 ♮ 6 4 2 6 6 4 2 7

Ob.
Vl.
Vla.
S.
der Zin - - - - - - - - ne,
A.
auf der Zin - - - ne, hoch auf der Zin - ne,
T.
ne, der Wächter sehr hoch auf der Zin - ne,
B.
- ne, der Wächter sehr hoch auf der Zin - ne,
Cont.
6 3 6 9 3 6 ♮ 6
5 5 5
40
Ob.
Tail.
Vl.
Vla.
S.
Cont.
6 6 7 6 6 7
5 ♮ 5

1.
Ob.
Tail.
Vl.
Vla.
S.
wach auf, du Stadt Je - - - -
A.
wach auf, wach auf, wach auf, du Stadt Je-ru - sa - lem, wach auf,
T.
wach auf, wach auf, wach auf, du Stadt Je - ru - sa - lem,
B.
wach auf, wach auf, wach auf, du Stadt Je - ru - sa - lem, wach auf,
Cont.

50

Ob.

Tail.

Vl.

Vla.

S. ru - - - sa - - - lem!

A. du Stadt Je - ru - sa - lem, wach auf, du Stadt Je -

T. du Stadt Je - ru - sa - lem, wach auf, du Stadt Je - ru - sa -

B. du Stadt Je - ru - sa - - lem, wach auf, du Stadt Je -

Cont.

6 5 7 6 5 6 4 3♭ 6 4 2 6 5♭ 7♭

Ob.
Tail.
Vl.
Vla.
S.
A.
ru - - sa - lem!
T.
lem, Je - ru - sa - lem!
B.
ru - - sa - lem!
Cont.

Ob.
Tail.
Vl.
Vla.
Cont.
6 6 9 5 6 5 9 5♭

Ob.
Tail.
Vl.
Vla.
Cont.
6 5 6 4 2 6 5 6 4 2 6 6 6 4 5 3

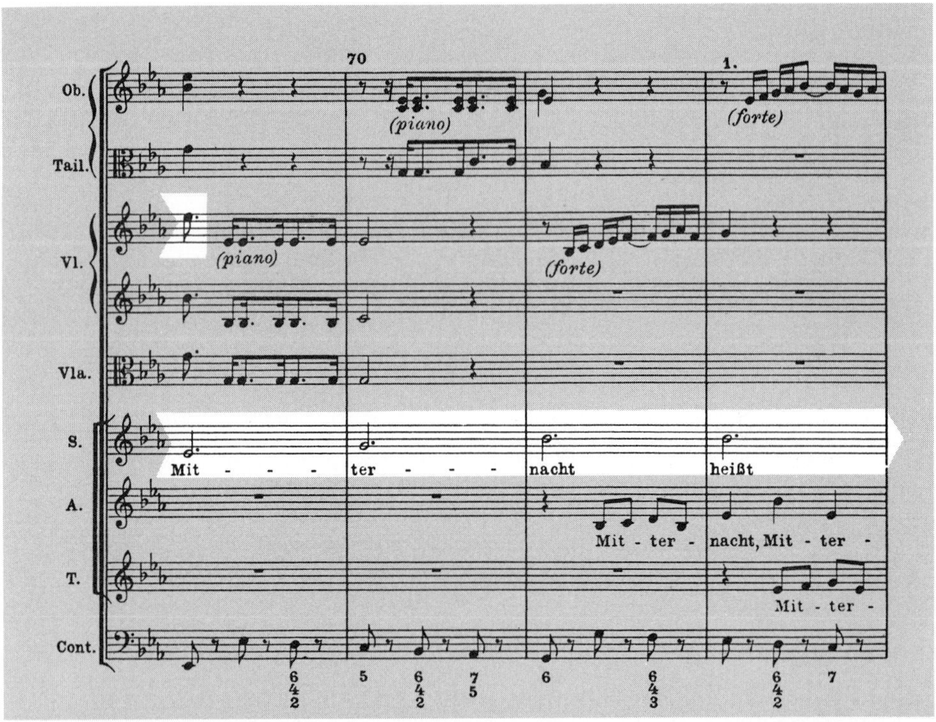

70
1.
Ob.
Tail.
Vl.
Vla.
S.
A.
T.
Cont.
(piano)
(forte)
(piano)
(forte)
Mit - - - ter - - - nacht heißt
Mit - ter - nacht, Mit - ter -
Mit - ter -

Ob.
Vl.
S.
A.
T.
B.
Cont.
die - - se Stun - - - - - - -
nacht heißt die - se Stun - de, heißt die - - se
nacht, Mit - ter - nacht heißt die - se Stun - de, die-se
Mit - ter - nacht, Mit - ter - nacht heißt die - se

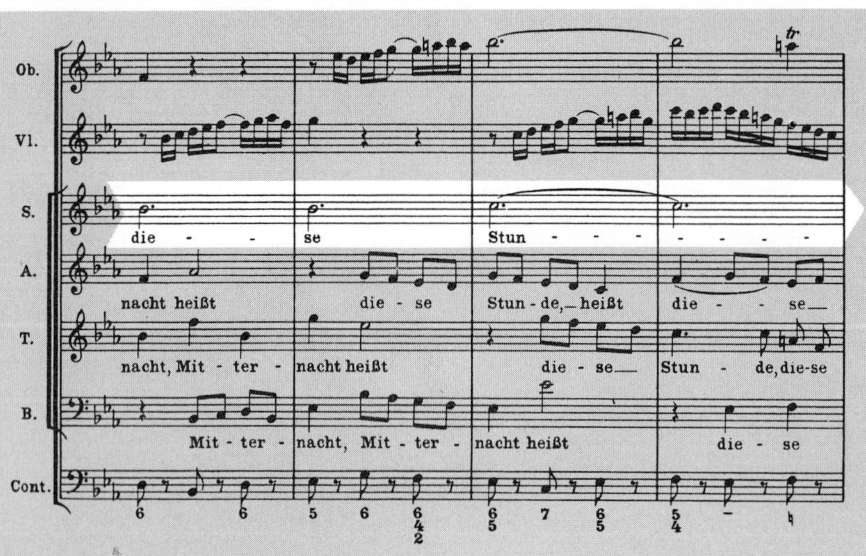

80
1.
Ob.
Tail.
Vl.
Vla.
S.
A
T.
B.
Cont.
de;
sie
Stun-de;
Stun - de;
Stun - de;
ru - - - fen
uns
mit
sie ru-fen uns mit hel - - - - - lem
sie ru-fen uns mit hel - - - - - - - - lem
sie ru-fen uns mit hel - - -

90

Ob.

Tail.

Vl.

Vla.

S.

de:

A.

Mun - de:

T.

Mun - de:

B.

Mun - de:

Cont.

6 6 6 5 6

Ob.
Tail.
Vl.
Vla.
S.
A.
T.
B.
Cont.
1.
wo seid ihr klu - - -
wo, wo, wo, wo, wo seid ihr klu-gen Jung-
wo, wo, wo, wo, wo seid ihr klu-gen Jung-
wo, wo, wo, wo, wo seid ihr, wo, wo, wo— seid

100

Ob.

Tail.

Vl.

Vla.

S. gen Jung - - frau - - - en?

A. frau-en, wo, wo seid ihr klu - gen Jung - frau - en, wo

T. frau - en, wo seid ihr, wo seid ihr klu-gen Jung - frau'n, wo seid

B. ihr, wo seid ihr klu - gen Jung - frau - - - en, wo seid ihr

Cont.

5 6/4/2 6/5 7 6/5 6/4/3♭ 6/4/2

Ob.
Tail.
Vl.
Vla.
S.
A. seid ihr klu - gen Jung-frau - en, wo, wo?
T. ihr, ihr klu - gen Jung-frau - en, wo, wo?
B. klu - gen Jung - frau - en, — wo, wo?
Cont.
6/5b 7b 5 6 6 6

Ob.
Tail.
Vl.
Vla.
Cont.
Ob.
Tail.
Vl.
Vla.
S.
A.
T.
B.
Cont.
Wohl
Wohl auf, wohl auf,
Wohl auf, wohl auf,
Wohl auf, wohl auf, wohl auf, wohl
Wohl auf, wohl auf, der Bräut' - gam

120
Ob.
Taill.
Vl.
Vla.
S.
auf, der Bräut' - - - gam
A.
der Bräut'gam kömmt, wohl auf, wohl auf, wohl auf! der Bräut'gam
T.
auf, wohl auf, wohl auf, der Bräut'gam kömmt, wohl auf, wohl
B.
kömmt, wohl auf, der Bräut'gam kömmt, wohl auf, der Bräut'gam
Cont.

Ob.
Tail.
Vl.
Vla.
S.
kömmt,
A.
kömmt, wohl auf, wohl auf,
steht
T.
auf, wohl auf, wohl auf,
steht auf, steht
B.
kömmt, wohl auf, wohl auf,
steht auf, steht auf,
Cont.

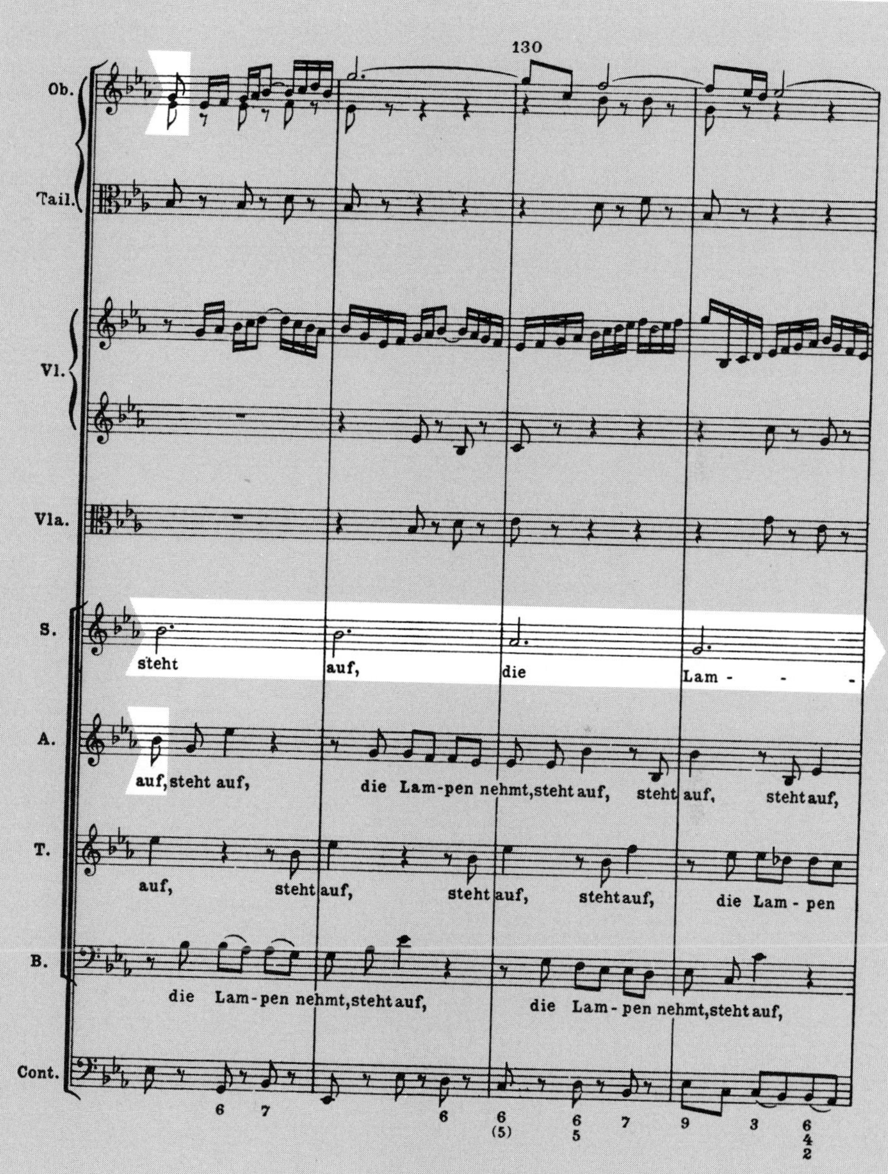
130
Ob.
Tail.
Vl.
Vla.
S.
steht auf, die Lam - - -
A.
auf, steht auf, die Lam-pen nehmt, steht auf, steht auf, steht auf,
T.
auf, steht auf, steht auf, steht auf, die Lam - pen
B.
die Lam-pen nehmt, steht auf, die Lam - pen nehmt, steht auf,
Cont.
6 7 6 6 (5) 6 5 7 9 3 6 4 2

Ob.
Tail.
Vl.
Vla.
S.
A.
T.
B.
Cont.
pen
nehmt!
die Lam-pen nehmt, steht auf, steht auf!
nehmt, steht auf, steht auf, steht auf, steht auf!
die Lam-pen nehmt, steht auf, steht auf!
Al - - -
140
- - - le - lu-ja, al-le-lu - ja,
Al - - -

1.
Ob.
Tail.
Vl.
Vla.
A.
T.
B.
Cont.
al-le-lu-ja,
al-le-lu - ja,
- - le - lu-ja, al-le-lu - ja,
Al - - - - -
6 5
7 ♮
6 4 2
6
9 8 6 7 6
6 4 2
tr
al-le-lu-ja,
al - le - lu - ja,
al-le-lu-ja,
al-le-lu - ja,
- - - le - lu-ja, al-le-lu - ja,
al - le-lu -
6 5
7
6
7 8 8
6 4 2
6 5
♮
6 4 2

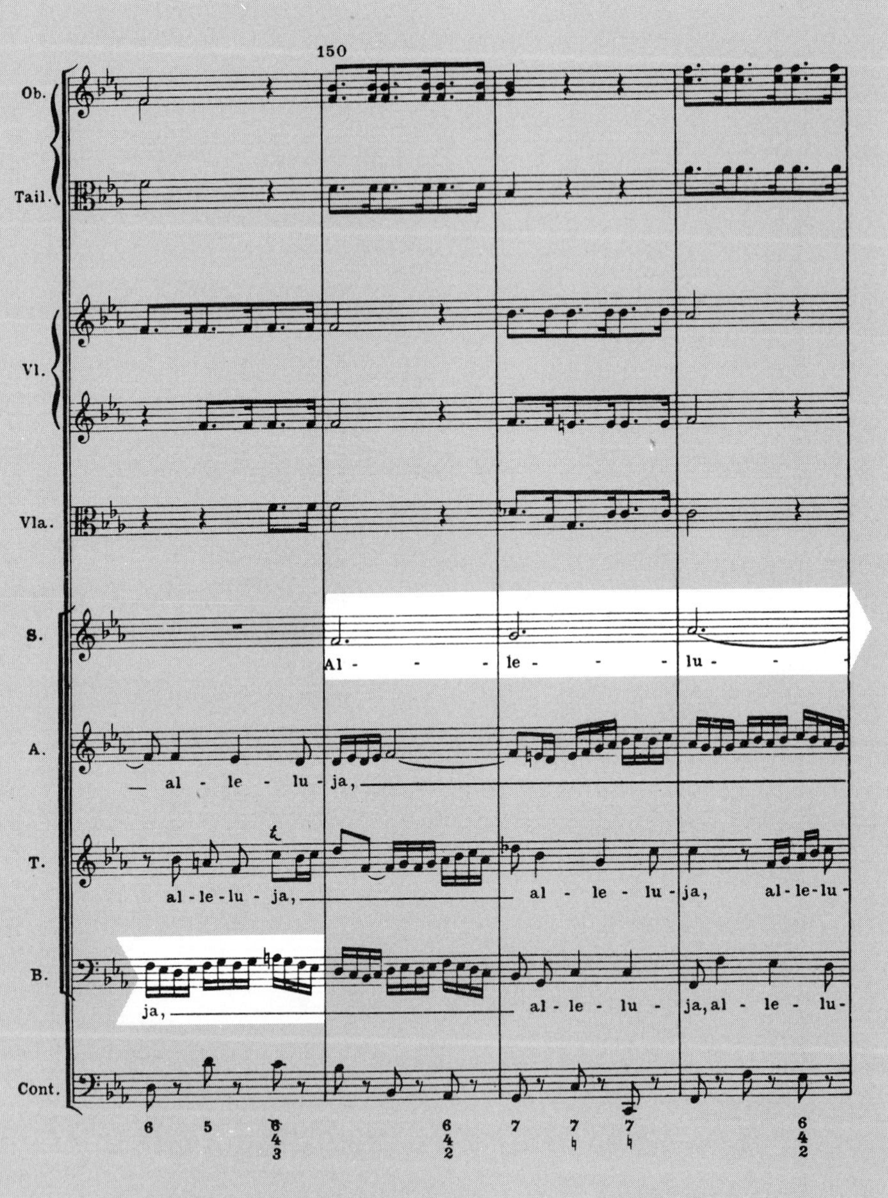
150
Ob.
Tail.
Vl.
Vla.
S.
Al - - - le - - - lu - -
A.
— al - le - lu - ja, ——
T.
al - le - lu - ja, —— al - le - lu - ja, al - le - lu -
B.
ja, —— al - le - lu - ja, al - le - lu -
Cont.
6 5 6 4 3 6 4 2 7 7 ♮ 7 ♮ 6 4 2

Ob.
Tail.
Vl.
Vla.
S.
- - - - ja!
A.
al - le - lu - ja, al - le - lu - ja!
T.
ja, al - le - lu - ja!
B.
ja, al - le - lu - ja, al - - - le - lu - ja!
Cont.
160
Ob.
Tail.
Vl.
Vla.
Cont.

Ob.
Tail.
Vl. I
S.
A.
T.
B.
Cont.
Macht euch be - - reit,
Macht euch be-reit, macht euch be-reit, be-reit, be-
Macht euch be-reit, macht euch be-reit, macht euch be - reit, be-
Macht euch be-reit, macht euch be-reit, macht euch be-reit, be-
Ob.
Tail.
Vl.
Vla.
S.
A.
T.
B.
Cont.
reit, macht euch be-reit, macht
reit, macht euch be-reit, macht
reit, macht euch be-reit,

170
Ob.
Tail.
Vl. I
S.
zu der Hoch - - - zeit,
A.
euch be - - reit, macht euch be - - reit, macht euch be -
T.
euch be - - reit, macht euch be - - reit, macht euch be -
B.
macht euch be - reit, zu der Hochzeit, macht euch be -
Cont.
6 5 6 6 5 7 6 5 6
Ob.
Tail.
Vl.
Vla.
S.
A.
reit zu der Hoch - zeit, macht euch be - reit zu der
T.
reit zu der Hoch - zeit, macht euch be - reit zu der
B.
reit zu der Hoch - zeit, macht euch be - reit zu der
Cont.
6 6 5♭ 6 5 7

180
1.

Ob.
Tail.
Vl.
Vla.
S. — ihr müs -
A. — Hoch - zeit, ihr, ihr,
T. — Hoch - zeit, ihr, ihr,
B. — Hoch - zeit, ihr, ihr,
Cont.

6 4 3 — 6 5 — 7 — 6 5 — 6 — 5 — 6

Ob.
Tail.
Vl.
Vla.
S.
set ihm ent - - - ge - - - gen
A.
ihr müs-set ihm ent-ge - gen gehn, ihr müs - - set ihm ent - ge - gen, ent -
T.
ihr müs - set ihm ent - ge - - gen gehn, ihm ent - ge - gen gehn
B.
müs-set ihm ent - ge - gen gehn, ihr müs - set ihm ent - ge-gen
Cont.
6 6 6 5 6 4 2 6 5 7 6 5

Ob.
Tail.
Vl.
Vla.
S.
gehn.
A.
ge-gen gehn, ihr müs-set ihm ent - ge - - - gen gehn.
T.
ihr müs - set ihm ent-ge-gen gehn, ent-ge - gen gehn.
B.
gehn, ihr müs - set ihm ent - ge - - - gen gehn.
Cont.
Dal Segno

Tenore
Continuo
Er kommt, er kommt,
der Bräut'gam kommt! Ihr Töch-ter
T.
Cont.
Zi - ons, kommt her - aus, sein Aus - gang
ei - let aus der Hö - he in
eu - er Mut - ter Haus.
Der Bräut'-gam kommt, der ei - nem
Re - he und jun-gen Hir-sche gleich auf
de - nen Hü-geln springt und euch das
Mahl der Hoch-zeit bringt.
Wacht auf, er - mun-tert euch! den
Bräut'gam zu em-pfan-gen; dort,
se - het, kommt er her-ge - gan-gen.

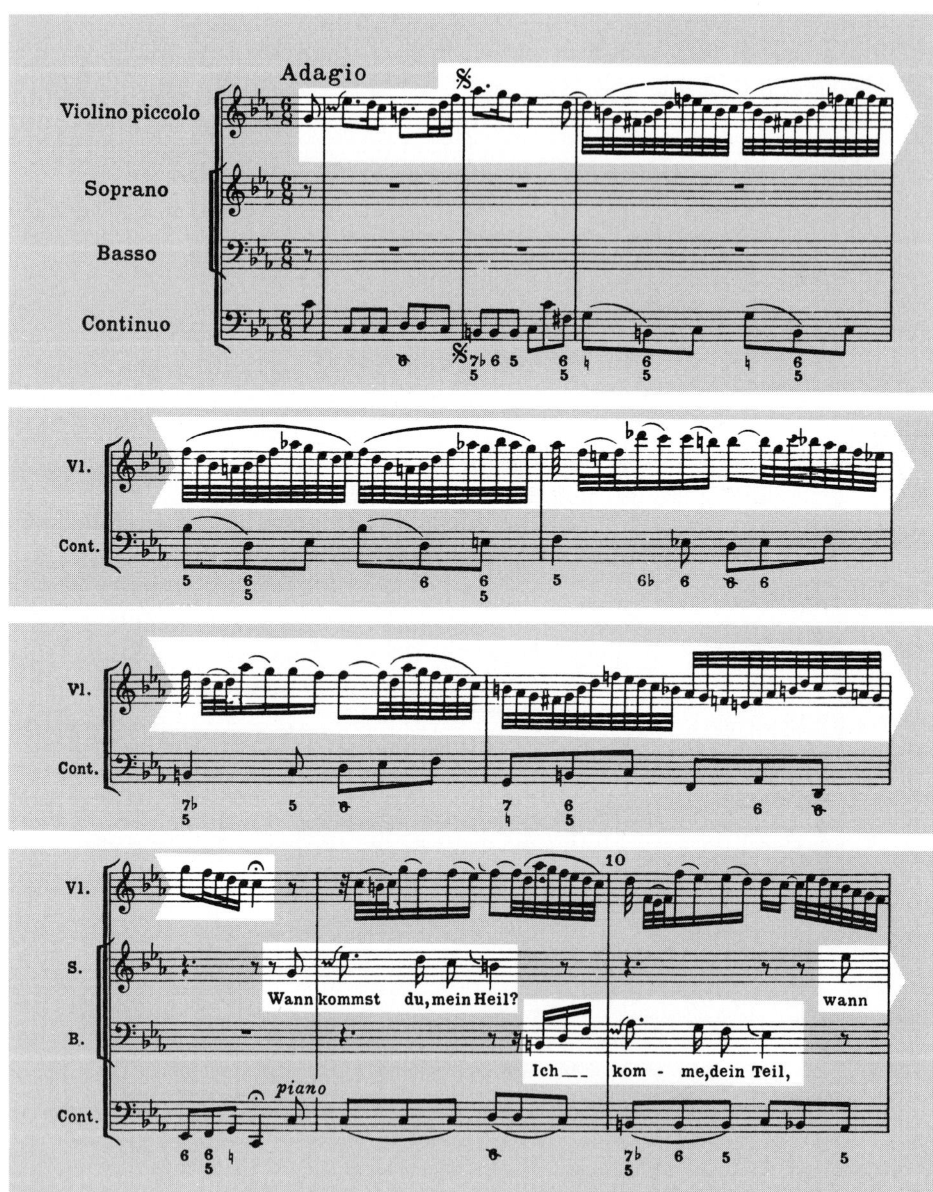
Adagio
Violino piccolo
Soprano
Basso
Continuo
Vl.
Cont.
Vl.
Cont.
Vl.
S.
B.
Cont.
piano
10
Wann kommst du, mein Heil?
wann
Ich __ kom - me, dein Teil,

Vl.
S.
B.
Cont.
kommst du, mein Heil, wann kommst du, mein
ich kom-me, dein Teil, ich_ kom-me,
Heil, mein Heil? Ich___ war- -te mit
dein Teil, dein Teil, ich komme, ich komme,
20
bren-nen-dem Ö - le; wann kommst du, mein Heil, wann
ich komme, ich___ kom-me, dein Teil,

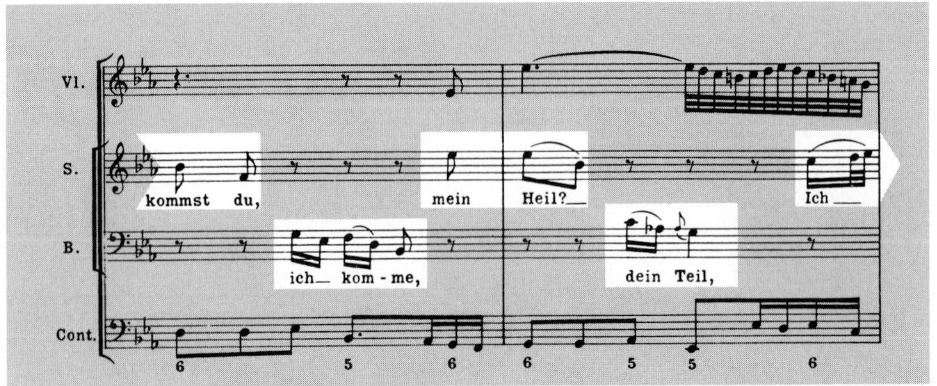
Vl.
S.
B.
Cont.
kommst du, mein Heil? Ich
ich kom - me, dein Teil,
6 5 6 6 5 5 6

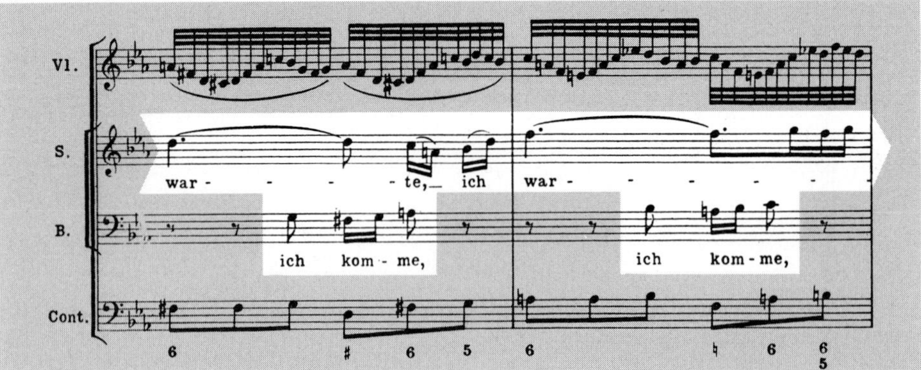
Vl.
S.
B.
Cont.
war - - te, ich war - - - - -
ich kom - me, ich kom - me,
6 ♯ 6 5 6 ♮ 6 6 5

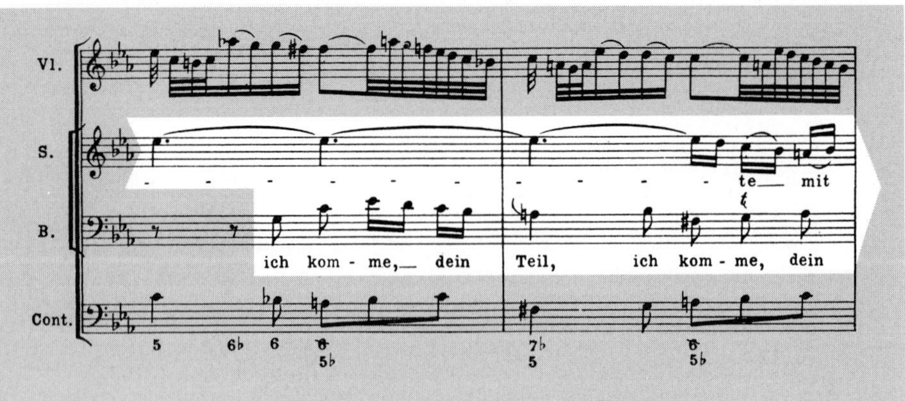
Vl.
S.
B.
Cont.
- - - - - - - - - - te mit
ich kom - me, dein Teil, ich kom - me, dein
5 6♭ 6 6 5♭ 7♭ 5 6 5♭

Vl.
S.
bren - nen - dem Ö - le, mit
brennen - dem Ö - le; wann
B.
Teil,
ich
kom - me, dein Teil,
Cont.
30
kommst du,
mein Heil? Ich
war- - -te mit brennendem Ö - le.
ich komme,
dein Teil,
ich komme!
Er - öff - ne den Saal,
Ich öff - ne den Saal,
ich

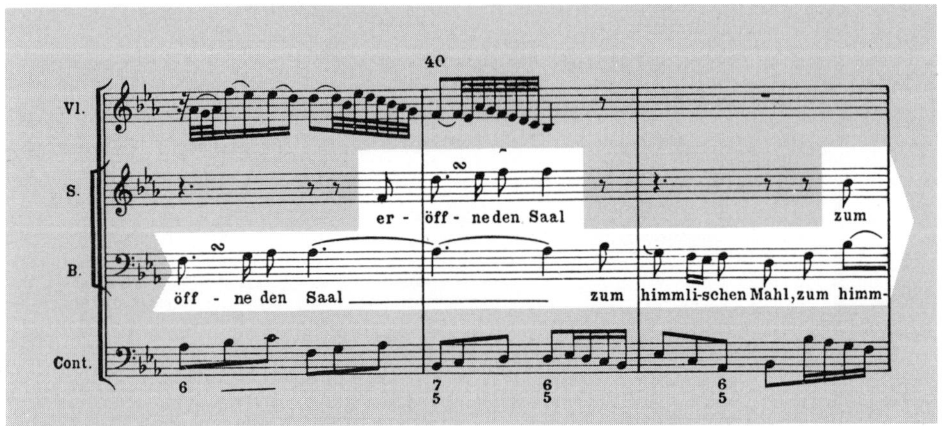
40
Vl.
S.
er - öff - ne den Saal
zum
B.
öff - ne den Saal
zum
himmli-schen Mahl, zum himm-
Cont.

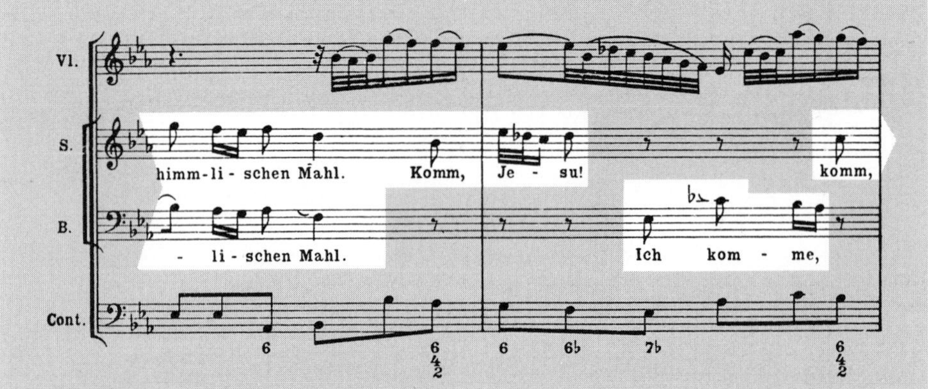
Vl.
S.
himm-li - schen Mahl.
Komm,
Je - su!
komm,
B.
- li - schen Mahl.
Ich kom - me,
Cont.

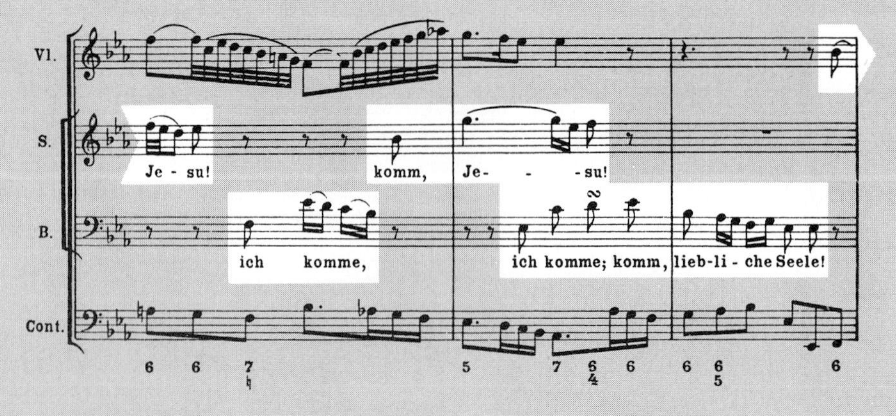
Vl.
S.
Je - su!
komm,
Je- - - su!
B.
ich komme,
ich komme; komm,
lieb-li - che Seele!
Cont.

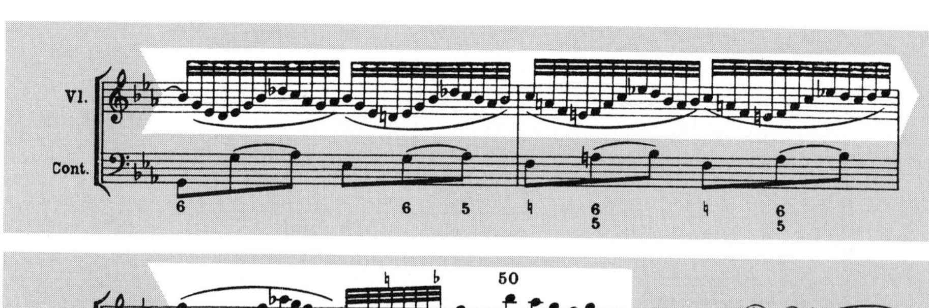
Vl.
Cont.

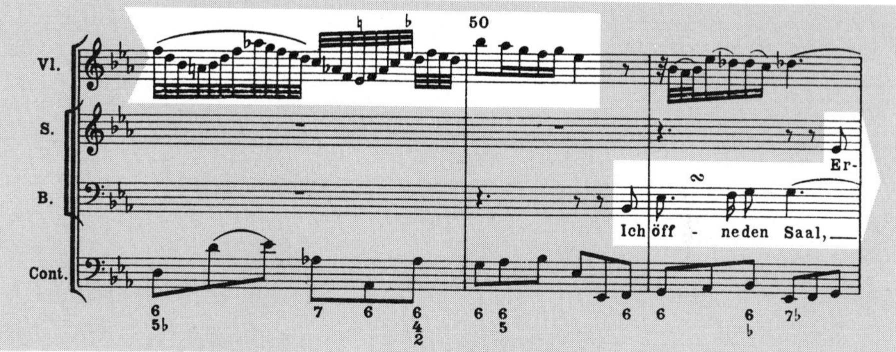
50
Vl.
S.
Er-
B.
Ich öff - ne den Saal,
Cont.

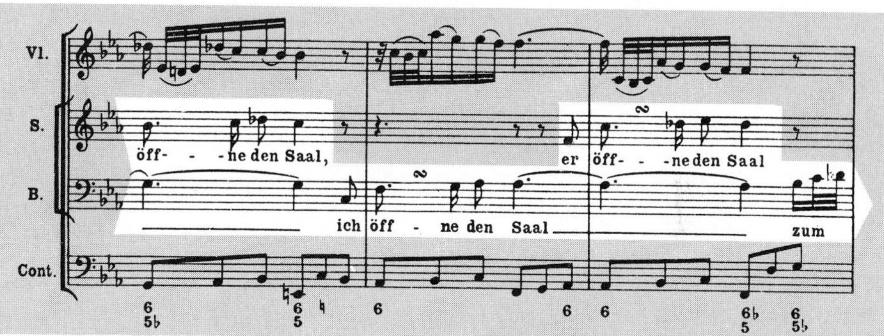
Vl.
S.
öff- - - ne den Saal, er öff- - - ne den Saal
B.
ich öff - ne den Saal zum
Cont.

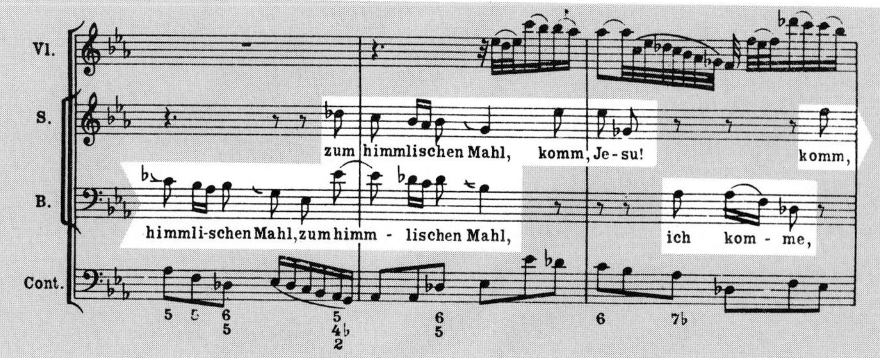
Vl.
S.
zum himmlischen Mahl, komm, Je - su! komm,
B.
himmli-schen Mahl, zum himm - lischen Mahl, ich kom - me,
Cont.

60
Vl.
S.
Je - su!
komm, Je - - - su!
B.
ich kom-me,
ich kom-me; komm', lieb-li - che See-le!
Cont.

Vl.
S.
Wann kommst du, mein Heil?
B.
Ich
Cont.

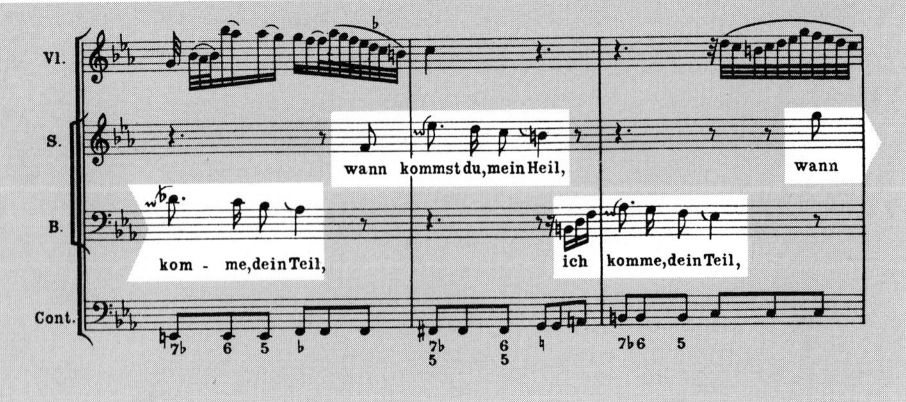
Vl.
S.
wann kommst du, mein Heil,
wann
B.
kom - me, dein Teil,
ich komme, dein Teil,
Cont.

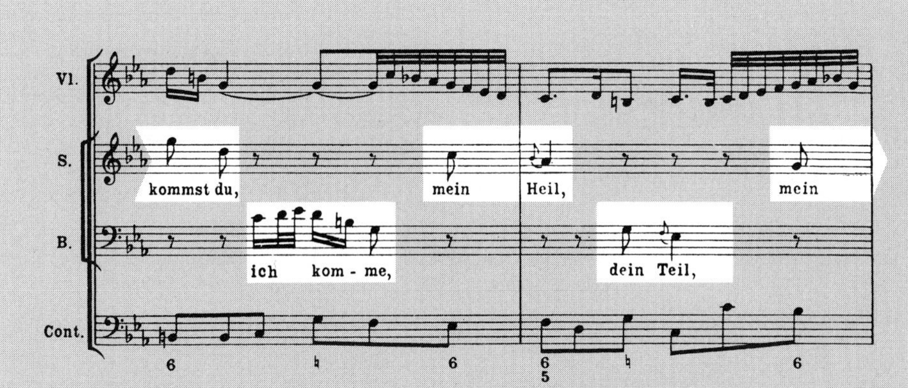
Vl.
S.
kommst du,
mein
Heil,
mein
B.
ich kom - me,
dein Teil,
Cont.

70
Vl.
S.
Heil?
ich
war- - -te, ich
war- - - -te,_ ich_
B.
dein Teil,
ich kom-me, dein Teil,
ich kom-me,
Cont.

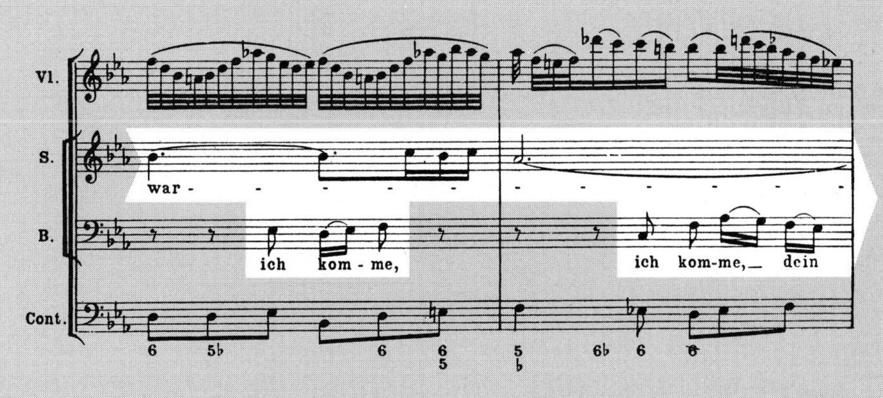
Vl.
S.
war- - - - - - - - - - - -
B.
ich kom - me,
ich kom-me,_ dein
Cont.

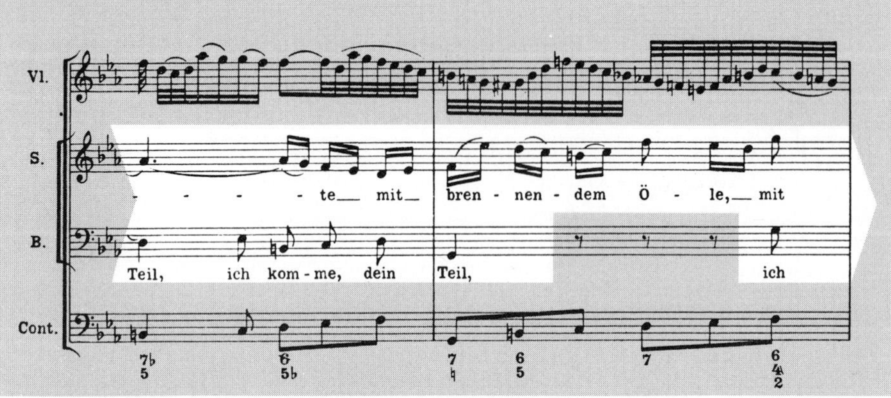
Vl.
S.
- - - - te— mit— bren - nen - dem Ö - le,— mit
B.
Teil, ich kom - me, dein Teil, ich
Cont.

Vl.
S.
brennen-dem Ö - le; wann kommst du, mein Heil,— ich—
B.
kom-me, dein Teil, ich kom-me, dein Teil,
Cont.

80
Vl.
S.
war - - - te— mit— bren - nen - dem Ö - le.
B.
ich kom - me!
Cont.
Dal Segno

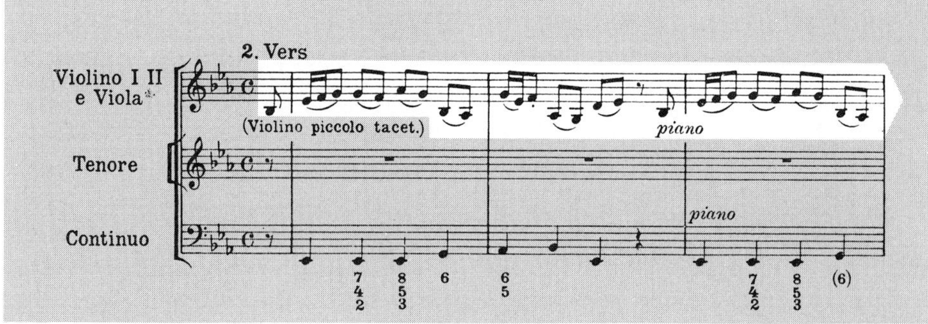
2. Vers
Violino I II e Viola
(Violino piccolo tacet.)
piano
Tenore
piano
Continuo

Vl.
Vla.
forte
forte
Cont.

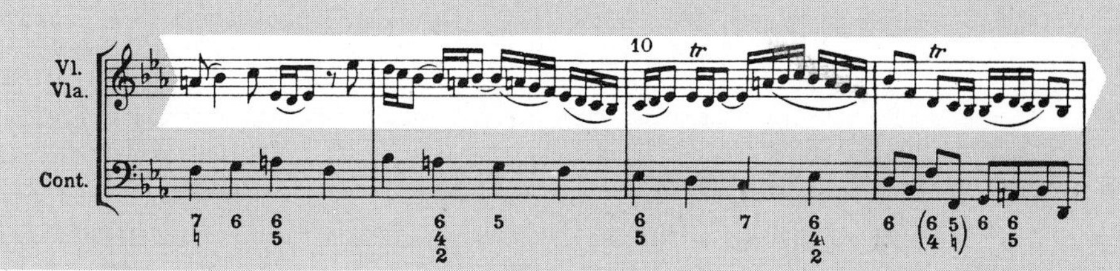
Vl.
Vla.
10
tr
tr
Cont.

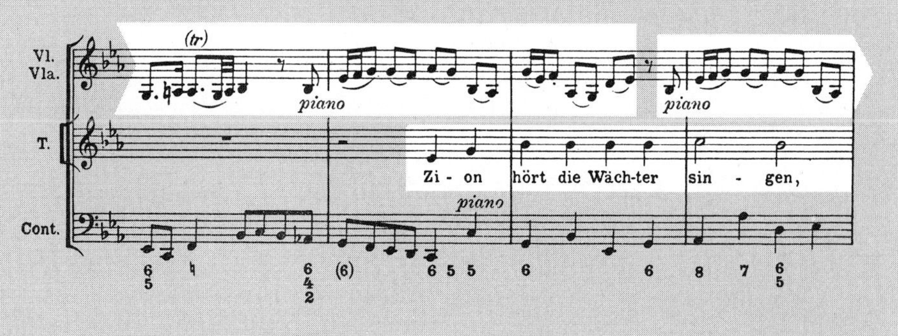
Vl.
Vla.
(tr)
piano
piano
T.
Zi - on hört die Wäch-ter sin - gen,
piano
Cont.

Vl. Vla.
T.
Cont.
das Herz tut ihr vor Freu - den sprin - gen,
20
sie wa - chet und steht ei - lend auf.
forte
piano
(piano)
(forte)
tr
30
(tr)
pp
Ihr Freund kommt vom Himmel

Vl.
Vla.
T.
Cont.
präch - tig,
von Gna-den stark, von Wahr - heit mäch -
40
tig,
ihr Licht wird hell, ihr_Stern geht auf.
forte
50
Nun komm, du wer - te
Kron,
Herr Je - su Got-tes Sohn.

Vl. Vla.
T.
Hos-si-an - na!
Cont.

60
Vl. Vla.
Cont.

Vl. Vla.
T.
Wir fol-gen all' zum Freu-den-saal
Cont.

Vl. Vla.
T.
und hal-ten mit das A-bend-mahl.
Cont.

Violino I e Violino piccolo.
piano
Violino II
Viola
Basso
So geh her-ein zu mir, du mir er-wähl-te
Continuo
Vl.
Vla.
B.
Braut! Ich ha-be mich mit dir in E-wig-keit ver-traut.
Cont
Vl.
Vla.
B.
Dich will ich auf mein Herz, auf meinen Arm gleich-wie ein Sie-gel set-zen, und
Cont.

Vl.
Vla.
B.
Cont.
dein be - trüb - tes Aug' er - göt - zen. Ver -
giß, o See-le, nun die Angst, den Schmerz, den du er - dulden müssen; auf meiner
Lin- ken sollst du ruh'n, und mei- ne Rech - te soll dich küs-sen.

Oboe Solo
Soprano
Basso
Continuo
Ob.
Cont.
S.
B.
piano
Mein Freund ist_mein!
Und
10
forte
Die Lie - be soll nichts schei - den;
ich bin dein! Die Lie - be soll nichts scheiden, nichts scheiden;

Ob.
Cont.
Ob.
piano
piano
S.
mein Freund ist_mein, die
B.
und ich ___ bin dein, die
Cont.
20
Ob.
piano sempre
S.
Lie - be_ soll __ nichts schei - - - den. Mein Freund ist_ mein,
B.
Lie - be_ soll __ nichts scheiden, nichts scheiden und
Cont.
Ob.
S.
mein Freund ist_mein, mein Freund ist_ mein, ___
B.
ich_ bin_ dein, und ich_ bin_ dein, und ich_ bin_
Cont.

Ob.
S.
B.
Cont.
die Lie - be soll nichts schei - den. Mein Freund ist
dein, die Lie - be soll nichts schei - den und
30
mein, die Liebe soll nichts schei-den. Mein Freund ist mein, die Liebe soll nichts
ich bin dein, und ich bin dein, und ich bin dein, und
schei-den, die Lie - be soll nichts schei - den, die Lie - be
ich bin dein, die Lie - be soll nichts schei - den, die Lie -
soll nichts schei - den. Mein Freund ist mein,
- be soll nichts schei - den und ich bin

Ob.
S.
B.
Cont.
forte
die Lie- - -be soll nichts schei - den.
dein, die Lie - be— soll nichts schei- - -den.
40
Ich
piano
will mit dir, ich will mit dir in Him - mels Ro - sen
Du sollst mit mir, du sollst mit mir in Him - mels Ro- -

50
Vl.
S.
wei- - den, ich will mit dir, ich will mit dir in
B.
- sen wei- - - -den, du sollst mit mir, du sollst mit
Cont.

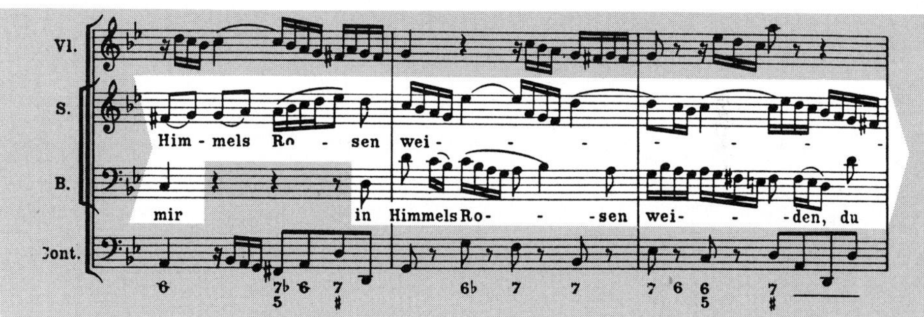
Vl.
S.
Him - mels Ro - sen wei- - - - - - -
B.
mir in Himmels Ro- - sen wei- - -den, du
Cont.

Vl.
piano
S.
-den, ich will mit dir in
B.
sollst mit mir in Him - mels Ro - sen
Cont.

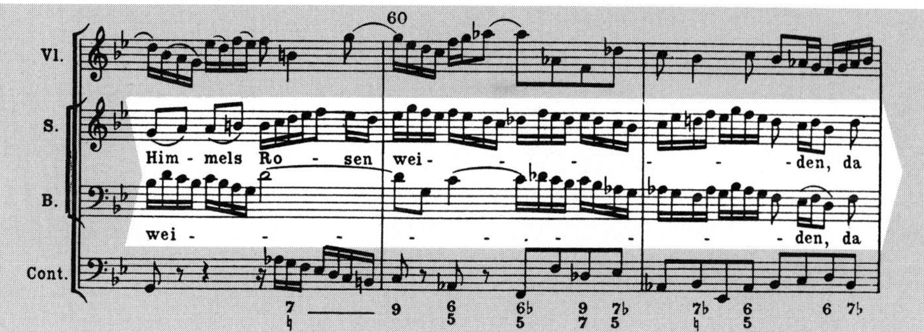
60
Vl.
S.
Him - mels Ro - sen wei- - - -den, da
B.
wei - - - - - - - -den, da
Cont.

Ob.
S.
B.
Cont.

S.: Freu - de die Fül-le, da Won-ne wird sein, da Freu-de die Fül-le,

B.: Freu - de die Fül-le, da Won-ne wird sein, da

Ob. *forte*

S.: da Freu - de die Fül-le, da Won-ne wird sein,

B.: Won-ne wird sein, da Freu - de die Fül-le, da Won-ne wird sein,

70

Ob. *piano*

S.: da Freude die Fül - le, da Won-ne wird sein, da Won-

B.: da Freu-de die Fül - le, da

S.: - - - - - - - ne, Won-ne wird sein!

B.: Won-ne wird sein, da Won - - - - - - ne wird sein!

Da Capo dal Segno

Soprano
Violino piccolo in 8a,
Corno, Oboe I, Violino I
col Soprano
Alto
Oboe II, Violino II
coll' Alto
Tenore
Taille e Viola
col Tenore
Basso
Continuo
Vers 3
Glo-ri - a sei dir ge - sun - gen mit Menschen-
Von zwölf Per - len sind die Pfor - ten an dei - ner
Glo - ri - a sei dir ge - sun - gen mit Men - schen-
Von zwölf Per - len sind die Pfor - ten an dei - ner
Glo - ri - a sei dir ge - sun - gen mit Menschen-
Von zwölf Per - len sind die Pfor - ten an dei-ner
Glo- -ri - a sei dir ge - sun - gen mit Men-schen-
Von zwölf Perlen sind die Pfor - ten an dei - ner

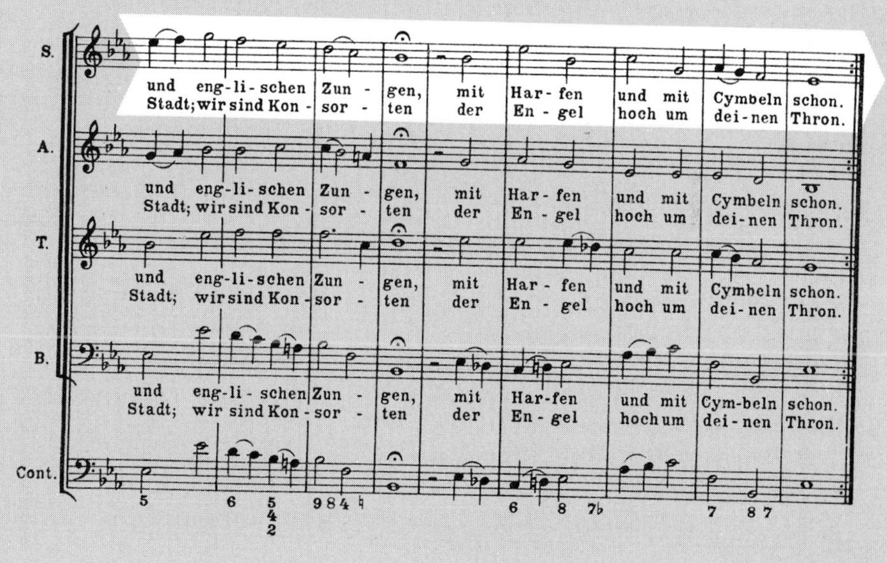
S.
A.
T.
B.
Cont.
und eng-li-schen Zun - gen, mit Har-fen und mit Cymbeln schon.
Stadt; wir sind Kon - sor - ten der En - gel hoch um dei-nen Thron.
und eng-li-schen Zun - gen, mit Har - fen und mit Cymbeln schon.
Stadt; wir sind Kon - sor - ten der En - gel hoch um dei-nen Thron.
und eng-li-schen Zun - gen, mit Har - fen und mit Cymbeln schon.
Stadt; wir sind Kon - sor - ten der En - gel hoch um dei-nen Thron.
und eng-li - schen Zun - gen, mit Har-fen und mit Cym-beln schon.
Stadt; wir sind Kon - sor - ten der En - gel hoch um dei - nen Thron.

S.
Kein Aug' hat je ge - spürt, kein Ohr hat je ge - hört sol - che Freu-
A.
Kein Aug' hat je_ ge - spürt, kein Ohr hat je_ ge - hört sol - che Freu-
T.
Kein Aug' hat je ge - spürt, kein Ohr hat je_ ge - hört sol - che Freu-
B.
Kein Aug' hat je_ ge - spürt, kein Ohr hat je_ ge - hört sol - che Freu-
Cont.
6 7 6 6 8 7 5 (5) 6 6— 8 7 9 3 6 5 6 7 6

S.
de. Des sind wir froh, i - o, i - o! e - wig in dul - ci ju - bi - lo.
A.
de. Des sind wir froh, i - o, i - o! e - wig in_ dul - ci ju - bi - lo.
T.
de. Des sind wir froh, i - o, i - o! e - wig in dul - ci ju - bi - lo.
B.
de. Des sind wir froh, i - o,_ i - o! e - wig in_ dul - ci ju - bi - lo.
Cont.
6 5 6 5 5 6 6 8 7 5 6 6 7 8 7

Translation

I

Wachet auf, ruft uns die Stimme
der Wächter sehr hoch auf der Zinne,
wach auf, du Stadt Jerusalem!

Mitternacht heisst diese Stunde;
sie rufen uns mit hellem Munde:
wo seid ihr klugen Jungfrauen?

Wohl auf, der Bräut'gam kömmt,
steht auf, die Lampen nehmt!
Alleluja!
Macht euch bereit zu der Hochzeit,
ihr müsset ihm entgegen gehn.

"Awake," the voice of watchmen
calls us from high on the tower,
"Awake, you city of Jerusalem!"

Midnight is this very hour;
they call to us with bright voices:
"Where are you, wise virgins?"

Take cheer, the Bridegroom comes,
arise, take up your lamps!
Hallelujah!
Prepare yourselves for the wedding,
you must go forth to meet him.

II

Er kommt, er kommt, der Bräut'gam kommt!
Ihr Töchter Zions, kommt heraus,
sein Ausgang eilet aus der Höhe
in euer Mutter Haus.

Der Bräut'gam kommt, der einem Rehe
und jungem Hirsche
gleich auf denen Hügeln springt
und euch das Mahl der Hochzeit bringt.

Wacht auf, ermuntert euch!
den Bräut'gam zu empfangen;
dort, sehet, kommt er hergegangen.

He comes, he comes, the Bridegroom comes!
Daughters of Zion, come forth,
he is hurrying from on high
into your mother's house.

The Bridegroom comes, who like a roe
and a young hart
leaping upon the hills
brings you the wedding meal.

Wake up, bestir yourselves
to receive the Bridegroom;
there, look, he come along.

III

Wann kommst du, mein Heil?
Ich komme, dein Teil.
Ich warte mit brennendem Öle;
Eröffne den Saal
zum himmlischen Mahl.
Ich öffne den Saal
zum himmlischen Mahl.
Komm Jesu!
komm, liebliche Seele!

Soul: When will you come, my salvation?
Jesus: I am coming, your own.
Soul: I am waiting with burning oil.
Throw open the hall
to the heavenly banquet!
Jesus: I open the hall
to the heavenly banquet.
Soul: Come, Jesus!
Jesus: Come, lovely Soul!

IV

Zion hört die Wächter singen,
das Herz tut ihr vor Freuden springen,
sie wachet und steht eilend auf.

Zion hears the watchmen singing,
for joy her very heart is springing,
she wakes and rises hastily.

Ihr Freund kommt von Himmel prächtig,
von Gnaden stark, von Wahrheit mächtig,
Ihr Licht wird hell, ihr Stern geht auf.

Nun komm, du werte Kron,
Herr Jesu Gottes Sohn.
Hosianna!
Wir folgen all'
zum Freudensaal
und halten mit das Abendmahl.

From heaven comes her friend resplendent,
sturdy in grace, mighty in truth,
her light shines bright, her star ascends.

Now come, you worthy crown,
Lord Jesus, God's own Son,
Hosanna!
We all follow
to the joyful hall
and share the Lord's Supper.

V

So geh herein zu mir,
du mir erwählte Braut!
Ich habe mich mit dir
in Ewigkeit vertraut.
Dich will ich auf mein Herz,
auf meinen Arm
gleich wie ein Siegel setzen,
und dein betrübtes Aug' ergötzen.
Vergiss, o Seele,
nun die Angst, den Schmerz,
den du erdulden müssen;
auf meiner Linken sollst du ruh'n,
und meine Rechte soll dich küssen.

Come enter in with me,
my chosen bride!
I have pledged my troth
to you in eternity!
I will set you as a seal upon my heart,
and as a seal upon my arm
and restore delight to your sorrowful eye.
Forget now, o soul,
the anguish, the pain,
which you had to suffer;
on my left you shall rest,
and my right shall kiss you.

VI

Mein Freund ist mein!
Und ich bin dein!
Die Liebe soll nichts scheiden.
Ich will mit dir in Himmels Rosen weiden,

Du sollst mit mir in Himmels Rosen weiden,

da Freunde die Fülle, da Wonne wird sein!

Soul: My friend is mine!
Jesus: and I am his!
Both: Love shall separate nothing!
Soul: I will feed with you among heaven's roses,
Jesus: You shall feed with me among heaven's roses,
Both: There fullness of joy, there rapture shall be!

VII

Gloria sei dir gesungen
mit Menschen-und englischen Zungen,
mit Harfen und mit Cymbeln schon.

Von zwölf Perlen sind die Pforten
an deiner Stadt; wir sind Konsorten
der Engel hoch um deinen Thron.

Gloria be sung to you
with men's and angels' tongues,
with harps and beautiful cymbals.

Of twelve pearls are the gates
at your city; we are consorts
of the angels high about your throne.

Kein Aug' hat je gespürt,	No eye has ever sensed,
kein Ohr hat je gehört	no ear has ever heard
solche Freude.	such a delight.
Des sind wir froh,	Of this we rejoice,
io, io!	io, io,
ewig in dulci jubilo.	forever *in dulci jubilo.*

MOVEMENTS 1, 4, AND 7 BY PHILIP NICOLAI;
MOVEMENTS 2, 3, 5, AND 6 ANONYMOUS.

TRANSLATED BY
GERHARD HERZ

27. BACH, *Crucifixus* from Mass in B minor (c. 1740?)

e-ti-am pro no - bis, cru - ci -
fi - xus e - ti-am pro no-bis,
cru - ci - fi - - xus e - ti-am pro
cru-ci- fi - xus, cru - ci - fi - xus e -
fi-xus e - - ti-am pro no - - -
e - - ti-am pro no- - - bis, sub Pon-ti-o Pi-
no-bis e - ti-am pro
- ti-am pro no- - - - bis,
- bis sub Pon - ti - o Pi - - la - - to, pas- -
la - to, sub Pon-ti - o Pi-la - - to, pas- -
no - - bis sub Pon - ti-o Pi-la - - - to, pas- -
sub Pon - - ti - - o Pi - la- - - to, pas- -

- sus et se - pul - - - tus est, pas - -
- sus et se - - pul - tus est, pas- -
sus, pas- - sus et se - pul - tus est, pas- -
- - - sus et se - pul - tus est, pas- -
- sus et se - pul - tus est, cru - -
- sus et se pul - tus est,
- sus et se - pul - - tus est,
sus et se - pul- - tus est,
- - ci - fi - xus e - ti - am pro no - - bis
cru - - - ci - fi - - xus e - ti - am pro
cru- - - ci - fi - - xus
cru- - - ci -

sub Pon-ti-o Pi - la - - - to pas - - -
no - bis sub Pon - ti-o Pi - la - - - to, pas - sus
e - ti-am pro no - bis,
fi - xus e - ti-am pro no - - - bis,
- - - - sus et se - pul - tus est, se -
et se - - - pul - - tus, se - pul - tus est, pas - -
pas - sus et se - pul - tus est, se -
pas - sus et se-pul - tus est, se -
pul - - tus est, se - - pul - - tus est.
- - sus et se - pul - - tus est.
pul - - - - tus, se - pul - - tus est.
pul - - tus est et se - pul - - tus est.
p
ppp

28. DOMENICO SCARLATTI (1685-1757),
Sonata in C minor, Kirkpatrick 12 (PUBL. 1738)

(r.h.)
20
tr
l.h.
r.h.
tr
tr
25
tr
tr
tr
tr

29. CHRISTOPH WILLIBALD GLUCK (1714-1787), Scenes from *Orphée et Euridice* (1762, rev. 1774)

Act II, Scene 1

A frightening, rocky landscape near the gates of the Underworld, veiled in a dark mist occasionally pierced by flames. The dance of the Furies and Monsters is interrupted by sounds of the lyre of the approaching ORPHEUS. When he comes into view they all join in the ensuing chorus.

No. 18 Dance of the Furies

Andante ben marcato
Soprano
Who can the mor - tal be, Wan - ton and
Alto
Quel est l'au - da - ci - eux qui dans ces
Tenor
Who can the mor - tal be, Wan - ton and
Bass
Quel est l'au - da - ci - eux qui dans ces
Andante ben marcato
f
bold is he, Who to this world of hate,
som - bres lieux o - se por - ter ses pas,
bold is he, Who to this world of hate,
som - bres lieux o - se por - ter ses pas,
Dar - ing a fright - 'ning fate, Has found the gate?
et de - vant le tré - pas ne fré - mit pas?
Dar - ing a fright - 'ning fate, Has found the gate?
et de - vant le tré - pas ne fré mit pas?

No. 20 Dance of the Furies

Vivace

1. 2.

attacca

No. 21 Chorus

(The Furies dance around Orpheus to frighten him.)
(Pendant le chœur les esprits dansent autour d'Orphée pour l'effrayer.)

world of hate, Dar - ing a fright - 'ning fate, Has found the gate?
ter ses pas, et de - vant le tré - pas ne fré - mit pas?
world of hate, Dar - ing a fright - 'ning fate, Has found the gate?
ter ses pas, et de - vant le tré - pas ne fré - mit pas?
B
Ter - ror shall strike his heart, Tear - ing his mind a - part, When howl - ing
Que la peur, la ter-reur s'em - pa - rent de son cœur à l'af - freux
Ter - ror shall strike his heart, Tear - ing his mind a - part, When howl - ing
Que la peur, la ter-reur s'em - pa - rent de son cœur à l'af - freux
B
sf
hell - hound's roar, Foam- drip - ping fangs a - jar, Bar him the door,
hur - le-ment du Cer - bère é - cumant et ru - gis - sant;
hell - hound's roar, Foam- drip - ping fangs a - jar, Bar him the door,
hur - le-ment du Cer - bère é - cumant et ru - gis - sant;
sf

C
When howl - ing hell - hound's roar, Foam-drip - ping fangs a - jar,
à l'af - freux hur - - le-ment du Cer - bère é - - - cu-mant
When howl - ing hell - hound's roar, Foam-drip - ping fangs a - jar,
à l'af - freux hur - - le-ment du Cer - bère é - - - cu-mant
C
sf sf sf
Bar him the door.
et ru-gis - sant!
Bar him the door.
et ru-gis - sant!
3
ff
D
Ter-ror shall strike his heart, Tear-ing his mind a-part, When howl - ing
Que la peur, la terreur s'em - pa - rent de soncœur à l'af - freux
Ter-ror shall strike his heart, Tear-ing his mind a-part, When howl - ing
Que la peur, la terreur s'em - pa - rent de soncœur à l'af - freux
D

hell - hound's roar, Foam-drip - ping fangs a - jar, Bar him the
hur - - le-ment du Cer - bère é - - cu-mant et ru - gis -
hell - hound's roar, Foam-drip - ping fangs a - jar, Bar him the
hur - - le-ment du Cer - bère é - - cu-mant et ru - gis -
attacca
No. 22 Solo with Chorus
Un poco lento
Orpheus Orphée
O.
Ah, have
Lais-sez-
Soprano Alto
door.
Tenor
sant!
Bass
door.
Un poco lento
fp
E
pit - y, have pit - y on me! Fu - ries! Mon - sters!
vous tou - cher par mes pleurs, spec - tres, lar - ves,
f
No! No!
Non! non!
No! No!
E
f p

Shad - ows so fear - ful, Oh hear my song so tear - ful, And your
om - bres ter - ri - bles! soy - ez, soy - ez sen - si - bles à l'ex-
No!
non!
No!
f
p
heart may heed my plea. Oh hear my song so
cès de mes mal - heurs, soy - ez, soy - ez sen -
tear - ful, And your heart may heed my plea, Yes, your
si - bles à l'ex-cès de mes mal - heurs, à l'ex-
heart may heed my plea.
cès de mes mal - heurs!
F
f
No! No!
Non! non!
No! No!
F
f
sf

Ah, have pi-ty, Ah, have pit-y, have pit-y on
Lais-sez-vous toucher, lais-sez-vous tou-cher par mes
No!
non!
No!
fp
me! Fu-ries! Mon-sters! Shad-ows so
pleurs, spec-tres, lar-ves, om-bres ter-
G
No! No!
Non! non!
No! No!
f
p
fear-ful, Oh hear my song so tear-ful, And your heart may heed my
ri-bles! soy-ez, soy-ez sen-si-bles à l'ex-cès de mes mal-
No!
non!
No!

H
plea.
heurs;
Fu - ries!
spec - tres,
Mon - sters!
lar - ves,
Shad - - ows so
om - - - bres ter -
No!
Non!
non!
No!
non!
No!
No!
No!
H
fear - ful,
ri - bles!
Oh hear my song so tear - ful,
soy - ez soy ez sen - si - bles
And your heart may heed my
à l'ex - cès de mes mal -
No!
non!
No!
plea,
heurs,
And your heart
a l'ex - cès
may
de
heed my plea,
mes mal - - heurs,
And your heart may heed my plea.
à l'ex - cès de mes mal - heurs!

No. 23 Chorus

(*The chorus answers Orpheus in a somewhat milder manner, showing signs of compassion*)
(***Le chœur apaisé répond à Orphée avec un peu plus de pitié dans l'expression.***)

I Animato
Who? Here is for life no room, Nothing but night and gloom,
qui? C'est le sé - jour af-freux des re-mords dé - vo-rants,
Who? Here is for life no room, Nothing but night and gloom,
qui? C'est le sé - jour af-freux des re-mords dé - vo-rants,
I Animato
Here is for life no room, Noth - ing but night and gloom, None but the
c'est le sé - jour af - freux des re - mords dé - vo-rants et des gé -
Here is for life no room, Noth - ing but night and gloom, None but the
c'est le sé - jour af - freux des re - mords dé - vo - rants et des gé -
cries of The damned in their doom, e - ter - nal doom.
mis - - se - ments et des tour - ments, et des tour - ments.
cries of The damned in their doom, e - ter - nal doom.
mis - - se - ments et des tour - ments, et des tour - ments.

No. 24 Solo

Un poco lento
Orpheus *Orphée*
o.
p
All the tor - ments Hell has to
Ah! la flam - me qui me dé -
of - fer Hun - - dred fold my heart must
vo - - re, est cent fois plus cru - elle en -
K
suf-fer, my heart must suf - fer. The world has
co - re, plus cru-elle en - co - re; l'en - fer n'a
nev - er known such grief As that from which I seek re -
point de tour-ments pa - reils à ceux que je res -
lief, As that from which I seek re - - lief.
sens, pa - reils à ceux que je res - - sens.

No. 25 Chorus

(*In a milder manner*) (*Encore plus apaisé.*)

fu - ry wild, Turn-ing our hearts beguiled Peace - - ful and mild.
nos ef-forts, il cal-me la fu-reur de nos trans-ports?
fu - ry wild, Turn-ing our hearts beguiled Peace - - ful and mild.
nos ef-forts, il cal-me la fu-reur de nos trans-ports?
No. 26 Solo
Un poco lento
Orpheus Orphée
Here be - fore - you I im - plore you So your
La ten - dres-se qui me pres-se, cal-me
wrath may soon a - bate. Tears shall tell you and com-pel you To al-
ra vo - tre fu - reur, oui, mes lar-mes, mes a - lar-mes flé-chi-
low me through the gate. Tears shall tell you and com-pel you To al-
ront vo-tre ri - gueur; mes a - lar-mes, mes lar-mes, fle-chi-
low me through the gate, To al - low me through the gate.
ront vo - - tre ri - gueur, flé-chi-ront vo - - tre ri - gueur.

No. 27 Chorus

(Almost completely subdued) (Encore plus doux.)
Andante
Soprano
Alto
Tenor
Bass
Beau-ty un-known to us, Warm and me-lod-i-ous, Melt-ing our
Quels chants doux et touchants, quels ac-cords ra-vis-sants! De si ten-
wrath a-way, Hold-ing our hearts in sway O-pen his way!
dres accents ont su nous dés-ar-mer et nous char-mer.
Allegro
So through the por-tals wide In may the mor-tal stride. He by the singer's art Conquered the
Qu'il descende aux en-fers! les che-mins sont ou-verts. Tout cède à la douceur de son art

monsters' heart, Winning his bride. He by the sing - er's art
en-chan-teur, il est vain-queur. Tout cède à la dou-ceur
monsters' heart, Winning his bride. He by the sing - er's art
en-chan-teur, il est vain-queur. Tout cède à la dou-ceur

dim. poco a poco
Con-quered the mon - sters' heart, Win - ning his bride. **M** So through the
dim. poco a poco
de son art en - - chan-teur, il est vain - queur. Qu'il des-cende
dim. poco a poco
Con-quered the mon - sters' heart, Win - ning his bride. So through the
dim. poco a poco
de son art en - - chan-teur, il est vain - queur. Qu'il des-cende

dim. poco a poco **M**

por - tals wide In may the mor - tal stride. He by the sing - er's art Conquered the
aux en-fers! les che-mins sont ou-verts. Tout cède à la dou-ceur de son art
por - tals wide In may the mor - tal stride. He by the sing - er's art Conquered the
aux en-fers! les che-mins sont ou-verts. Tout cède à la dou-ceur de son art

N
poco calando
monsters' heart, Winning his bride.
He by the sing - er's art
en-chan-teur, il est vain - queur.
Tout cede à la dou-ceur
monsters' heart, Winning his bride.
He by the sing - er's art
en-chan-teur, il est vain - queur.
Tout cede à la dou-ceur
N
poco calando
Con-quered the mon - sters' heart,
Winning his bride,
de son art en - - chanteur,
il est vain-queur,
Con-quered the mon - sters' heart, Win - ning his bride,
de son art en - - chanteur, il est vain - queur,
Win - ning his
il est vain -
p
pp
win - ning his bride.
il est vain - queur.
win - ning his bride.
il est vain - queur.
win - ning his bride.
il est vain - queur.
bride,
queur,
win - ning his bride.
il est vain - queur.
smorzando

No. 43, *J'ai perdu mon Euridice*

voice so — sad — and — sigh - ing In — tears and ter - ror, In fears and — sor - row —
poux, ton é - poux fi - dè - le; en - tends ma — voix qui t'ap - pel - le, ma voix qui t'ap-
Tempo I
cry - ing. Now my love has gone for - ev - er. All my days have turned to night. From my —
pel - le! J'ai per - du mon Eu - ri - di - ce, rien n'é - ga - le mon mal - heur; sort cru-
heart, — gone for - ev - er Ev - 'ry — ray - of — hope and — light, None can —
el! — quel - le ri - gueur! rien n'é - ga - le — mon — mal - heur! je — suc-
Moderato
Adagio
know my - bit - ter - plight. Can you hear me, are you near me? No sound has
combe à — ma — dou - leur! Eu - ri - di - ce, Eu - ri di - ce! Mor - tel si-
found me. Si - lence a - round me! Sorrow has crowned me. All has end - ed in pain and
len - ce! Vaine es - pé - ran - ce! Quel - le souf - fran - ce! Quel tour - ment — dé - chi - re mon

Tempo I P
fright. Now my love has gone for - ev - er. All my days have turned to
cœur! J'ai per - du mon Eu - ri - di - ce, rien n'é - ga - le mon mal -
p
fp
night. From my heart, gone for - ev - er Ev - 'ry ray of hope and
heur; sort cru - el! quel - le ri - gueur, rien n'é ga - le mon mal -
sf
sf
cresc.
light, hope and light Have died for - ev - er None can know my bit - ter
heur! sort cru - el! quel - le ri - gueur! je suc - combe à ma dou -
mf
cresc.
p
cresc.
f
ff
plight, my bit - ter plight, my bit - ter plight.
leur, à ma dou - leur, à ma dou - leur!
f
ff
sf
sf

30. FRANZ JOSEPH HAYDN (1732-1809), Second and fourth movements from Symphony No. 94 in G major ("Surprise") (1791)

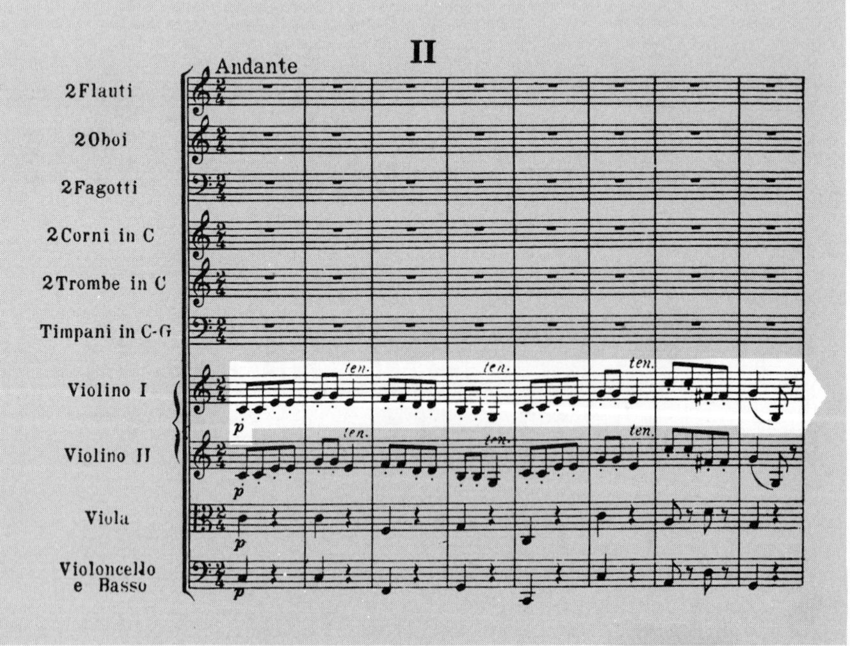

Reprinted with permission of Ernst Eulenburg Ltd., London-Zürich, from the Eulenburg miniature score.

Fl.
Ob.
Fg.
Cor. (C)
Tr. (C)
Tp.
Vl.
Vla.
Vc. e B.
10
ten.
pizz.
arco
[pp]
ff

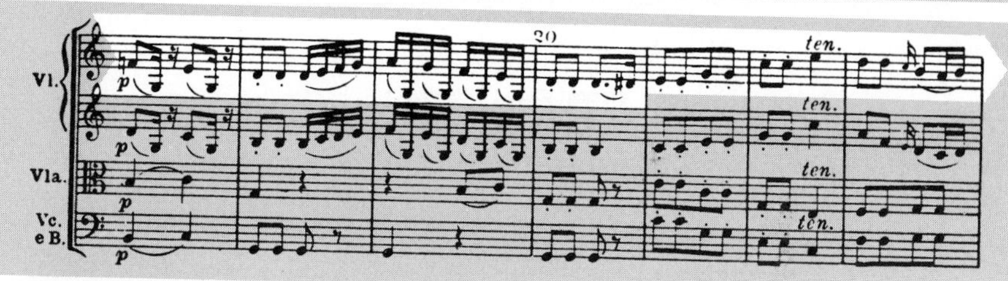
Vl.
Vla.
Vc. e B.
20
ten.
p

Fl.
Ob.
Cor. (C)
Vl.
Vla.
Vc. e B.
30
1.
ten.
p
pp

Fl.
Ob.
Fg.
Cor. (C)
Tr. (C)
Tp.
Vl.
Vla.
Vc. e B.
f
p
sf
ten.

Fl.
Vl.
Vla.
Vc. e B.
1.
40
[sf]
ten.
f
p

Vl.
Vla.
Vc. e B.
ten.

Minore
50
zu 2
ten.
ff
p
f
Fl.
Ob.
Fg.
Cor. (C)
Tr. (C)
Tp.
Vl.
Vla.
Vc. e B.

60
Fl.
Ob.
Fg.
Cor. (C)
Tr. (C)
Tp.
Vl.
Vla.
Vc. e B.
Fl.
Ob.
Fg.
Cor. (C)
Tr. (C)
f
Tp.
f
Vl.
Vla.
Vc. e B.

Minore
50
zu 2
ten.
Fl.
Ob.
Fg.
Cor. (C)
Tr. (C)
Tp.
Vl.
Vla.
Vo. e B.
ff
p
f

60
Fl.
Ob.
Fg.
Cor. (C)
Tr. (C)
Tp.
Vl.
Vla.
Vo. e B.
f

Fl.
Ob.
Fg.
Cor. (C)
Tr. (C)
Tp.
Vl.
Vla.
Vc. e B.
70
zu 2
p

Maggiore
ten.
ten.
Ob.
Fg.
Vl.
Vla.
Vc. e B.
p

80
1.
p
ten.
Fl.
Ob.
Fg.
Vl.
Vla.
Vc. e B.
ten.
ten.

3
90
sf
tr
Fl.
Ob.
Vl.
ten.
ten.
ten.
ten.

Fl.
Ob.
Vl.
ten.
ten.
100
Cor. (C)
p
zu 2
ff
Fg.
Tr. (C)
Tp.
6
Vla.
Vc. e B.

110
Fl.
Ob.
Fg.
Cor. (C)
Tr. (C)
Tp.
Vl.
Vla.
Vc. e B.
p
p dolce
p dolce
p
p

120
ten.
Fg.
Vl.
Vla.
Vc. e B.
ten.
130
zu 2
Fl.
Ob.
Fg.
Cor. (C)
Tr. (C)
Tp.
Vl.
Vla.
Vc. e B.

Fl.
Ob.
Fg.
Cor. (C)
Tr. (C)
Tp.
Vl.
Vla.
Vc. e B.
140
zu 2
[ff]
ff

Fl.
Ob.
Fg.
Cor. (C)
Tr. (C)
Tp.
Vl.
Vla.
Vc. e B.
1.
ten.
p
pp
150

IV
Finale Allegro molto
2 Flauti
2 Oboi
2 Fagotti
2 Corni in G
2 Trombe in C
Timpani in D-G
Violino I
Violino II
Viola
Violoncello e Basso

Fl.
Vl.
Vla.
Vc. e B.
10

Fl.
Vl.
Vla.
Vc. e B.
20
Vl.
Vla.
Vc. e B.
30
1.
p
Fl.
Fg.
Vl.
Vla.
Vc. e.B.

Fl.
Ob.
Fg.
Cor. (G)
Tr. (C)
Tp
Vl.
Vla.
Vc. e B.
tr

zu 2
40
Fl.
Ob.
Fg.
Cor. (G)
Tr. (C)
Tp.
Vl.
Vla.
Vc. e B.
f

Fl.
Ob.
Fg.
Cor. (G)
Tr. (C)
Tp.
Vl.
Vla.
Vc. e B.
50

Fl.
Ob.
Fg.
Cor. (G)
Tr. (C)
Tp.
Vl.
Vla.
Vc. e B.
60

Fl.
Ob.
Fg.
Cor. (G)
Tr. (C)
Tp.
Vl.
Vla.
Vc. e B.
70

Fl.
Ob.
Fg.
Cor. (G)
Tr. (C)
Tp.
Vl.
Vla.
Vc. e B.
pizz.
p

80
Fl.
Ob.
1.
Fg.
Cor. (G)
Tr. (C)
Tp.
Vl.
Vla.
Vc. e B.
(Cello)
p arco

Fl.
Ob.
Fg.
Cor. (G)
Tr. (C)
Tp.
Vl.
Vla.
Vc. e B.
f arco

90
zu 2
Fl.
Ob.
Fg.
Cor. (G)
Tr. (C)
Tp.
Vl.
Vla.
Vc. e B.

100
Fl.
Ob.
Fg.
Cor. (G)
Tr. (C)
Tp.
Vl.
Vla.
Vc. e B.
p
1.

110
zu 2
Fl.
Ob.
Fg.
Cor. (G)
Tr. (C)
Tp.
Vl.
Vla.
Vc. e B.
f
zu 2

120
Fl.
Ob.
Fg.
Cor. (G)
Tr. (C)
Tp.
Vl.
Vla.
Vc. e B.
f

130
Fl.
Ob.
Fg.
Cor. (G)
Tr. (C)
Tp.
Vl.
Vla.
Vc. e B.
Fl.
Ob.
Fg.
Cor. (G)
Tr. (C)
Tp.
Vl.
Vla.
Vc. e B.

140
Fl.
Ob.
Fg.
Cor. (G)
Tr. (C)
Tp.
Vl.
p
pp
p
Vla.
p
Vc. e B.
p

1.
p
150
Fl.
Ob.
1.
Fg.
p
Cor. (G)
Tr. (C)
Tp.
Vl.
p
p
Vla.
p
Vc. e B.
p

zu 2
Fl.
Ob.
Fg.
Cor. (G)
Tr. (C)
Tp.
Vl.
Vla.
Vc. e B.
160

170
Fl.
Ob.
Fg.
Cor. (G)
Tr. (C)
Tp.
Vl.
Vla.
Vc. e B.
sf

190
Fl.
Ob.
Vl.
Vla.
Vc.
e B.

zu 2
200
Fl.
Ob.
zu 2
Fg.
Cor. (G)
Tr. (C)
Tp.
Vl.
Vla.
Vc. e B.

Fl.
Ob.
Fg.
Cor. (G)
Tr. (C)
Tp.
Vl.
Vla.
Vc. e B.

210
Fl.
Ob.
Fg.
Cor. (G)
Tr. (C)
Tp.
Vl.
Vla.
Vc. e B.
1.
p
pizz.

Fl.
Ob.
Fg.
Cor. (G)
Tr. (C)
Tp.
Vl.
Vla.
Vc. e B.
1.
p

220
zu 2
Fl.
Ob.
Fg.
Cor. (G)
Tr. (C)
Tp.
Vl.
Vla.
Vc. e B.
arco
pizz.
230

zu 2
Fl.
Ob.
Fg.
Cor. (G)
Tr. (C)
Tp.
arco
arco
Vl.
Vla.
Vc. e B.
240

Fl.
Ob.
Fg.
Cor. (G)
Tr. (C)
Tp.
Vl.
Vla.
Vc. e B.
250

Fl.
Ob.
Fg.
Cor. (G)
Tr. (C)
Tp.
Vl.
Vla.
Vc. e B.
260
f
[ff]

31. HAYDN, String Quartet in C major, Opus 76, No. 3 (1797)

10
fz
fz
fz
fz
tr
tr
tr
tr
tr
tr
20
tr
tr
fz
fz
tr
fz

tr
fz
6
ff
p
f
30
fz
p
f
ff

p
p
p
p
pp
pp
pp
pp
f
f
f
f
40
tr
tr
tr
tr
tr

tr
1.
p
2.
f
50

60
tr
f
p

f
fz
fz
fz
sempre
70

fz
p
pp
f
80
tr

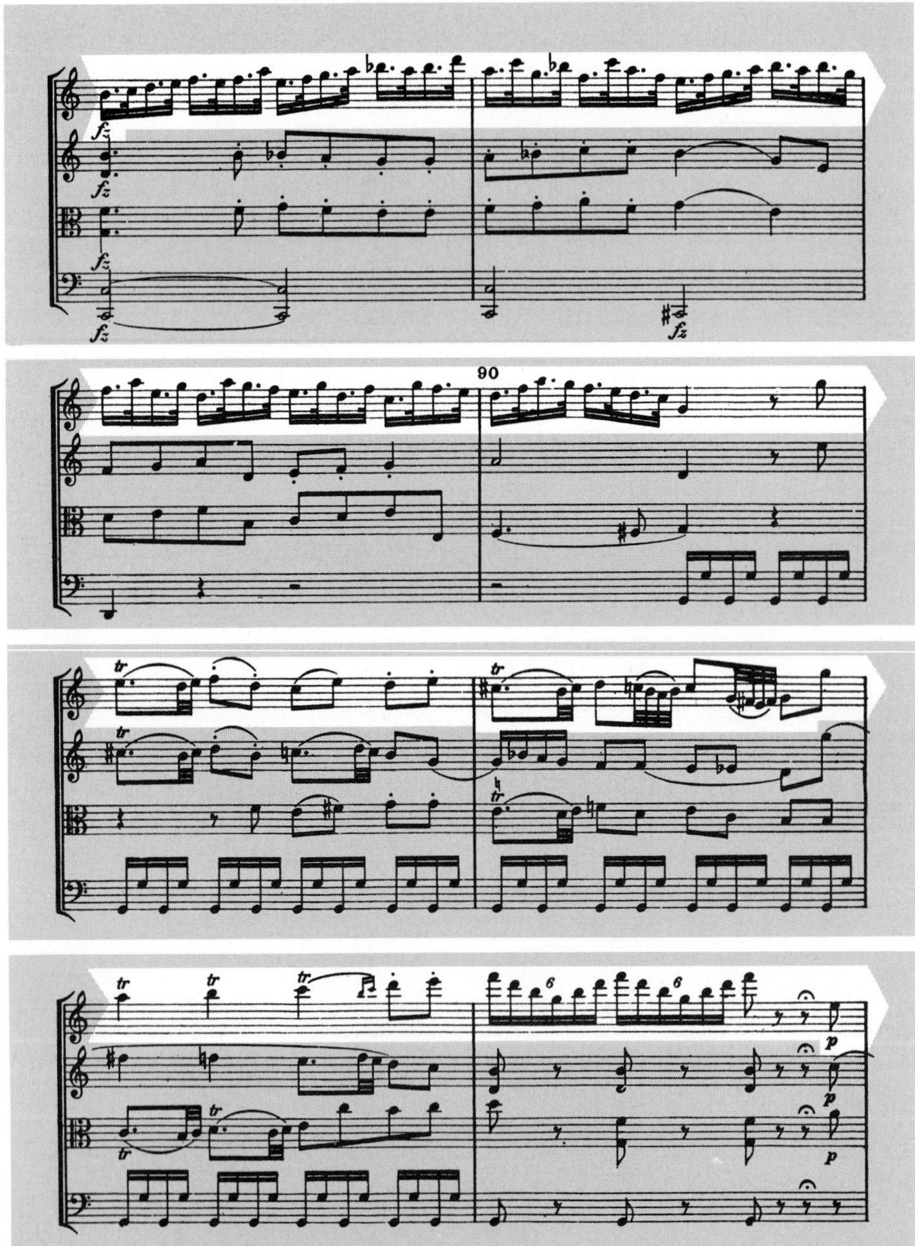
fz
fz
fz
fz
fz
90
tr
tr
p
p
p

fz
f
fz
100
p
la seconda volta più presto

110
8
8
tr
1.
2.
f
p

II
Poco adagio; cantabile
p dolce
p dolce
p dolce
p dolce
10
fz
fz
fz
fz
fz
fz
fz
fz
p
p
p
p
fz
fz
fz
fz
fz
fz
fz
fz
p
p
p
p
20
Var. I
sempre piano

30
fz
fz
p
p

fz
fz
p
p
40
Var. II
p
p
p
p

50
fz
fz
fz
fz
60

Var. III
p
p
p
p
70

Var. IV

100
pp
III
Menuett. Allegro
f
10

20
f
f
p
p
f
f
p
p
30
f
f
f
40
50

Trio
60
70
80
90
M.D.C.

IV
Finale. Presto
f
p
10
3
20

30
fz
p
p
fz
p
fz
fz
p
fz
40
f
f
f
f
3
3
3
3

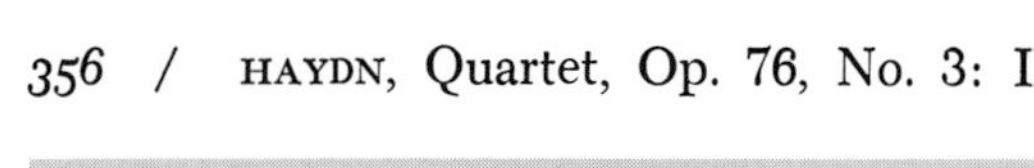

50
fz
fz
fz

fz
fz
fz

60

70
1.
2.
p
p
p
f
f
f
f

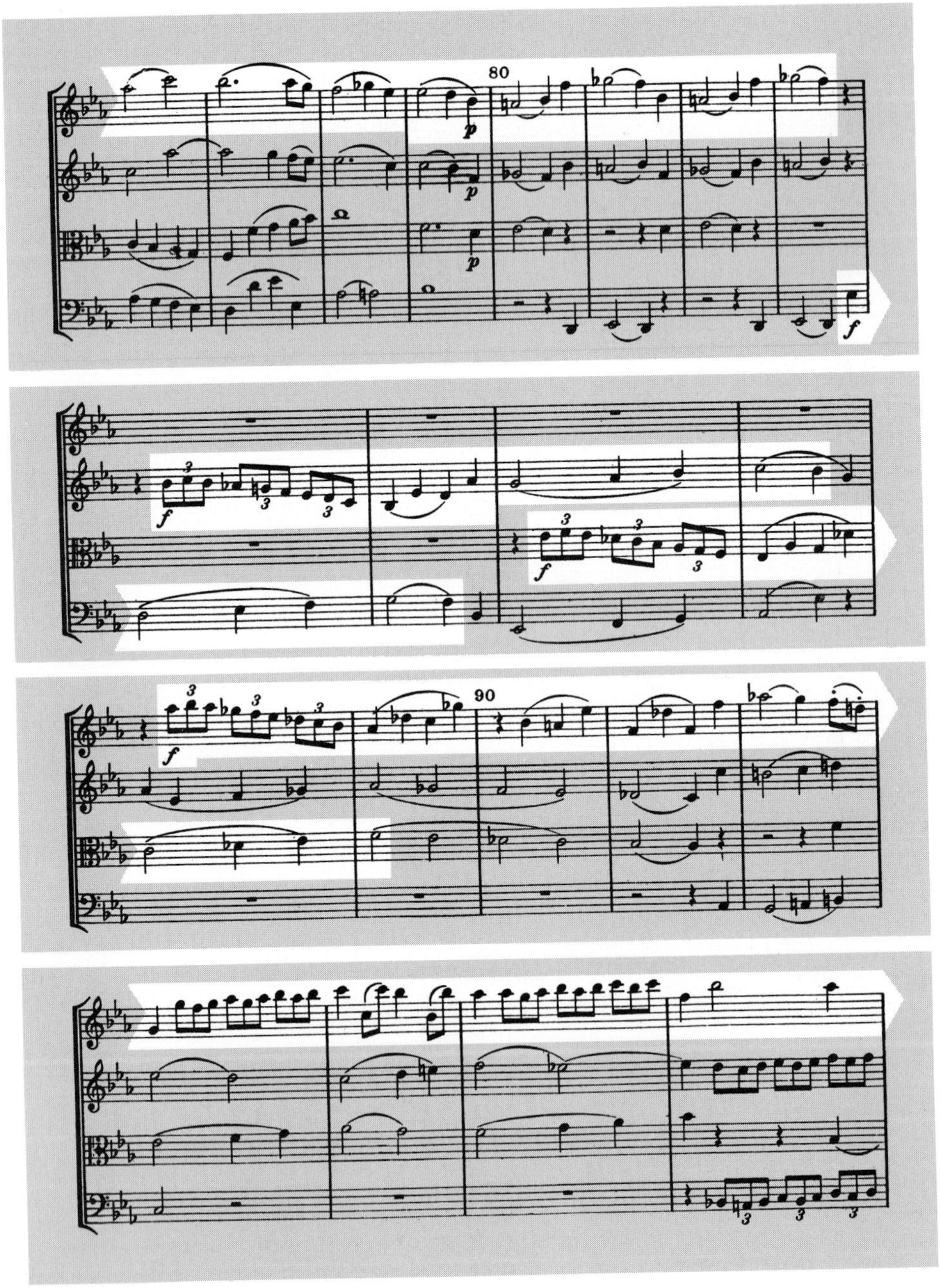
80
p
p
p
p
f
f
f
90
f
3
3
3
3
3
3
3
3
3
3
3

100
3
fz
fz
fz
fz
fz
fz

110

120

130

pp
p
pp
f
p
pp
f
p
pp
f
140
fz
fz
fz
fz
fz
fz

180
Fine

32. WOLFGANG AMADEUS MOZART (1756-1791), Piano Concerto in C major, K. 467 (1785)

Reprinted with permission of Ernst Eulenburg Ltd., London-Zürich, from the Eulenburg miniature score.

10
Fl.
Ob.
Fag.
Cor. (C)
Trb. (C)
Timp.
Vl.
Vla.
Vlc. e Cb.

Fl.
Ob.
zu 2
Fag.
Cor. (C)
Trb. (C)
Timp.
Vl.
Vla.
Vlc. e Cb.

20
Fl.
Ob.
Fag.
Cor. (C)
zu 2
Trb. (C)
zu 2
Timp.
Vl.
Vla.
Vlc. e Cb.

Fl.
Ob.
Fag.
Cor. (C)
Trb. (C)
Timp.
Vl.
Vla.
Vlc. e Cb.

Fl.
Ob.
1.
1.
Fag.
Cor. (C)
Trb. (C)
Vl. I.
p
Vla.
Vlc. e Cb.

Fl.
Ob.
Fag.
Cor. (C)
Trb. (C)
Timp.
Vl.
Vla.
Vlc. e Cb.

50
Fl.
Ob.
zu 2
Fag.
Cor.
(C)
zu 2
Trb.
(C)
Timp.
Vl.
Vla.
Vlc. e
Cb.

Fl.
p
Ob.
p
Fag.
p
Cor.
(C)
Trb.
(C)
Timp.
Vl.
p
p
Vla.
p
Vlc. e
Cb.
p

Fl.
tr
f
Ob.
zu 2
Fag.
Cor. (C)
Trb. (C)
Timp.
Vl.
tr
Vla.
Vlc. e Cb.

SOLO
Fl.
Ob.
Fag.
Cor. (C)
Trb. (C)
Klav.
Vl.
Vla.
Vlc. e Cb.
p

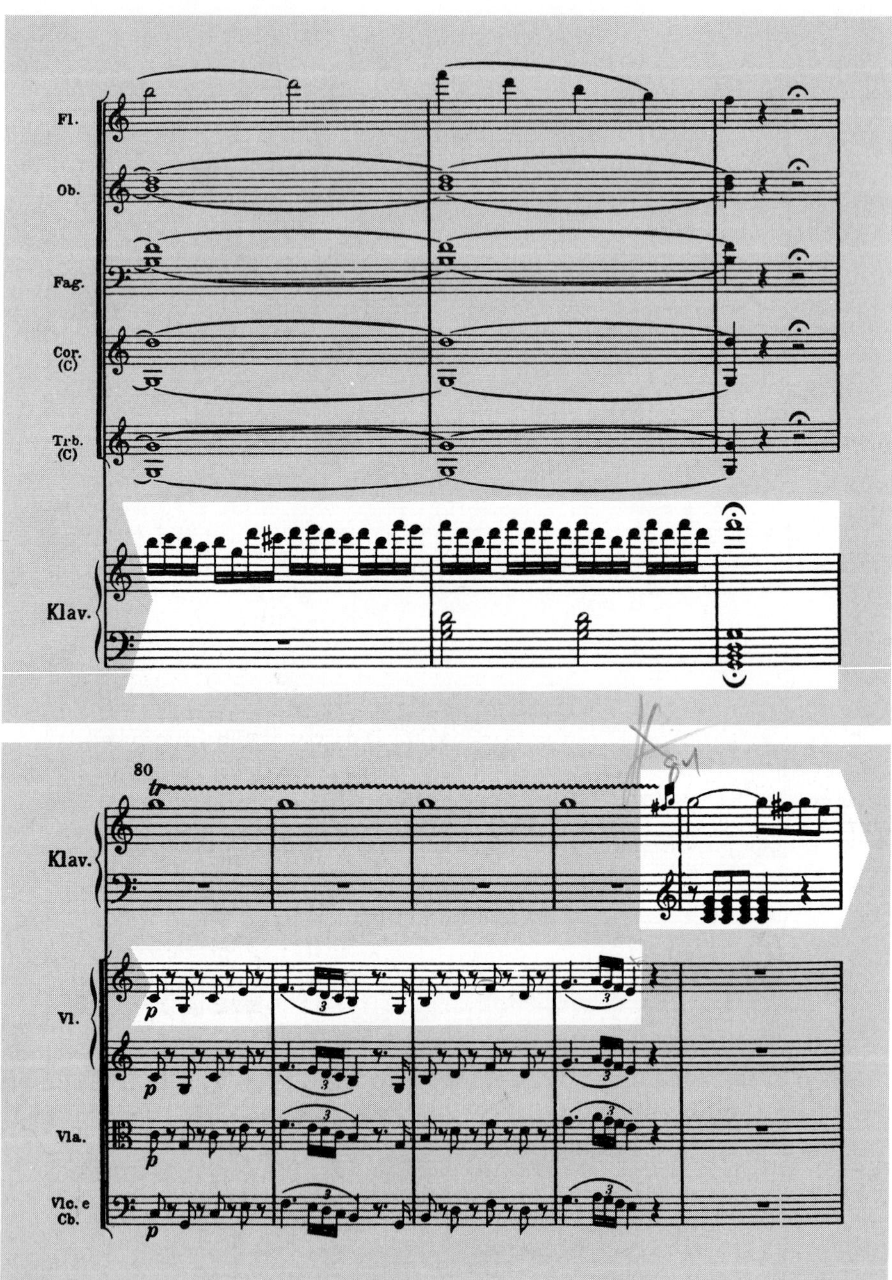
Fl.
Ob.
Fag.
Cor. (C)
Tr·b. (C)
Klav.
80
Klav.
Vl.
Vla.
Vlc. e Cb.

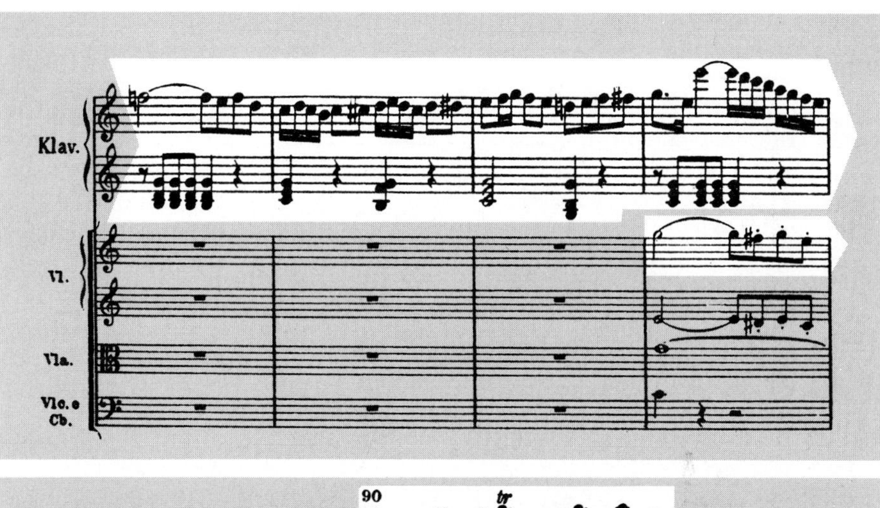

90
Fl.
Ob.
Fag.
Cor.
(C)
Trb.
(C)
Timp.
Klav.
Vl.
Vla.
Vlc. e
Cb.
tr
p

Klav.
Vl.
Vla.
Vlc. e
Cb.

Klav.
Vl.
Vla.
Vlc. e
Cb.

100
Klav.
Vl.
Vla.

TUTTI.
SOLO.
Fl.
Ob.
zu 2
Fag.
zu 2
Cor. (C)
Trb. (C)
Timp.
Klav.
Vl.
Vla.
Vlc. e Cb.

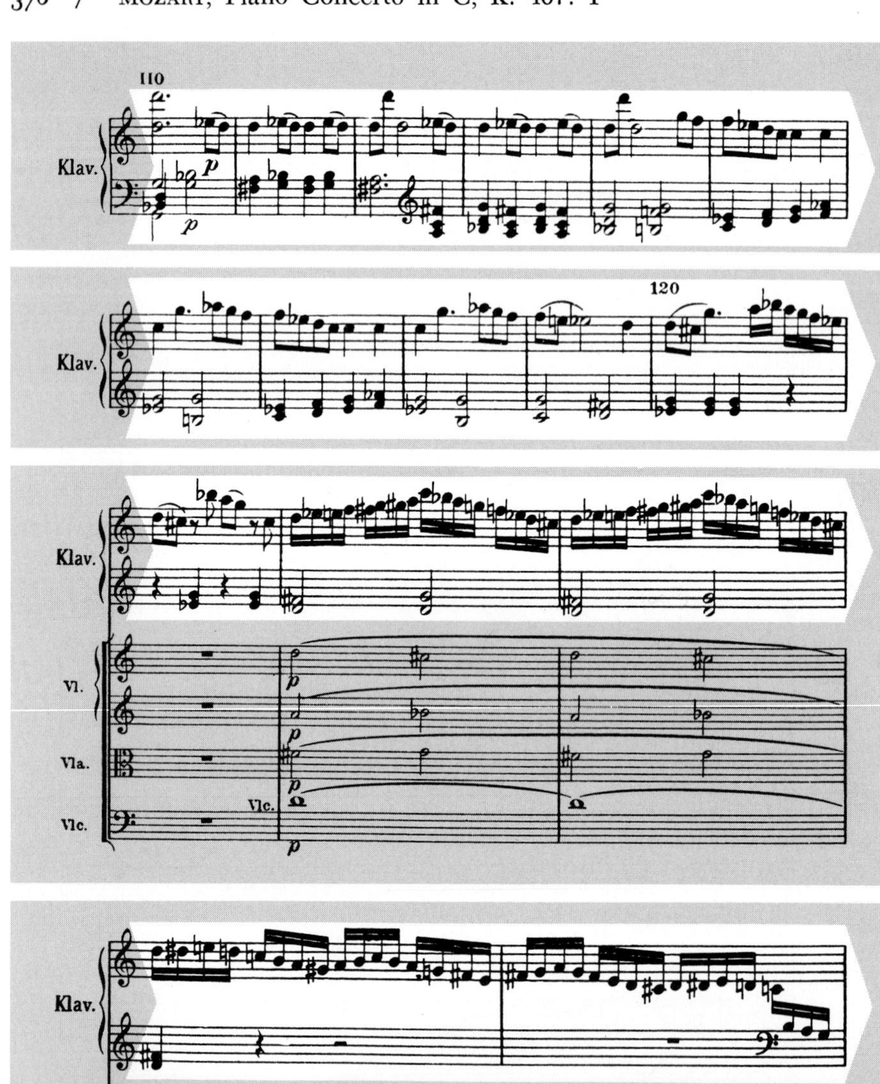
110
Klav.
p
p
120
Klav.
Klav.
Vl.
p
p
Vla.
p
Vlc.
Vlc.
p
Klav.
Vl.
Vla.
Vlc.

Klav.
130
Klav.
Vl.
[p]
[p]
Vla.
[p]
Bassi.
Vlc. e Cb.
[p]
Fl.
[p]
Ob.
1.
[p]
Fag.
[p]
Klav.
Vlc. e Cb.
[p]

140
Fl.
Ob.
Fag.
Klav.
Vlc. e Cb.

Fl.
Klav.

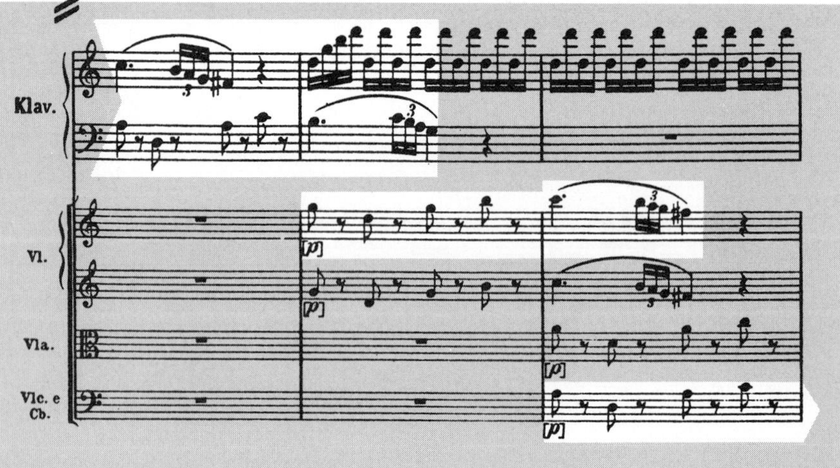
Klav.
Vl.
[p]
[p]
Vla.
[p]
Vlc. e Cb.
[p]

Fl.
Ob.
Fag.
Klav.
Vl.
Vla.
Vlc. e Cb.
[p]
[p]
p

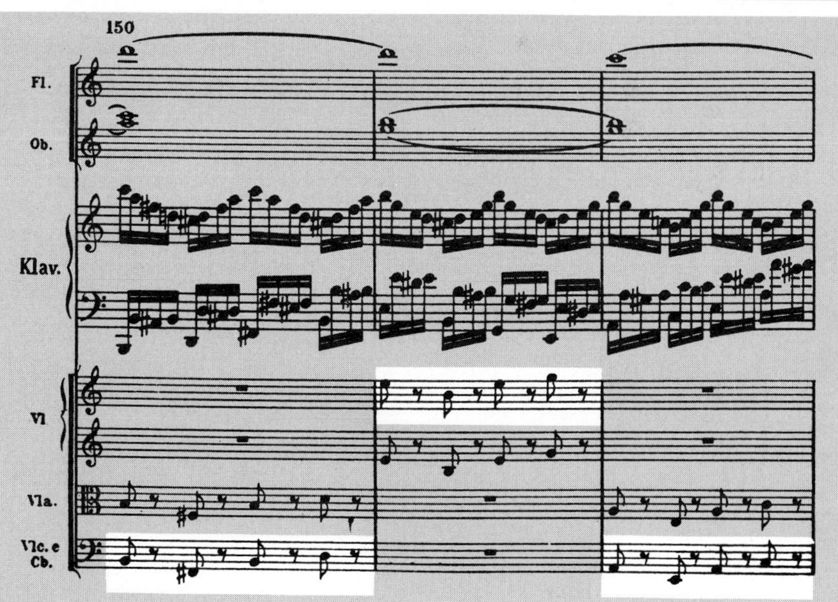

Fl.
Ob.
Klav.
Vl.
Vla.
Vlc. e Cb.

160
Klav.
Vl.
Vla.
Vlc. e Cb.

Fl.
Ob.
Fag.
Cor. (C)
Klav.

Klav.

Klav.
Vl.
Vla.
Vlc. e Cb.

170
Klav.

Klav.

Klav.
Vl.
Vla.
Vlc. e Cb.

180
Klav.
Vl.
Vla.
Vlc. e Cb.
Klav.
Vl.
Vla.
Vlc. e Cb.
Ob.
Klav.
Vl.
Vla.
Vlc. e Cb.

Fl.
Ob.
Fag.
Klav.
Vl.
Vla.
Vlc. e Cb.
Vlc.
190
1.
Vlc.

Fl.
Ob.
Fag.
Klav.
Vl.
Vla.
Vlc. e Cb.
Bassi
TUTTI
Fl.
Ob.
zu 2
Fag.
Cor. (C)
Trb. (C)
Timp.
Klav.
Vl.
Vla.
Vlc. e Cb.

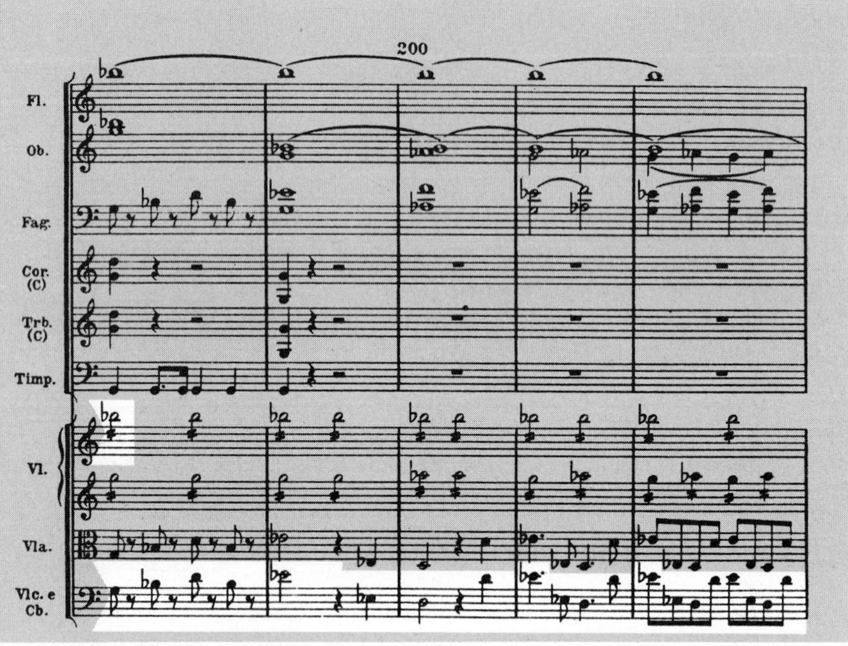
200
Fl.
Ob.
Fag.
Cor. (C)
Trb. (C)
Timp.
Vl.
Vla.
Vlc. e Cb.

Fl.
Ob.
Fag.
zu 2
Cor. (C)
zu 2
Trb. (C)
zu 2
Timp.
Vl.
Vla.
Vlc. e Cb.
p

210
Fl.
Ob.
Fag.
Vl.
Vla.
Vlc. e Cb.

Vl.
Vla.
Vlc. e Cb.

220
Fl.
Ob.
p
p
Vl.
Vla.
Vlc. e Cb.

SOLO.
Fl.
Ob.
Klav.
Vl.
Vla.
Vlc. e Cb.
230
Fag.

Fl.
Ob.
1.
Fag.
Klav.
Vl.
Vla.
Vlc. e
Cb.

Fl.
Ob.
Fag.
1.
Klav.
Vl.
Vla.
Vlc. e
Cb.

Fl.
Ob.
Fag.
1.
Klav.
Vl.
Vla.
Vlc. e
Cb.

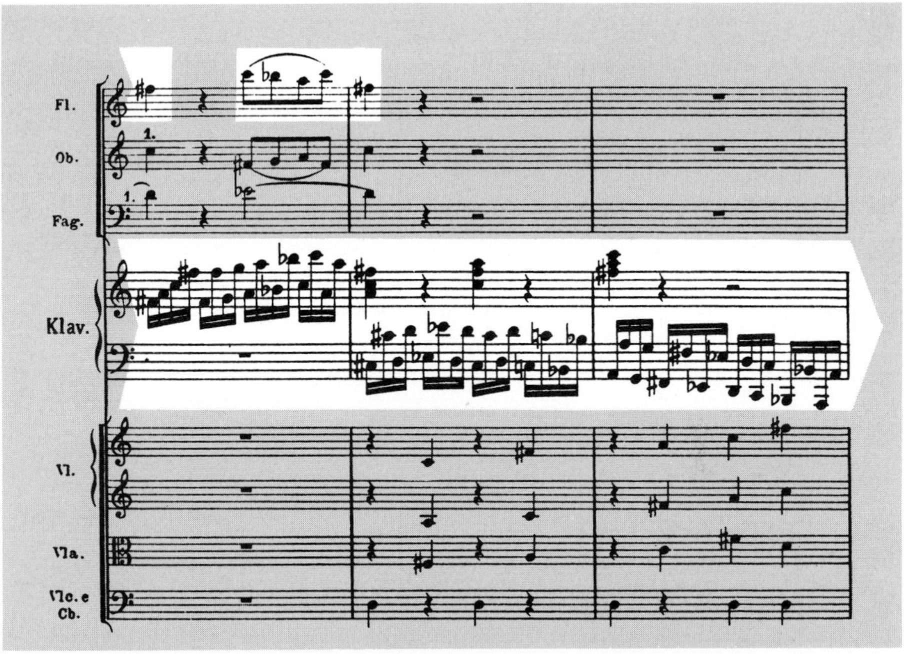

Fl.
Ob.
Fag.
Klav.
Vl.
Vla.
Vlc. e Cb.

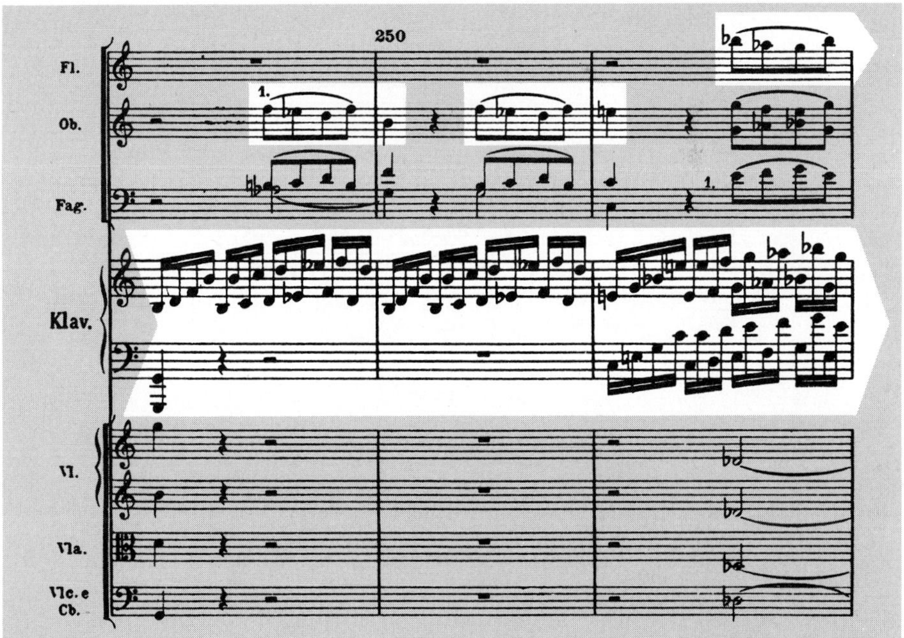

250

Fl.
Ob.
Fag.
Klav.
Vl.
Vla.
Vlc. e Cb.

Fl.
Ob.
Fag.
Klav.
Vl.
Vla.
Vlc. e Cb.

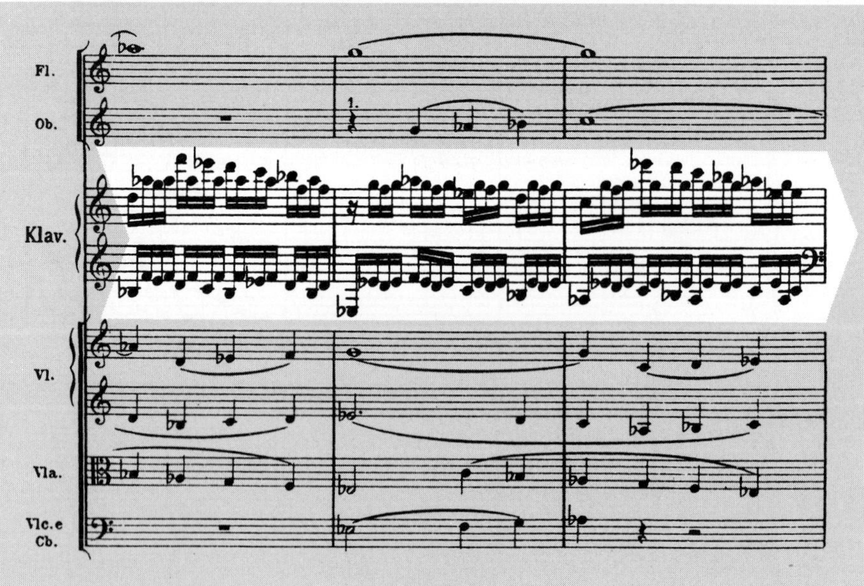

Fl.
Ob.
1.
Klav.
Vl.
Vla.
Vlc. e
Cb.

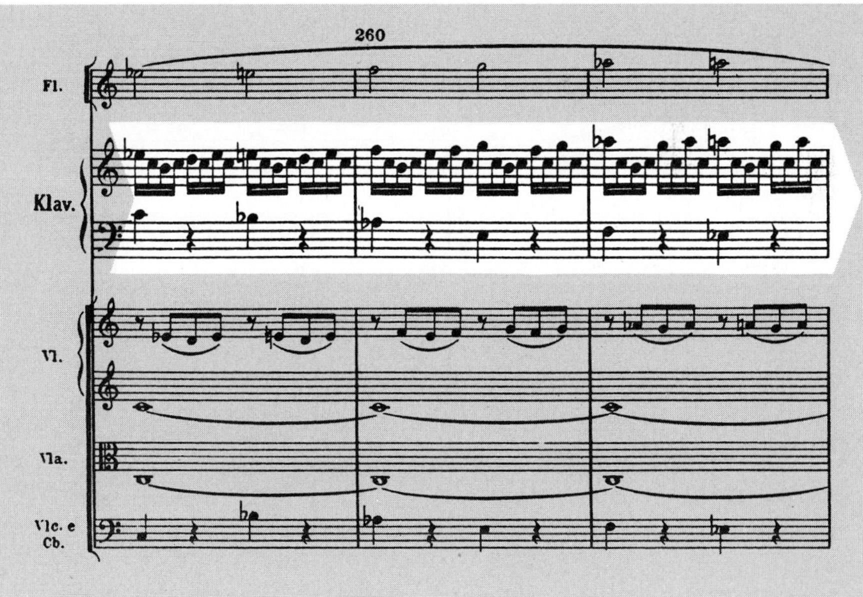
260
Fl.
Klav.
Vl.
Vla.
Vlc. e
Cb.

Fl.
Klav.
Vl.
Vla.
Vlc. e
Cb.

Fl.
Klav.
6
Vl.
Vla.
Vlc. e
Cb.

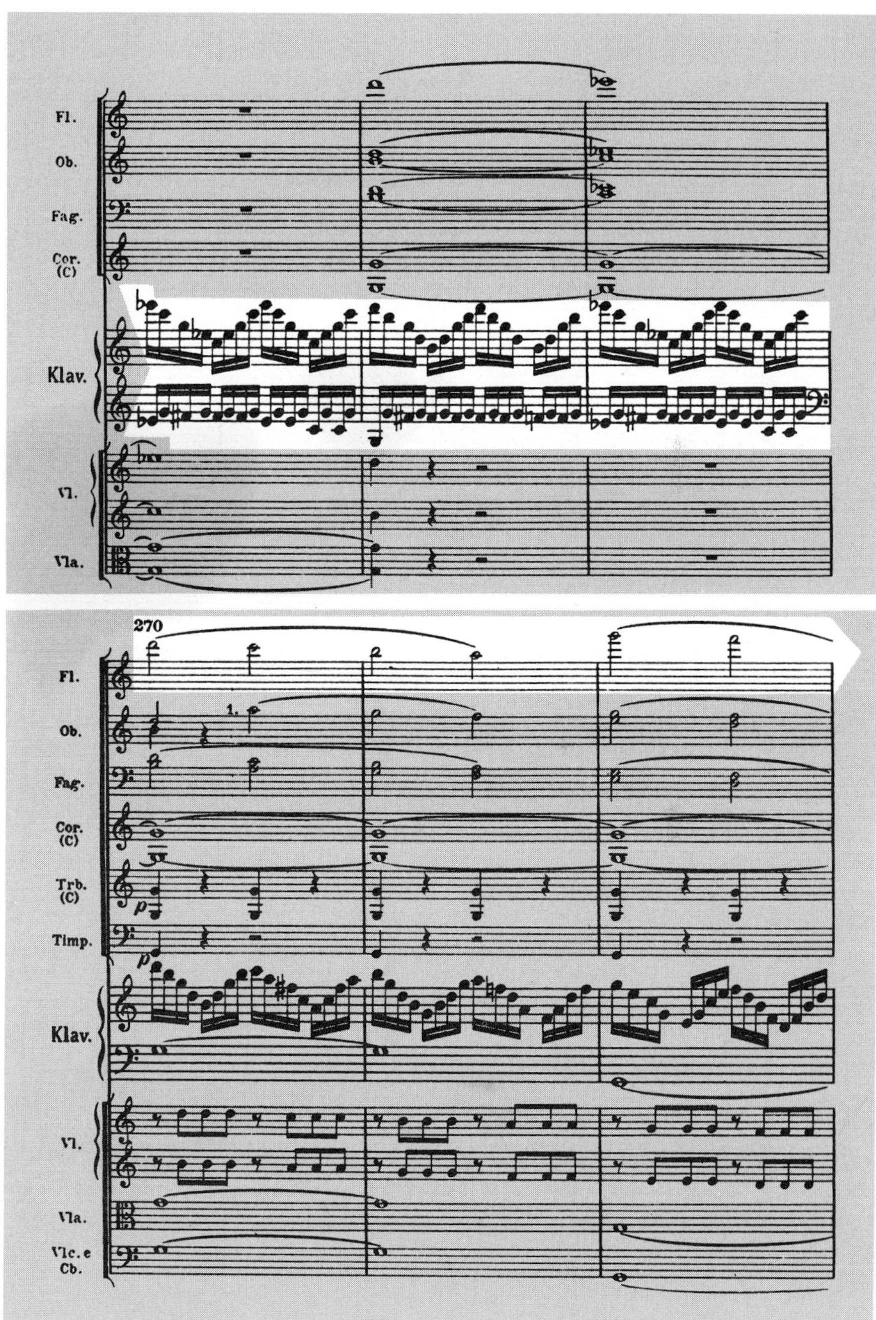
Fl.
Ob.
Fag.
Cor. (C)
Klav.
Vl.
Vla.
270
Fl.
Ob.
1.
Fag.
Cor. (C)
Trb. (C)
Timp.
Klav.
Vl.
Vla.
Vlc. e Cb.

TUTTI

Fl.
Ob.
Fag.
Cor. (C)
Trb. (C)
Timp.
Klav.
Vl.
Vla.
Vlc. e Cb.

280
Fl.
Ob.
Fag.
Cor. (C)
Trb. (C)
Timp.
Vl.
Vla.
Vlc. e Cb.

Fl.
Ob.
Fag.
zu 2
Cor. (C)
Trb. (C)
Timp.
Vl.
Vla.
Vlc. e Cb.

290

Fl.
Ob.
Fag.
Cor. (C)
Trb. (C)
Timp.
Vl.
Vla.
Vlc. e Cb.

SOLO.
Fl.
Klav.
Vl.
p

300
Fl.
Ob.
Klav.
p

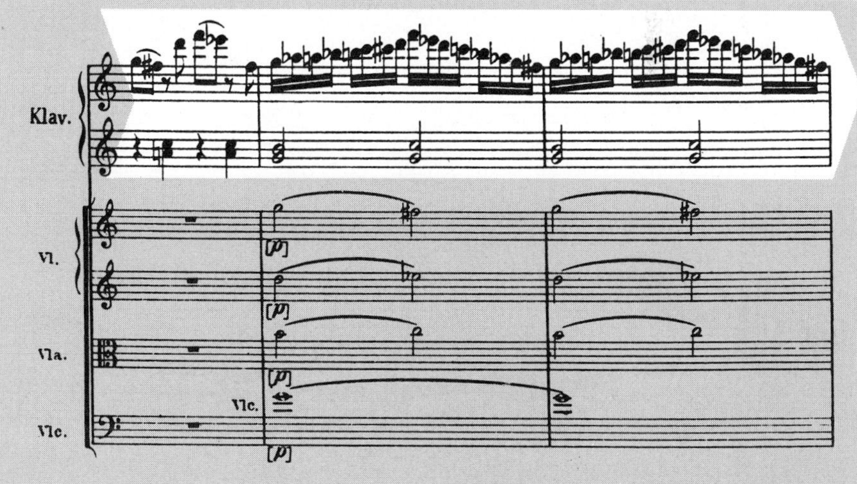
Klav.
Vl.
Vla.
Vlc.
[p]

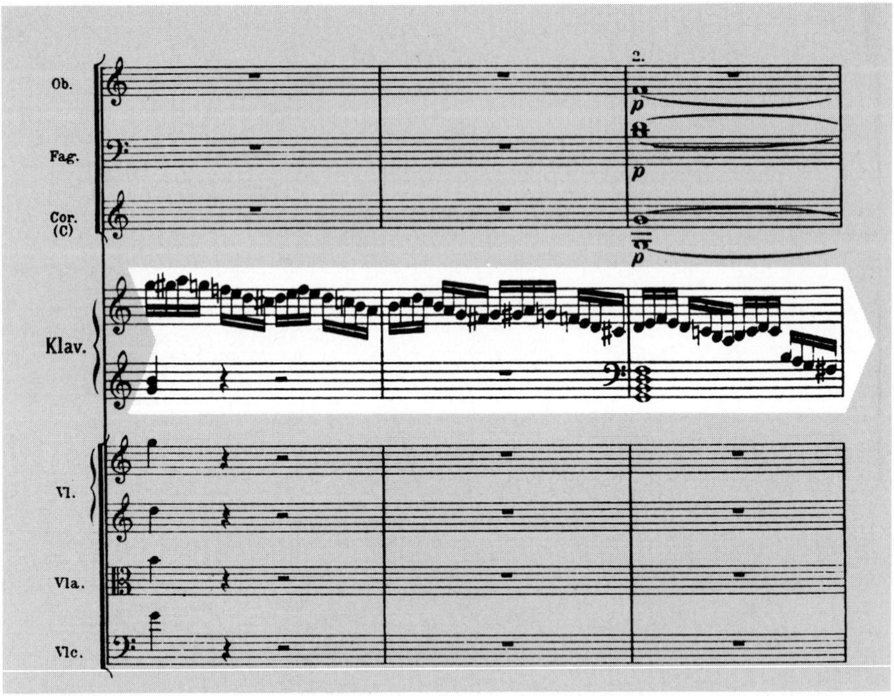

2.
Ob.
p
Fag.
p
Cor. (C)
p
Klav.
Vl.
Vla.
Vlc.

Fl.
Ob.
Fag.
Cor. (C)
Klav.
Vl.
[p]
[p]
Vla.
[p]
Bassi.
Vlc. e Cb.
[p]

320
Fl.
Ob.
Fag.
Klav.
Vlc. e Cb.
[p]
[p]
[p]

Fl.
Ob.
1.
Klav.

Klav.
330
Vl.
[p]
[p]

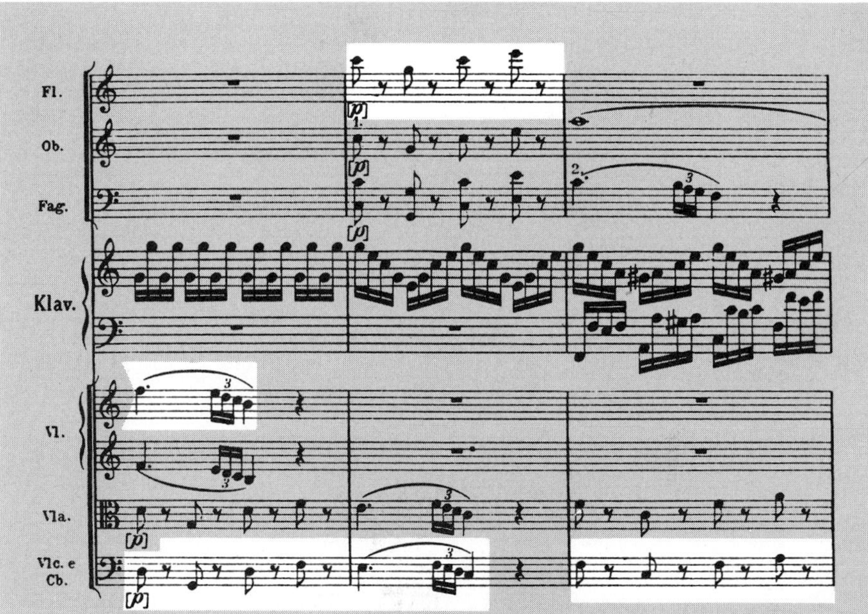
Fl.
Ob.
Fag.
Klav.
Vl.
Vla.
Vlc. e Cb.
[p]
1.
2.
3

Fl.
Ob.
Fag.
Klav.
Vl.
Vla.
Vlc. e Cb.
[p]
1.
2.
3

Fl.
Ob.
Fag.
Klav.
Vl.
Vla.
Vlc. e Cb.

340
Klav.
Vl.
Vla.
Vlc. e Cb.

Klav.
Vl.
Vla.
Vlc. e Cb.

Klav.
Vl.
Vla.
Vlc. e Cb.

350

Fl.
Ob.
Fag.
Cor. (C)
Klav.
Vl.
Vla.
Vlc. e Cb.

TUTTI.
SOLO.

Fl.
Ob.
Fag.
Cor. (C)
Trb. (C)
Klav.
Vl.
Vla.
Vlc. e Cb.

360
Ob.
Fag.
Trb. (C)
Klav.
Vla.
Vlc. e Cb.

Klav.

Klav.
tr
Vl.
[p]
Vla.
Vlc. e Cb.

Ob.
Fag.
[p]
[p]
Klav.
Vl.
Vla.
Vlc. e
Cb.

370
Ob.
Fag.
Klav.
Vl.
Vla.
Vlc. e
Cb.

Fl.
Ob.
2.
Fag.
2.
Klav.
Vl.
Vla.
Vlc. e Cb.

Fl.
Ob.
1.
1.
Fag.
Cor. (C)
p
Trb. (C)
p
Timp.
p
Klav.
Vl.
Vla.
Vlc. e Cb.

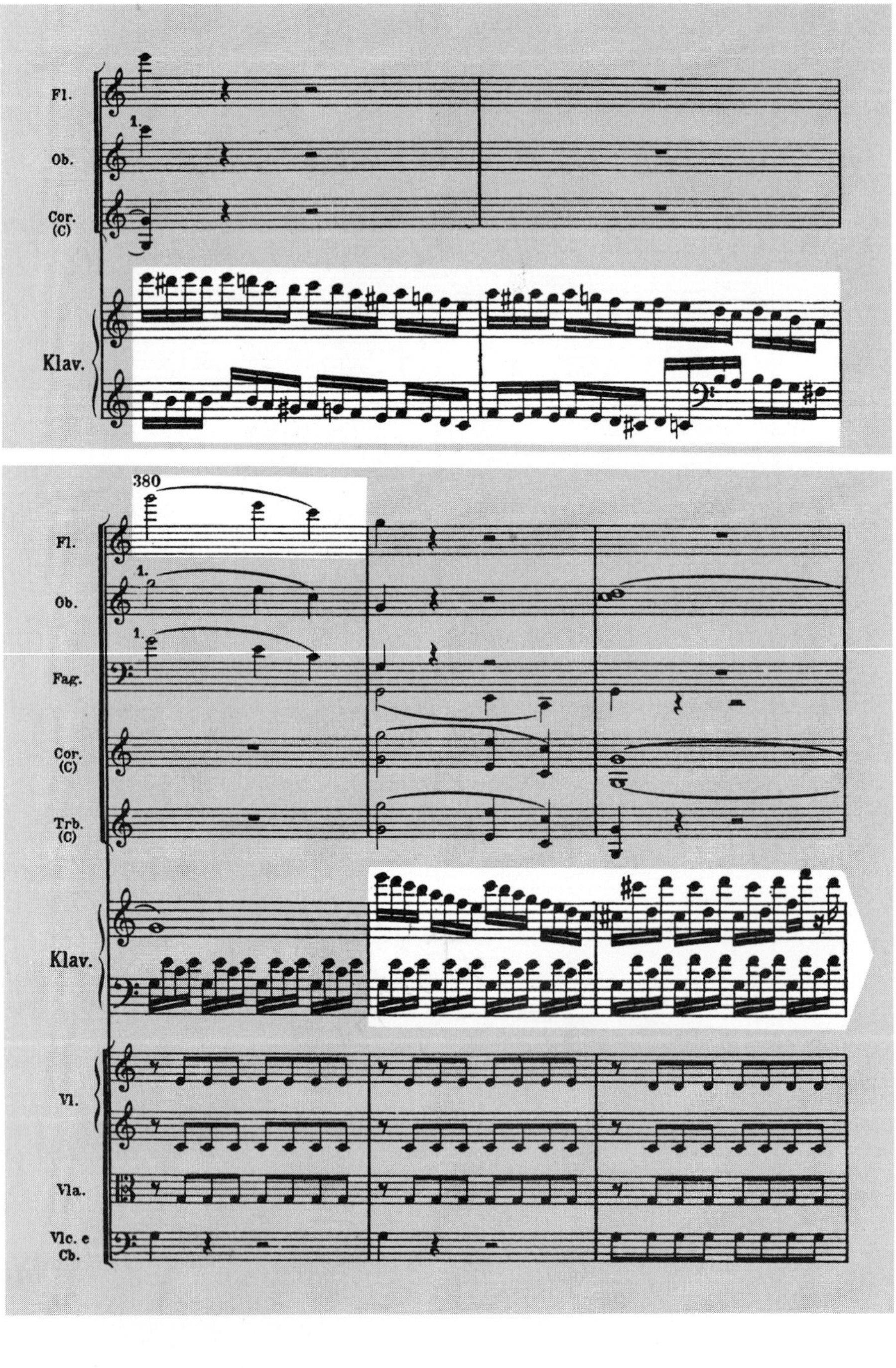

Fl.
1.
Ob.
Cor. (C)
Klav.

380
Fl.
1.
Ob.
1.
Fag.
Cor. (C)
Trb. (C)
Klav.
Vl.
Vla.
Vlc. e Cb.

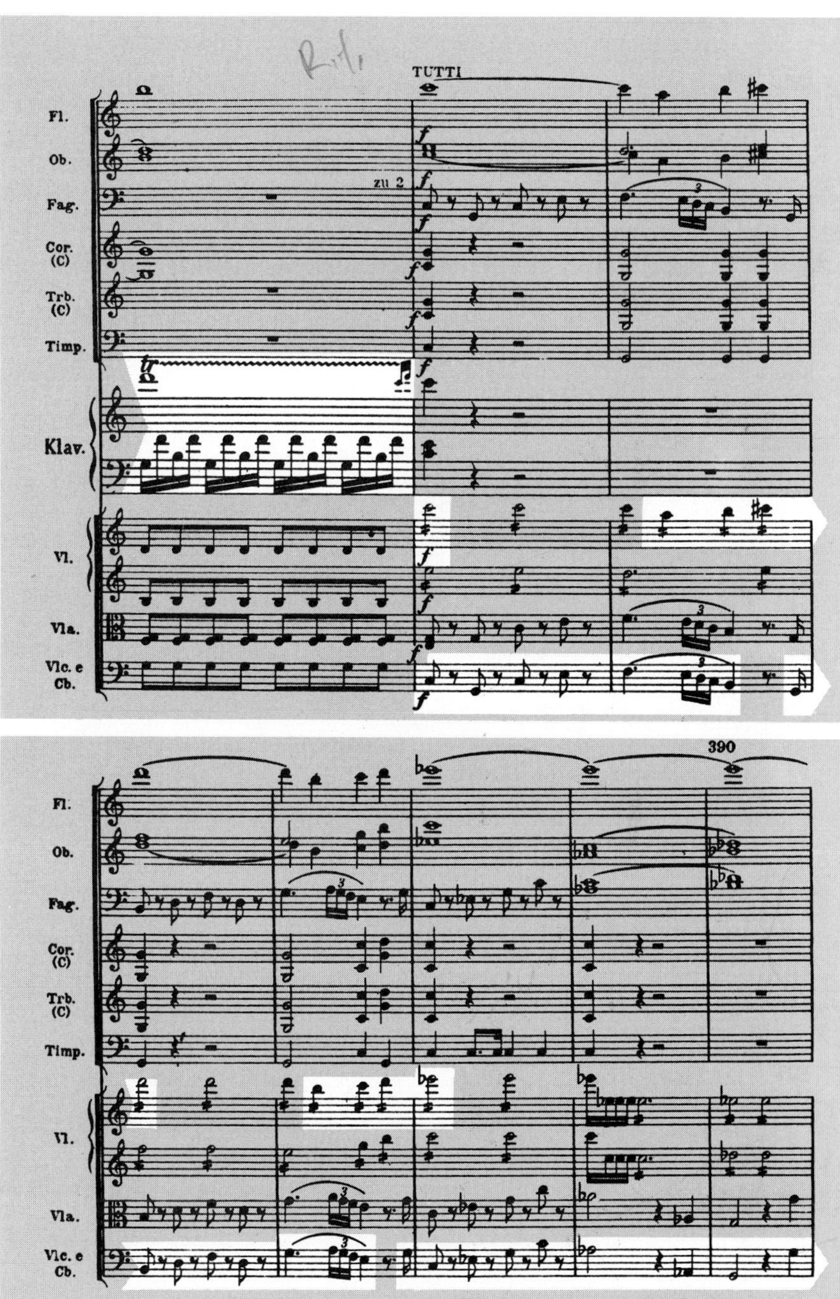
TUTTI
Fl.
Ob.
zu 2
Fag.
Cor. (C)
Trb. (C)
Timp.
Klav.
Vl.
Vla.
Vlc. e Cb.
390

* Mozart did not leave written-out cadenzas for this concerto. Modern pianists supply their own or choose from among various published cadenzas.

Fl.
Ob.
Fag.
Cor. (C)
Trb. (C)
Timp.
Vl.
Vla.
Vlc. e Cb.
zu 2

410
Fl.
Ob.
zu 2
Fag.
Cor. (C)
Trb. (C)
Timp.
Vl.
Vla.
Vlc. e Cb.
zu 2
1.

II.
Andante.
TUTTI
Flauto.
2 Oboi.
2 Fagotti.
2 Corni in F.
Klavier.
Con Sordino
Violino I.
Con Sordino
Violino II.
Con Sordino
Viola.
Violoncello e Contrabasso.
p Pizzicato
Fl.
Ob.
Fag.
Cor. (F)
Vl.
Vla.
Vlc. e Cb.

10
Fl.
Ob.
Fag.
Cor. (F)
Vl.
Vla.
Vlc. e Cb.
sfp
sf
p
f

Fl.
Ob.
Fag.
Cor. (F)
Vl.
Vla.
Vlc. e Cb.
1.
3

20
Fl.
Ob.
Fag.
Cor. (F)
SOLO
Klav.
pizz.
Vl.
pizz.
pizz.
Vla.
pizz.
Vlc. e Cb.

30
Fl.
Ob.
Fag.
Cor. (F)
Klav.
Vl.
Vla.
Vlc. e Cb.

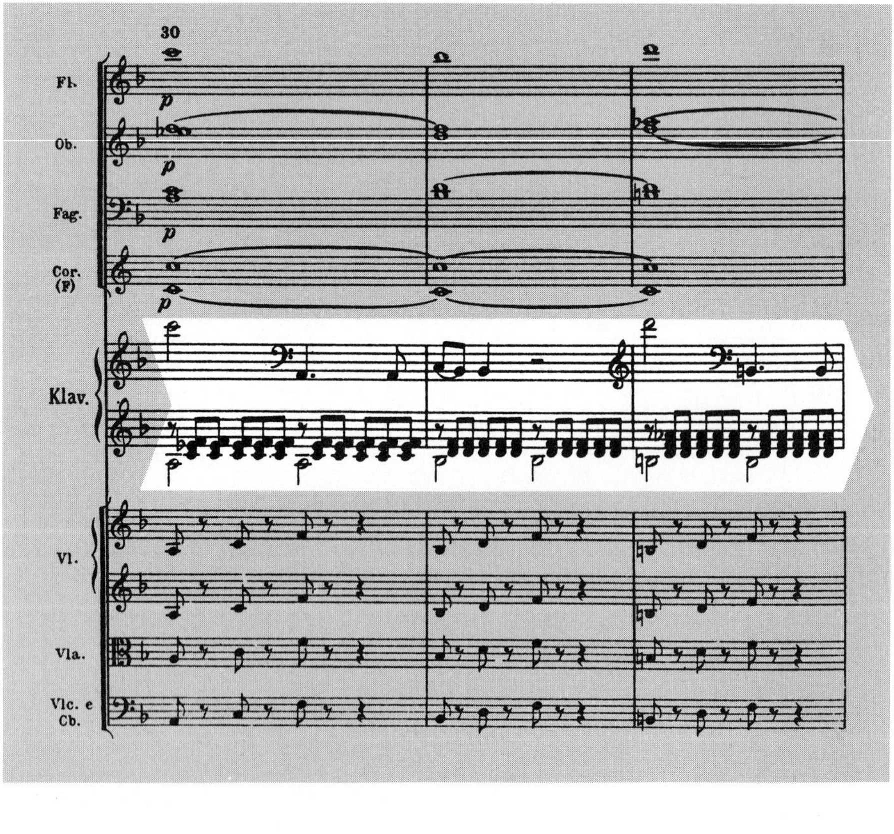

Fl.
Ob.
Fag.
Cor. (F)
Klav.
Vl.
Vla.
Vlc. e
arco
Fl.
Ob.
Fag.
Cor. (F)
Klav.
Vl.
Vla.
Vlc. e Cb.
arco
arco
arco

Fl.
[p]
Ob.
[p]
Fag.
[p]
Klav.
Vl.
Vla.
Vlc. e Cb.

50
Fl.
Ob.
Fag.
Klav.
Vl.
Vla.
Vlc. e Cb.

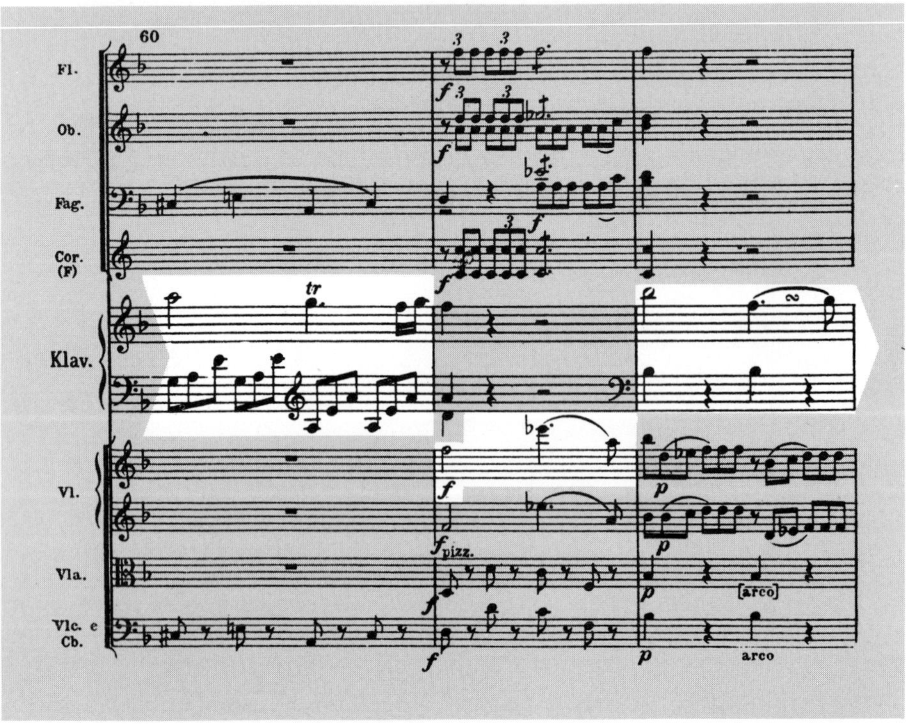

60
Fl.
Ob.
Fag.
Cor. (F)
Klav.
tr
Vl.
Vla.
Vlc. e Cb.
f
p
pizz.
[arco]
arco

Fl.
Ob.
Fag.
Klav.
Vl.
Vla.
Vlc. e Cb.
tr.
pizz.

70
Fl.
Ob.
Fag.
Klav.
Vl.
Vla.
Vlc. e Cb.
arco

Fl.
Ob.
Fag.
Klav.
pizz.
Vl.
Vla.
Vlc. e Cb.

Ob.
Fag.
Klav.
Vl.
Vla.
Vlc. e Cb.

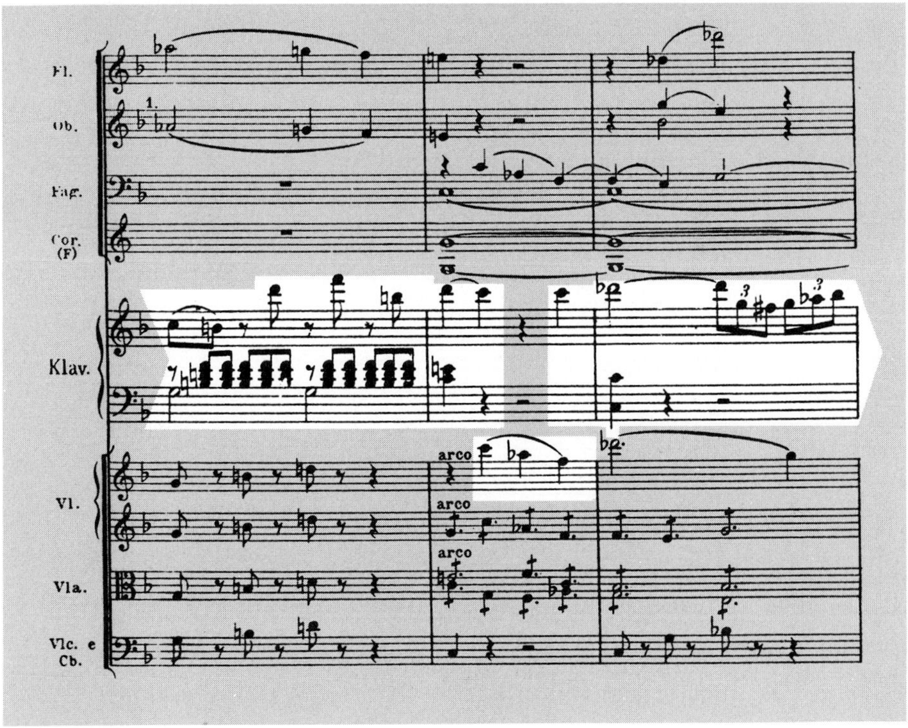

Fl.
1.
Ob.
Fag.
Cor. (F)
3
3
Klav.
arco
Vl.
arco
arco
Vla.
Vlc. e Cb.

Fl.
Ob.
Fag.
Cor. (F)
Klav.
Vl.
Vla.
Vlc. e Cb.

90

Fl.
1.
Ob.
1.
Fag.
Cor. (F)
Klav.
pizz.
Vl.
pizz.
pizz.
Vla.
Vlc. e Cb.

Fl.
Ob.
Fag.
Cor. (F)
Klav.
Vl.
Vla.
Vlc. e Cb.
1.
cresc.
p

Fl.
Ob.
Fag.
Cor. (F)
Klav.
Vl.
Vla.
Vlc. e Cb.
cresc.
f
p

100
Fl.
Ob.
Fag.
Cor. (F)
Klav.
Vl.
Vla.
Vlc. e Cb.

Fl.
Ob.
Fag.
Cor. (F)
pp
pp
pp
pp
Klav.
Vl.
Vla.
Vlc. e Cb.

III.
Allegro vivace assai.
TUTTI
Flauto.
2 Oboi.
2 Fagotti.
2 Corni in C.
2 Trombe in C.
Timpani in C-G.
Klavier.
Violino I.
Violino II.
Viola.
Violoncello e Contrabasso.

10

Fl.
Ob.
Fag.
Cor. (C)
Trb. (C)
Vl.
Vla.
Vlc. e Cb.

zu 2
zu 2
p
p
zu 2
f
f
f
f
f

20
SOLO

Fl.
Ob.
Fag.
Cor. (C)
Trb. (C)
Timp.
Klav.
Vl.
Vla.
Vlc. e Cb.

zu 2
f
f
f
f
p
p
p
p

TUTTI
30
Fl.
Ob.
Fag.
Cor. (C)
Trb. (C)
Timp.
Klav.
Vl.
Vla.
Vlc. e Cb.
40
zu 2
1.

Fl.
Ob.
Fag.
Cor. (C)
Trb. (C)
Timp.
Vl.
Vla.
Vlc. e Cb.

50

Fl.
Ob.
Fag.
Cor. (C)
Trb. (C)
Timp.
Vl.
Vla.
Vlc. e Cb.

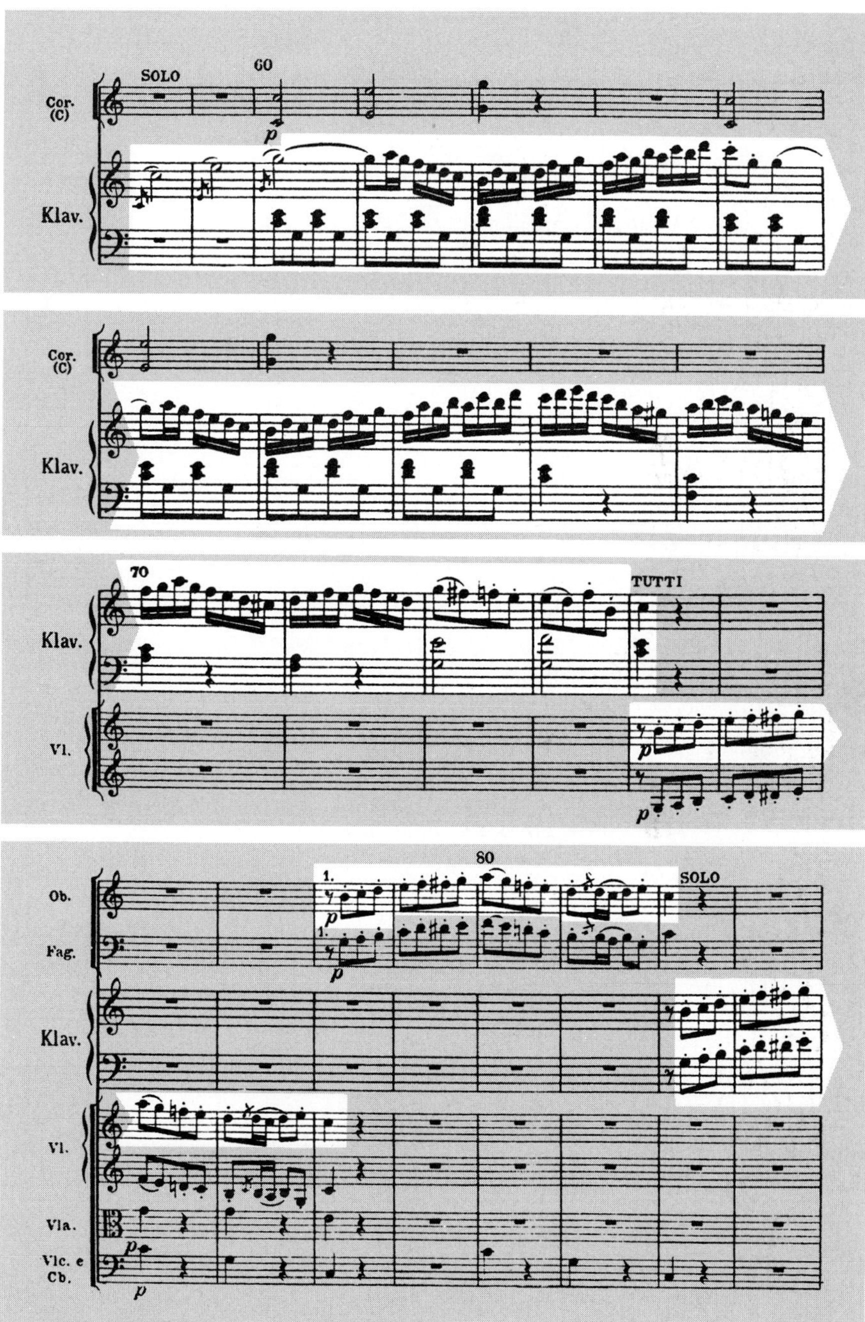
SOLO
60
Cor. (C)
p
Klav.
Cor. (C)
Klav.
70
TUTTI
Klav.
Vl.
p
p
80
SOLO
Ob.
1.
p
Fag.
1.
p
Klav.
Vl.
Vla.
Vlc. e Cb.
p
p

90
Klav.
Vl.
Vla.
Vlc. e Cb.

Klav.
Vl.
Vla.
Vlc. e Cb.

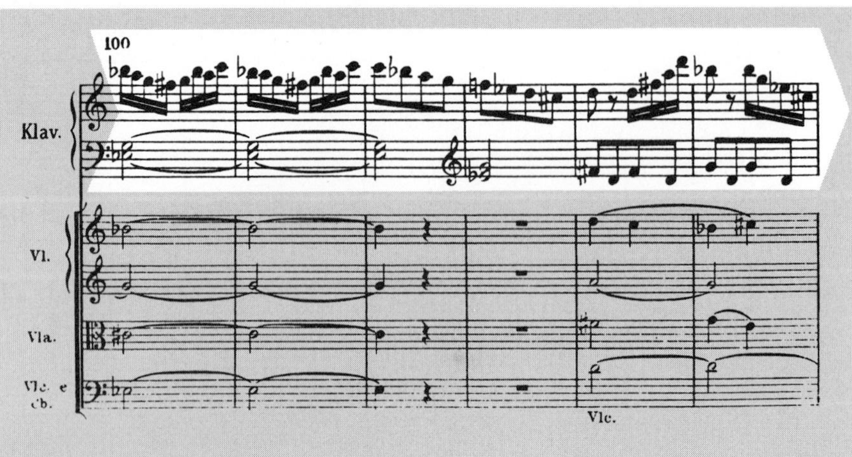
100
Klav.
Vl.
Vla.
Vlc. e Cb.
Vlc.

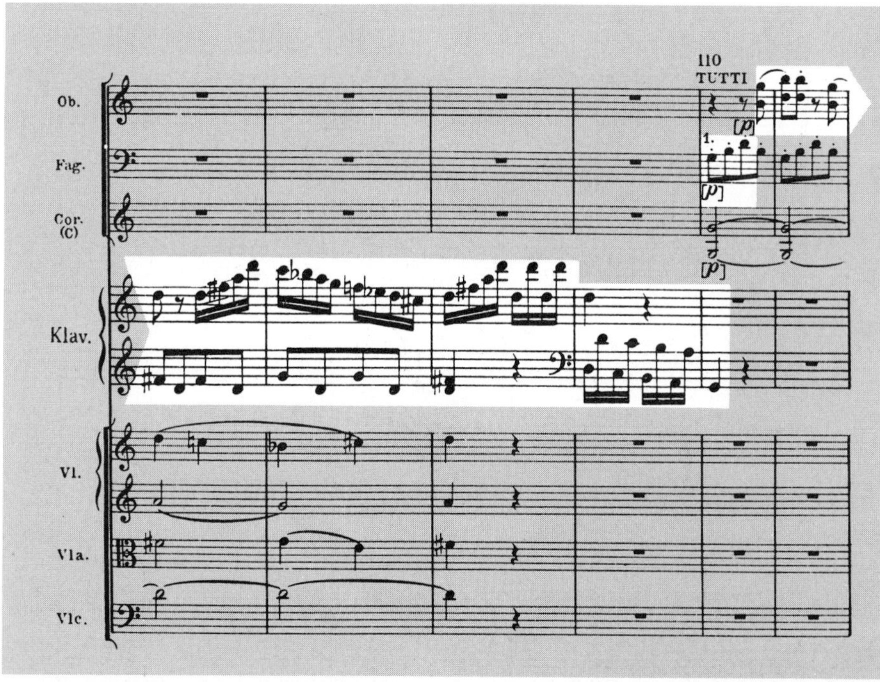

110
TUTTI
Ob.
[p]
Fag.
1.
[p]
Cor. (C)
[p]
Klav.
Vl.
Vla.
Vlc.

120
SOLO
Fl.
Ob.
Fag.
Cor. (C)
tr
tr
Klav.
Vl.
Vla.
Vlc. e Cb.

Fl.
Ob.
Fag.
Klav.
Vl.
Vla.
Vlc. e Cb.

140
Fl.
Ob.
Fag.
Klav.
Vl.
Vla.
Vlc. e Cb.

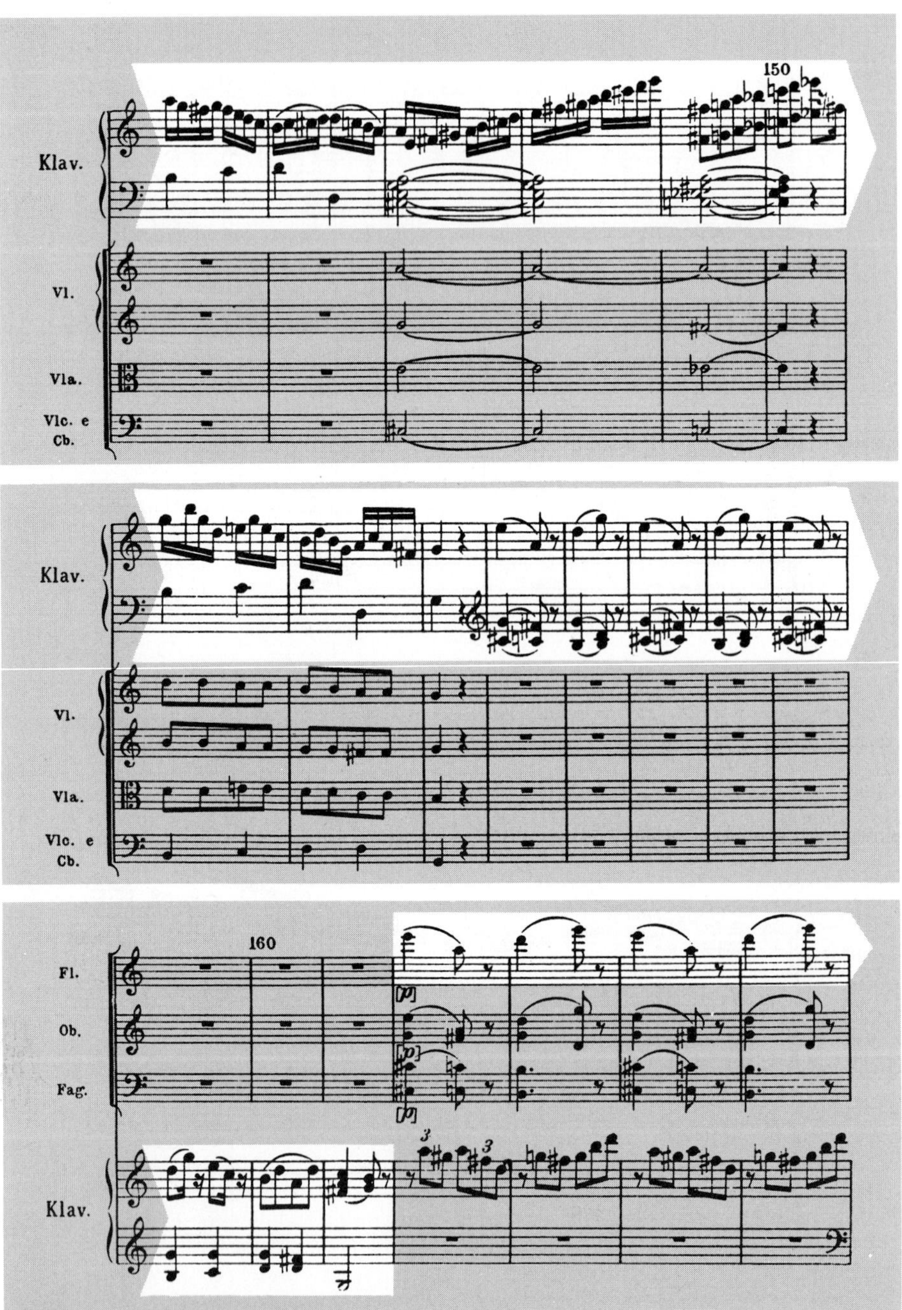
150
Klav.
Vl.
Vla.
Vlc. e
Cb.
Klav.
Vl.
Vla.
Vlc. e
Cb.
160
Fl.
Ob.
Fag.
[p]
[p]
[p]
3
3
Klav.

Fl.
Ob.
Fag.
Klav.
Vl.
Vla.
Vlc. e Cb.
170
p

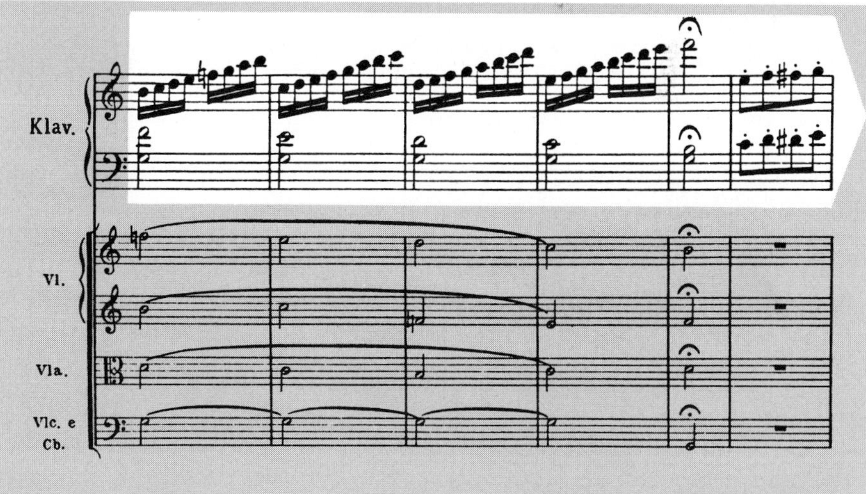

TUTTI
190
Fl.
Ob.
Fag.
Cor.
(C)
Trb.
(C)
Timp.
Vl.
Vla.
Vlc. e
Cb.

SOLO
200
Klav.
Vl.
Vla.
Vlc. e Cb.
p

Klav.
Vl.

210
Fl.
Ob.
Fag.
Cor. (C)
Klav.
p

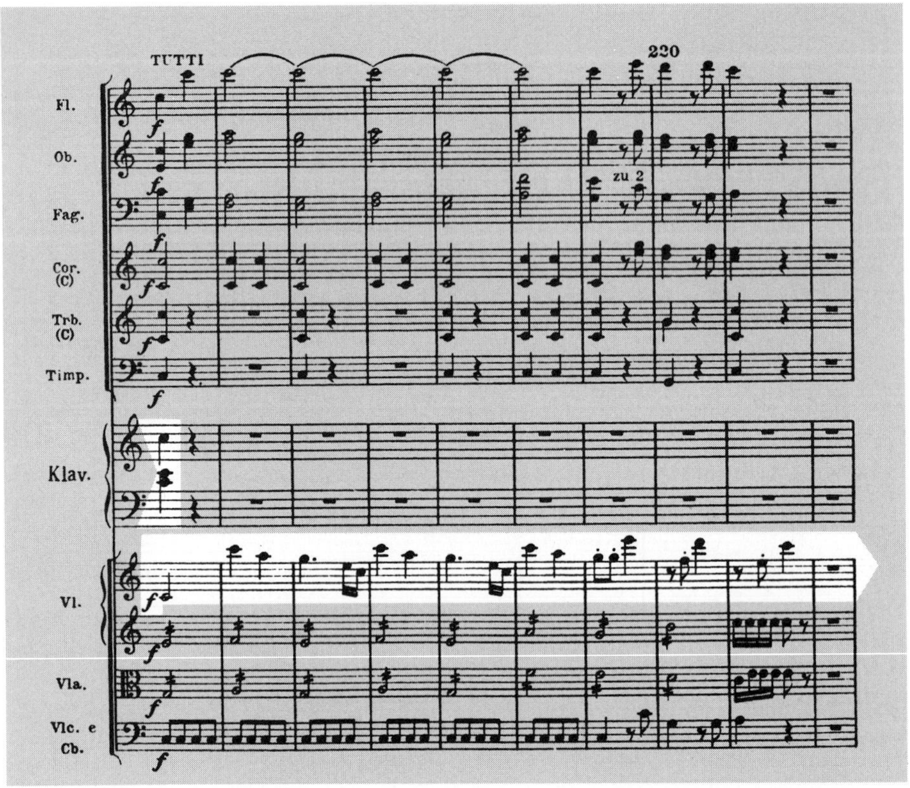

TUTTI
220
Fl.
Ob.
Fag.
zu 2
Cor. (C)
Trb. (C)
Timp.
Klav.
Vl.
Vla.
Vlc. e Cb.

230
Fl.
Ob.
Fag.
zu 2
Vl.
Vla.
Vlc. e Cb.

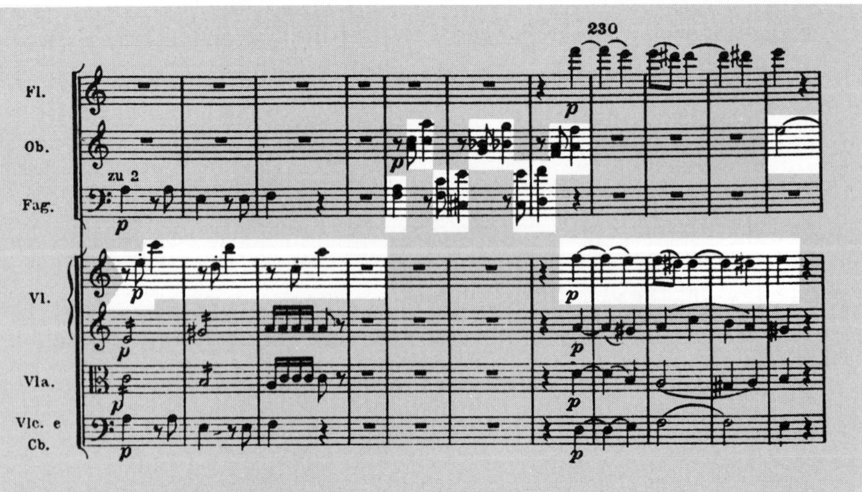

SOLO
240
Ob.
Fag.
Klav.
Vl.
Vla.
Vlc. e Cb.

Klav.

TUTTI
250
SOLO
Fl.
Ob.
Fag.
Klav.
Vl.
Vlc. e Cb.
[p]

260
Klav.
TUTTI
SOLO
TUTTI
SOLO
Fl.
Ob.
Fag.
[p]
Klav.
Vl.
Vla.
Vlc. e Cb.
270
Klav.
Vl.
Vla.
Vlc. e Cb.

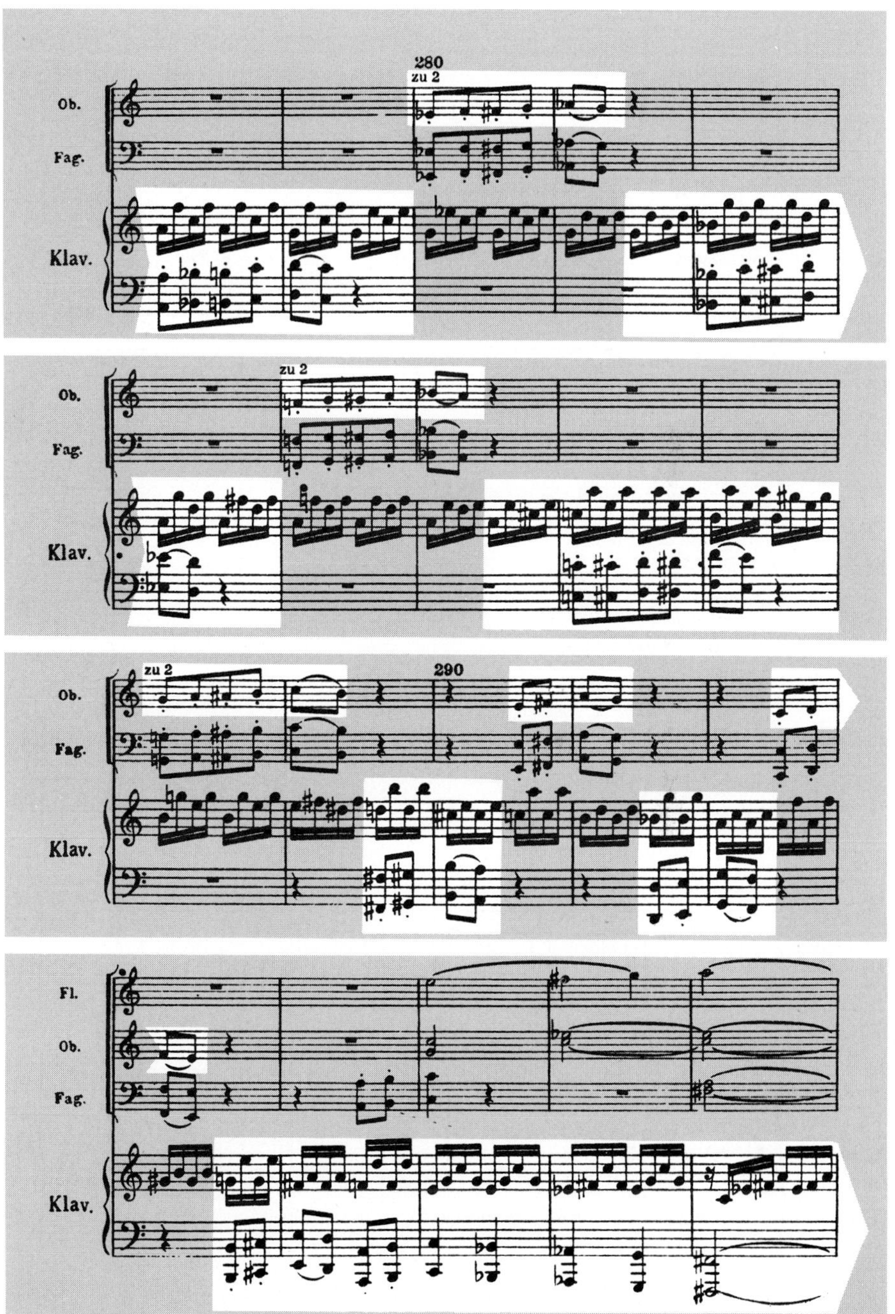
280
zu 2
Ob.
Fag.
Klav.
zu 2
Ob.
Fag.
Klav.
zu 2
290
Ob.
Fag.
Klav.
Fl.
Ob.
Fag.
Klav.

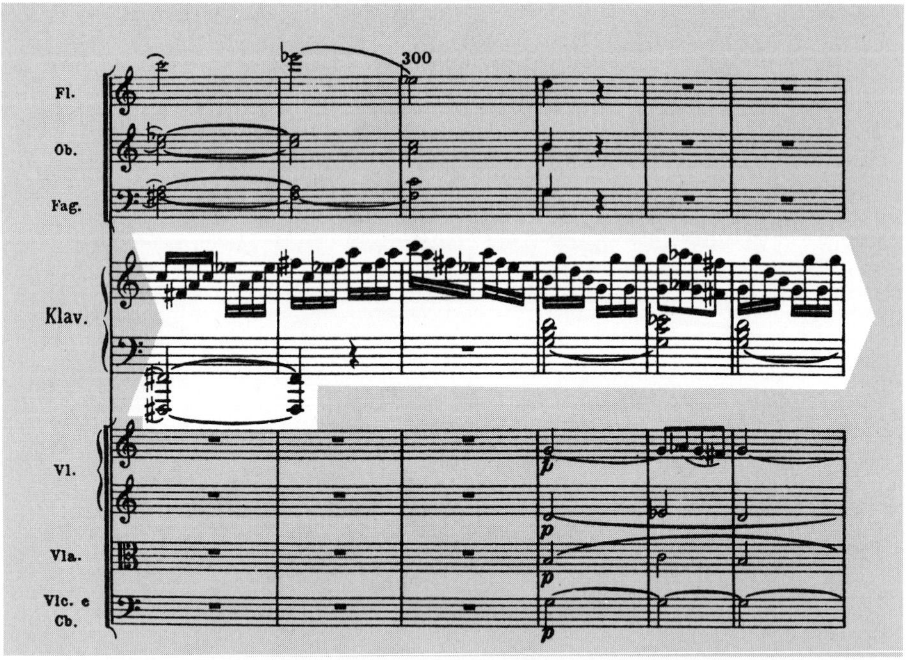

300

Fl.

Ob.

Fag.

Klav.

Vl.

p

p

Vla.

p

Vlc. e Cb.

p

SOLO
320
Ob.
Fag.
Klav.
Vl.
Vla.
Vlc. e Cb.
TUTTI
330
Fl.
Ob.
zu 2
Fag.
Cor. (C)
Trb. (C)
Timp.
Klav.
Vl.
Vla.
Vlc. e Cb.

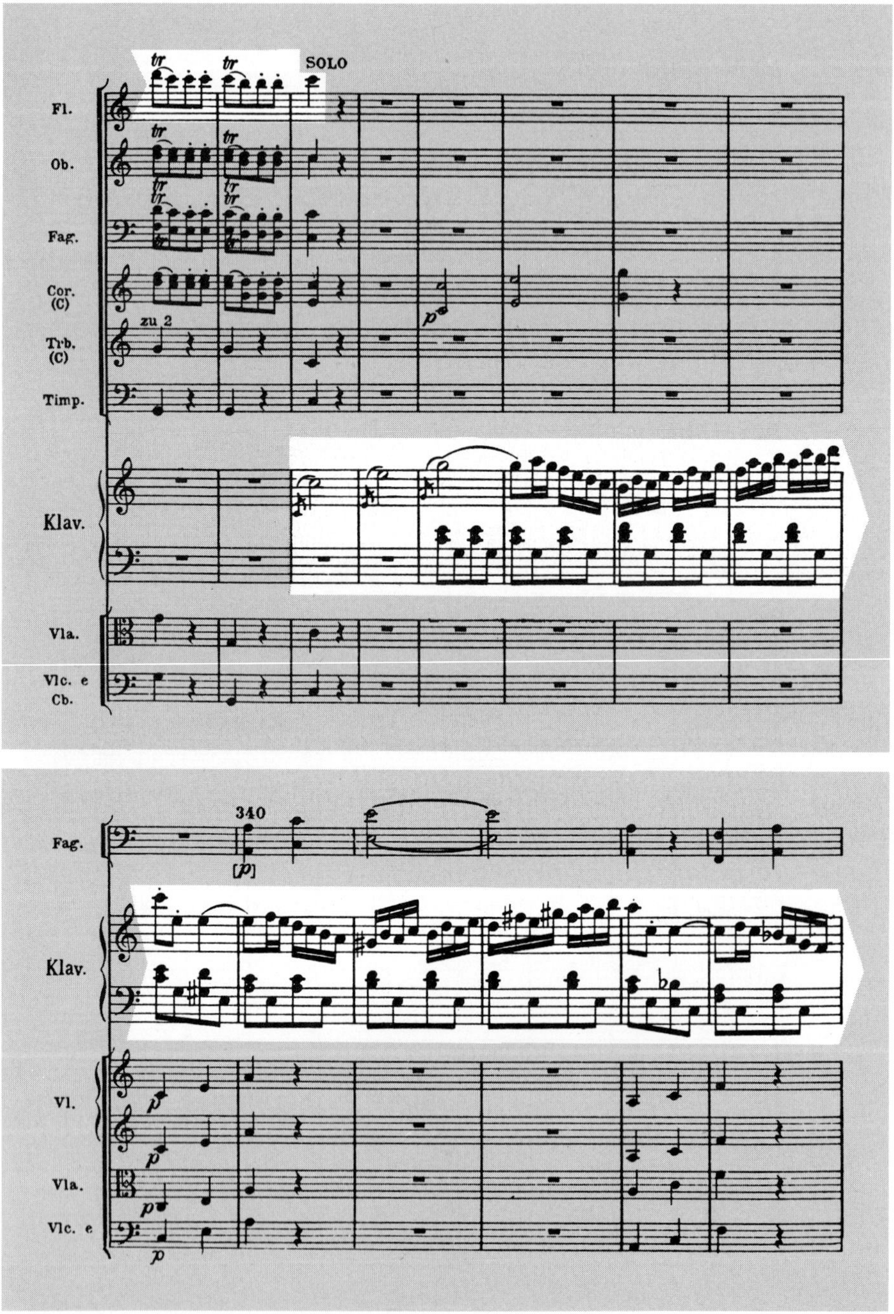

tr tr SOLO
Fl.
Ob.
Fag.
Cor. (C)
zu 2
Trb. (C)
Timp.
Klav.
Vla.
Vlc. e Cb.

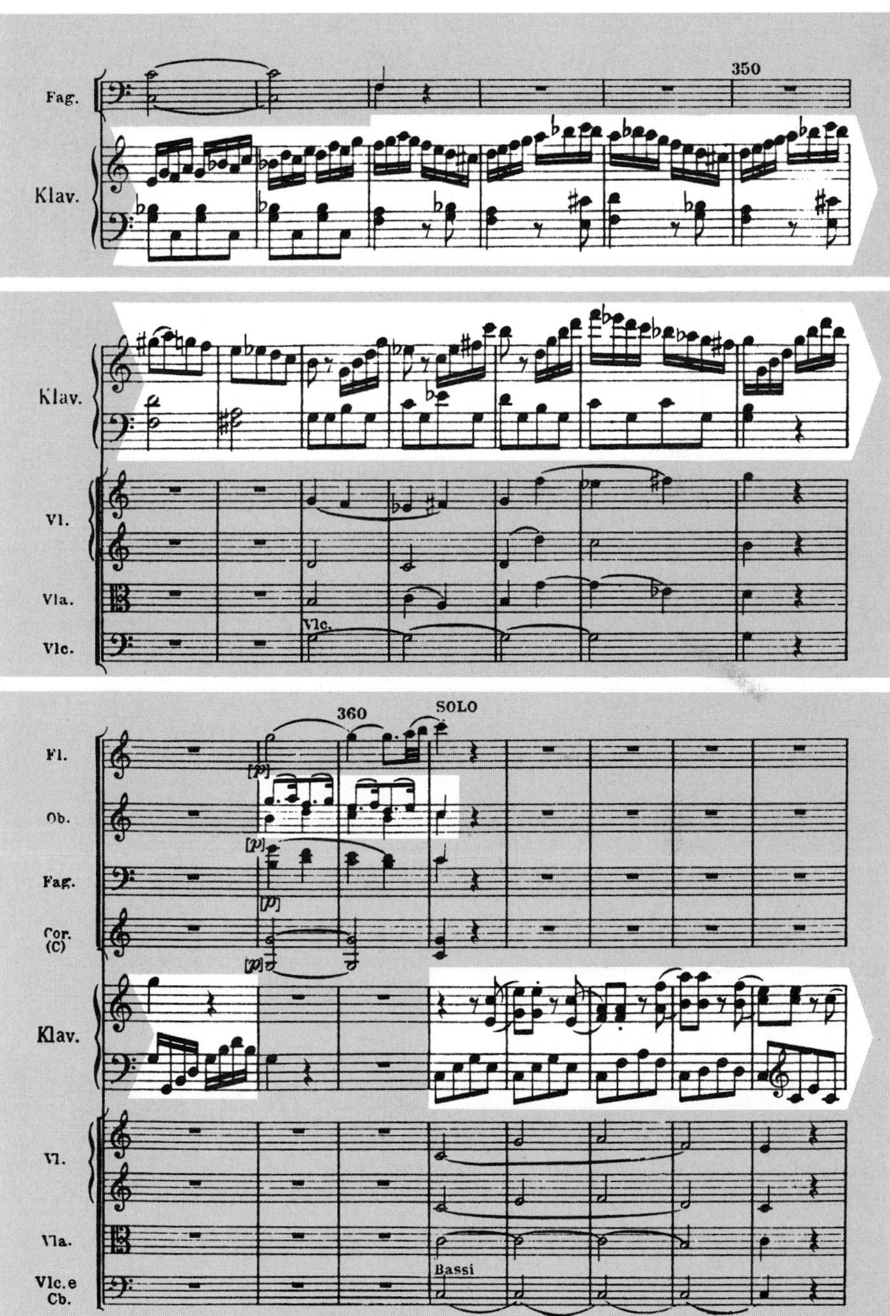

350
Fag.
Klav.
Klav.
Vl.
Vla.
Vlc.
Vlc.
360
SOLO
Fl.
Ob.
Fag.
Cor. (C)
Klav.
Vl.
Vla.
Bassi
Vlc. e Cb.

370

Ob.

Fag.

1.

Cor. (C)

Klav.

Vl.

Vla.

Vlc. e Cb.

380
Ob.
Fag.
Klav.
Vl.
Vla.
Vlc. e
Cb.
[p]

Fl.
Ob.
Fag.
Klav.
Vl.
Vla.
Vlc. e
Cb.
[p]

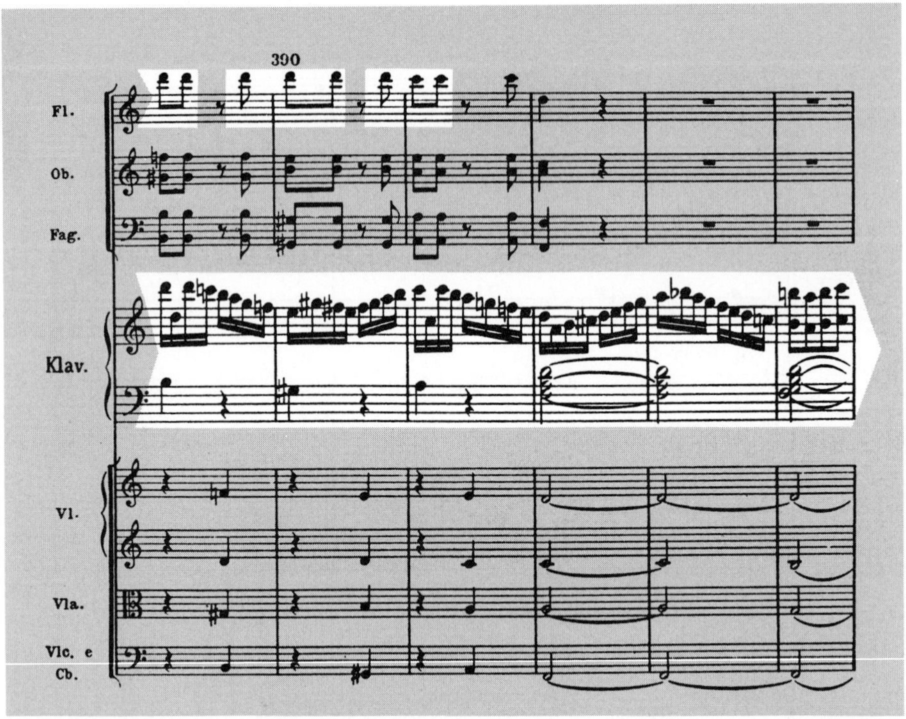

390

Fl.
Ob.
Fag.
Klav.
Vl.
Vla.
Vlc. e Cb.

400
Klav.
Vl.
Vla.
Vlc. e Cb.

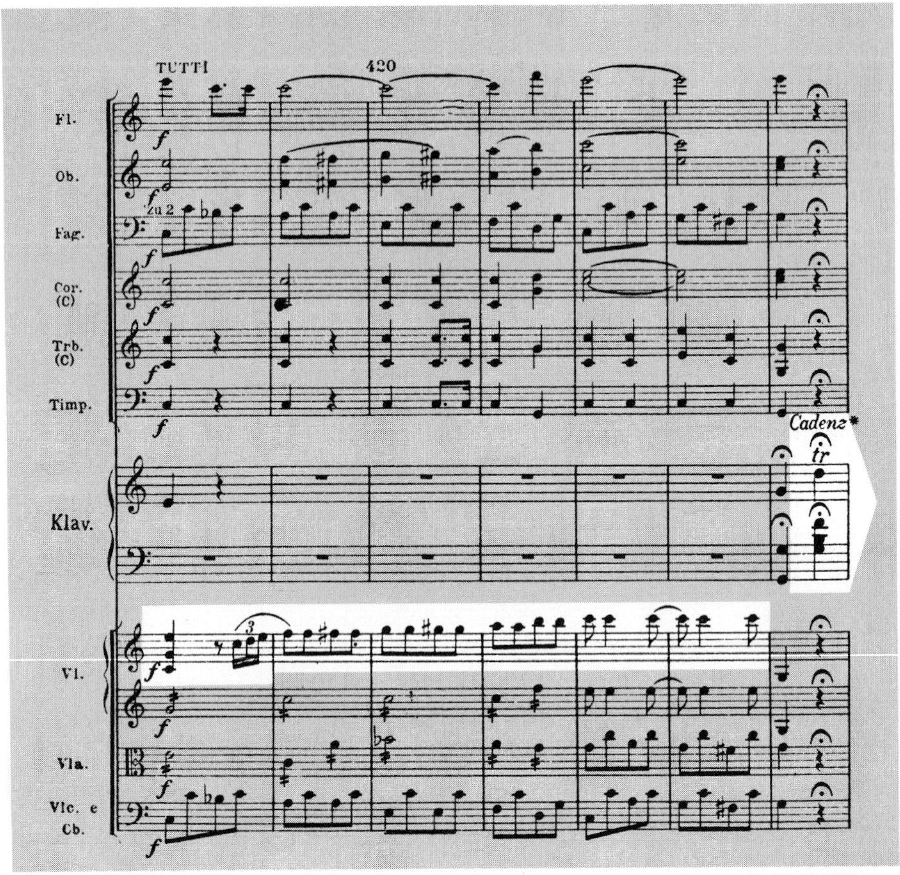

TUTTI
420
Fl.
Ob.
zu 2
Fag.
Cor. (C)
Trb. (C)
Timp.
Cadenz*
tr
Klav.
Vl.
Vla.
Vlc. e Cb.

430
Klav.
Vl.
Vla.
Vlc. e Cb.

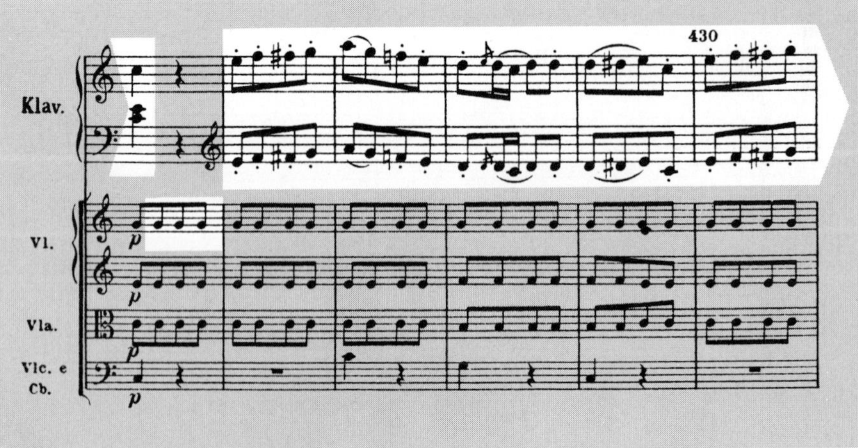

* See note on p. 412.

Fl.
Ob.
Fag.
Cor. (C)
Trb. (C)
Timp.
Klav.
Vl.
Vla.
Vlc. e Cb.

440
Fl.
Ob.
Fag.
Cor. (C)
Trb. (C)
Timp.
Klav.
Vl.
Vla.
Vlc. e Cb.

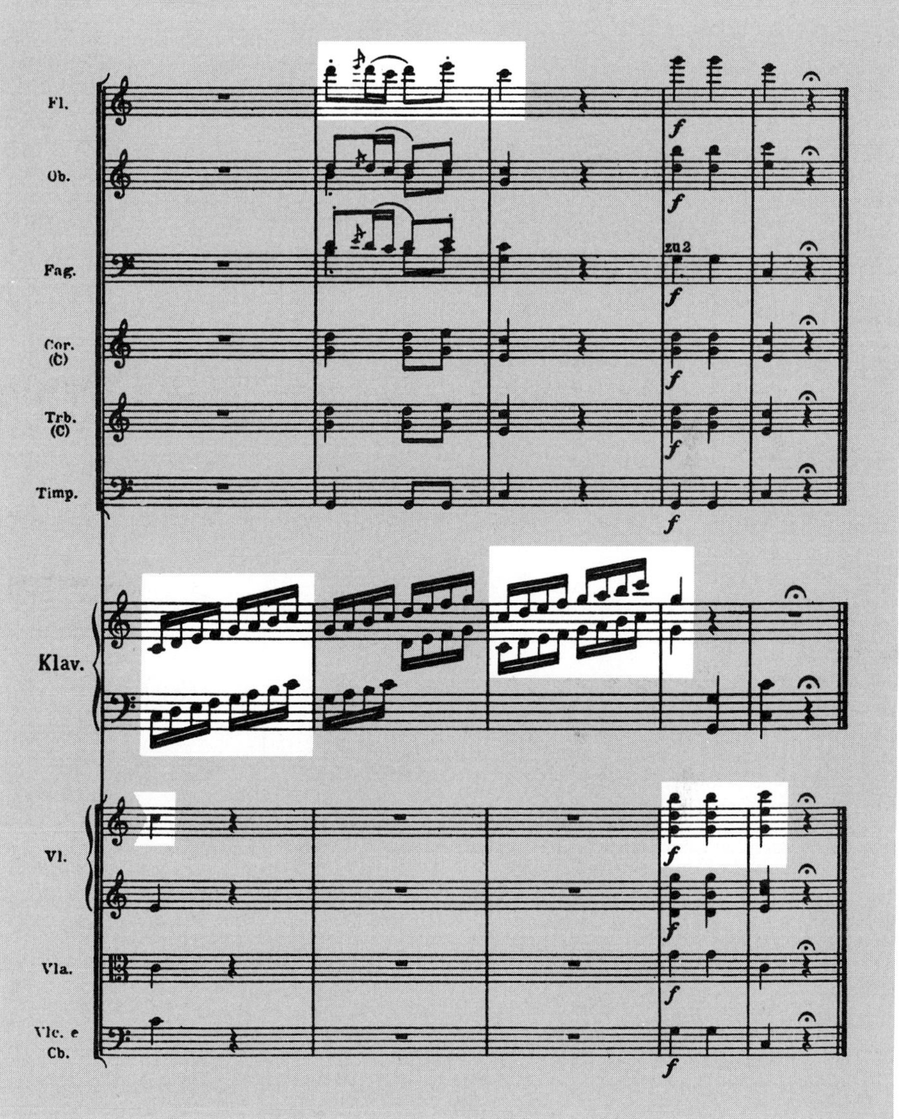
Fl.
Ob.
Fag.
zu 2
Cor. (C)
Trb. (C)
Timp.
Klav.
Vl.
Vla.
Vlc. e Cb.

33. MOZART, *Eine kleine Nachtmusik* (1787)

tr
tr
20
sf
p
cresc.
f
30
3
p

tr
tr
tr
tr
40
3
f
f
f
f
3

tr
tr
p
p
p
p

tr
tr
3
3
50
f
f
f
f

tr
tr
tr
tr
tr
tr
p
p
p
p

60
70

80
90

tr
sf
p
cresc.
f
100

110
120

tr
p
f
130

II
Romanze
Andante
p
f
10
cresc.
fp

20
p
p
p
p

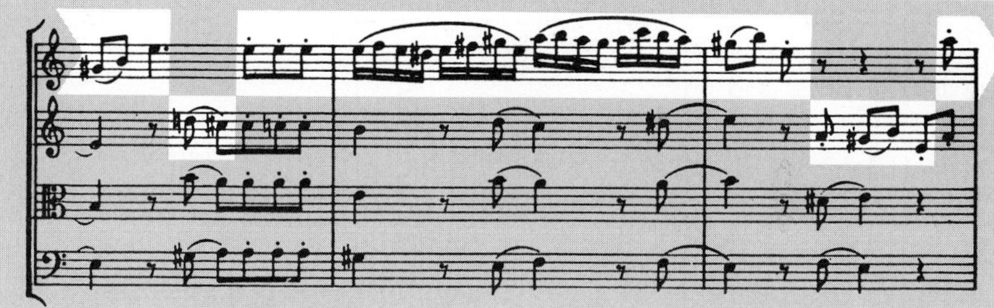

30

50
p
p
f
f
p

III

Menuetto
Allegretto

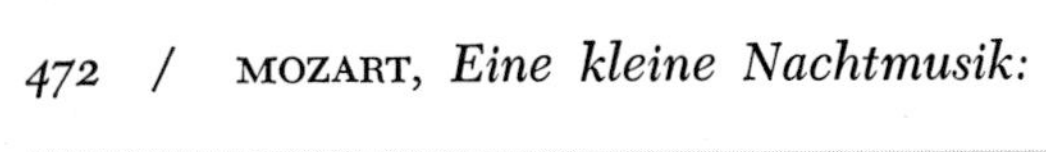

30

p

f

sotto voce

p

Menuetto da Capo.

IV

Allegro

p

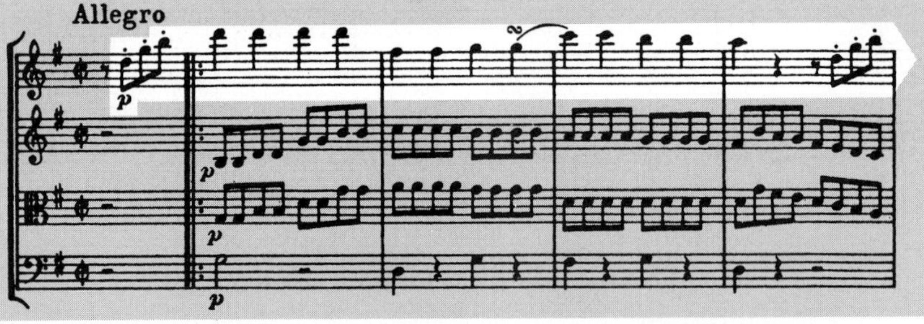

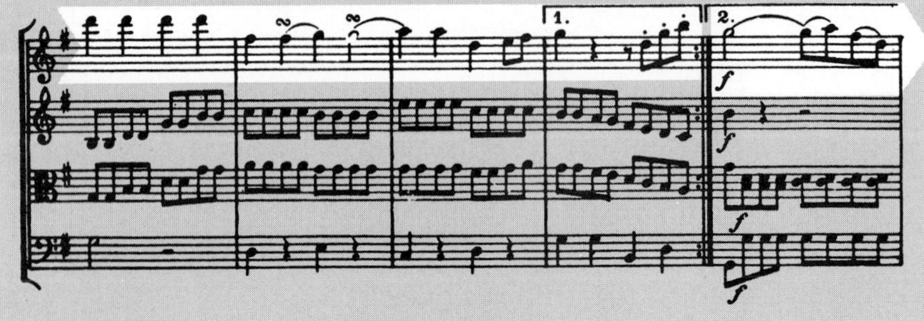

10
20

80
40

f
f
f
f
50
p
p
p
p
1.
2.
f
f
f
f
p
p
p
p
60

80
f
p
f
p
f
p
f
p
fp
fp
fp
90

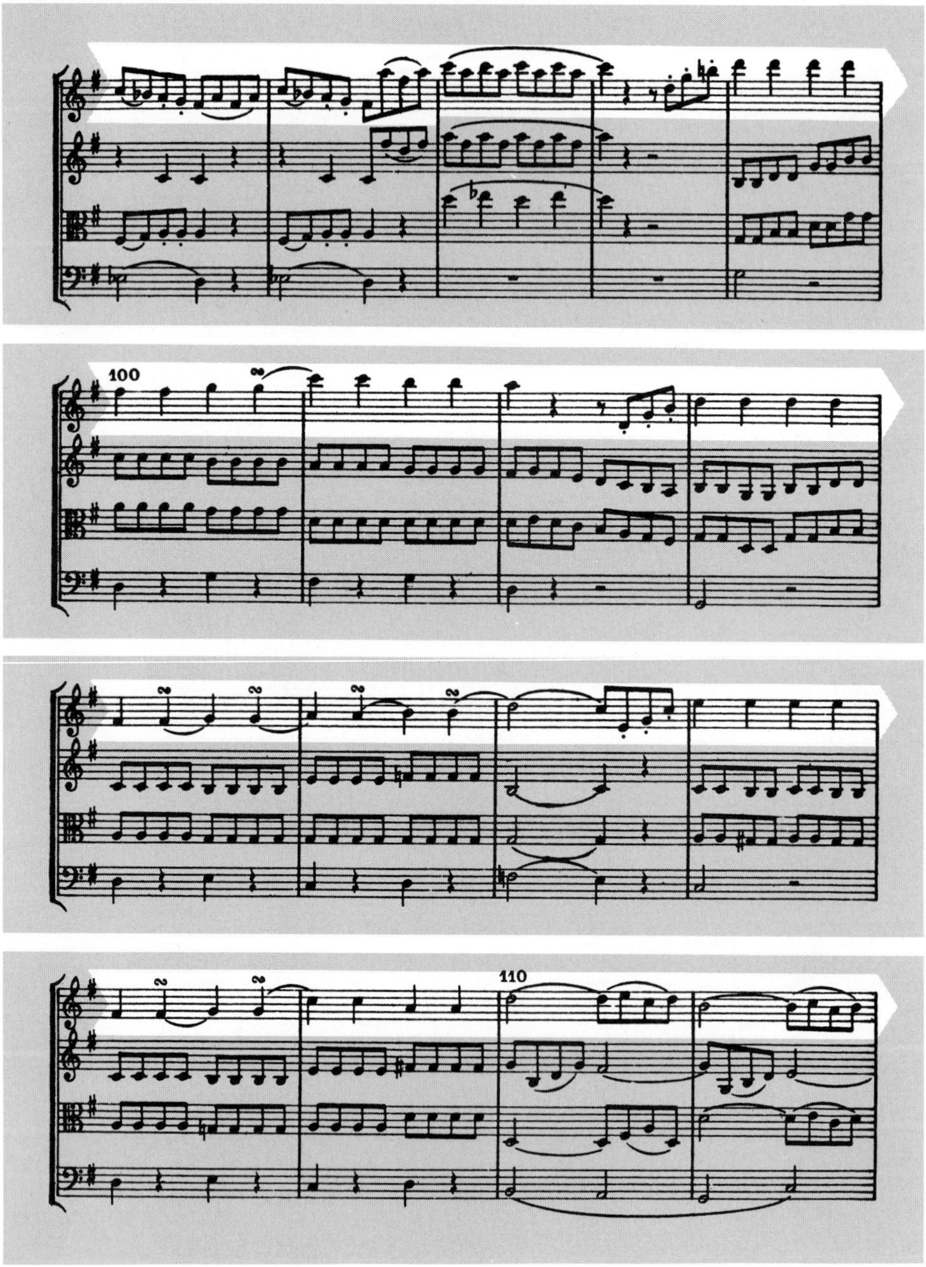

120
f
p
f
p
f
p
f

CODA

130

140

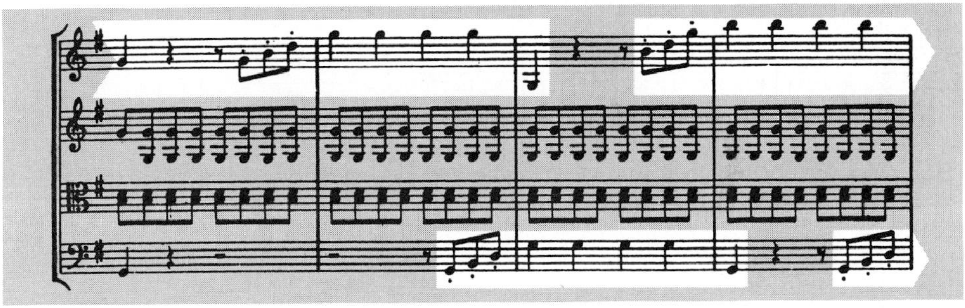

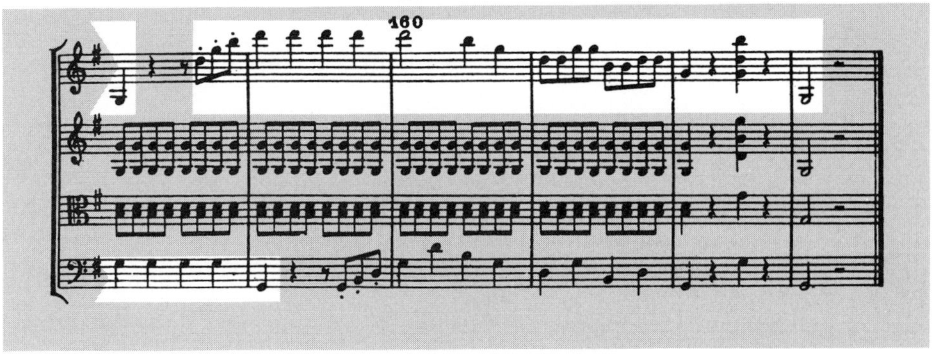

34. MOZART, Three excerpts from *Don Giovanni* (1787)
No. 1, Introduction

L.
vo-glio più ser - vir, e non vo-glio più ser - vir, no, no, no,
more a ser - vant be, Would no more a ser - vant be, No, no, no,
p
(facing the palace)
no, no, no, non vo-glio più ser-vir. Oh che ca-ro galant-
no, no, no, I would a mas - ter be. What a dif-fer-ence be-
sf p sf p
uo-mo! Voi star den-tro col-la bel-la, ed io far la sen-ti
tween us! Warm you lie in arms of beau-ty While I freeze on sen-try
sf p sf p
nel - la, la sen - ti - nel - la, la sen - ti - nel - la! Vo - glio
du - ty, on sen - try du - ty, on sen - try du - ty; I would
fp
far il gen - til - uo - mo, e non vo-glio più ser -
like to play the mas - ter, Would no more your serv - ant
f tr fp
vir, e non vo-glio più ser - vir, No, no, no, no, no, no, non vo-glio
be, Would no more your serv - ant be, No, no, no, no, no, no, I would a

L.
più ser-vir. Ma mi par, che ven-ga gen-te; ma mi par, che venga
mas - ter_ be. What was that? We're in for trou-ble. What was that? We're in for
gen-te; non mi vo-glio far sen-tir, ah non mi vo-glio far sen-tir, non mi
trou-ble. This is not the life for me, no, This is not the life for me. This is
cresc.
f
p
vo - glio far sen - tir, No, no, no, no, no, non mi vo - glio far sen-
not the life for me, No, no, no, no, no, This is not the life for_
tir.
me.
Tutti.
(Hides himself.)
cresc.
f
Donna Anna. (Holding Don Giovanni firmly by the arm.)
A.
Non spe-rar, se non m'uc-ci - di, ch'io ti la - sci fug-gir mai.
(her voice sti-fled by agita-tion.)
No, you won't, you shan't es-cape me, I will nev-er_ let_ you_ go.
Strings.
Tutti.
fp
fp
fp
f
p
f

A.
G.
L.
Donna Anna. (her voice gaining strength)
Don Giovanni. (Trying to conceal his features.)
Non spe-
No, you
Don-na fol-le! indar-no gri-di, chi son io, tu non sa-prai.
Do not scream! wake the house hold. Kiss me, dear, and let me go!
You'll
Leporello.
Che tu-
Mas- ter
Str.
fp
f
p
rar, se non m'uc-ci-di, ch'io ti la-sci fug-gir mai, non spe-
won't, you shan't es-cape me! I shall nev-er let you go! No, you
Don-na fol-le! in-dar-no gri-di, chi son io tu non sa-
Do not scream! wake the house-hold. Kiss me, dear, and let me
You'll
mul-to! o ciel! che gri-di! Il pa-
curs-ing, the la-dy scream-ing, How am
(with full strength.)
rar, ch'io ti la-sci fug-gir mai. Gen-te! ser-vi al tra-di-to-re!
won't, I will nev-er let you go! Fire and mur-der! Save me! Seize him!
(almost
prai, no, tu non sa-prai. Ta-ci, e
go! Now! Now let me go. Stop that
dron in nuo-vi guai.
I to get a-way?
fp
cresc.

(freeing herself)
A.
hissing; tries to cover her mouth)
Scel-le-ra-to! Scel-le-ra-to!
Fire and mur-der! Try to stop me!
G.
tre-ma al mio fu-ro-re! Scon-si-glia-ta! Scon-si-glia-ta!
noise or I shall hurt you. Stop, I tell you! Stop, I tell you!
L.
Sta a ve-
It's a
Str. & Cor.
f p cresc. fp p
(turning to the palace)
Gen-te! ser-vi! Co-me fu-ria di-spe-ra-ta ti sa-
Help me! Save me! (seizing her roughly) From my un-re-lent-ing fu-ry You shall
Ta-ci, e tre-ma! Que-sta fu-ria di-spe-
Must I hurt you? From her un-re-lent-ing
der che il li-ber-ti-no mi fa-rà pre-ci-pi-tar. Che tu-
ver-y pret-ty pick-le, And I can-not get a-way Mas-ter
Tutti.
f
prò per-se-gui-tar. Co-me fu-ria di-spe-ra-ta, di-spe-
nev-er get a-way. From my un-re-lent-ing, my a-veng-ing
ra-ta mi vuol far pre-ci-pi-tar, Que-sta fu-ria di-spe-
fu-ry I had bet-ter get a-way. From her un-re-lent-ing
mul-to! oh ciel, che gri-di!
curs-ing, the la-dy scream-ing,

A.
G.
L.
ra - ta, ti sa - prò per -
fu - ry You shall nev - - - - er
ra - ta mi vuol far pre -
fu - ry I had bet - - - ter
Sta a veder che il li - ber - ti - no mi fa - rà pre - ci - pi - tar, sta a veder che il li - ber -
Well, we're in a pret - ty pick - le; How am I to get a - way? Well, we're in a pret - ty
se - - gui - tar. Scel - le - ra - to! Scel - le -
get a - way. Fire and mur - der! Try to
ci - - pi - tar. Scon - si - gliata! Scon - si -
get a - way. Stop, I tell you! Stop, I
ti - no mi fa - rà preci - pi - tar.
pick - le; How am I to get a - way?
ra - to! Gen - te! ser - vi! Co - me fu - ria di - spe -
stop me! Save me! Help me! From my un - re - lent - ing
glia - ta! Ta - ci, e tre - ma! Que - sta
tell you! I shall hurt you. From her
Sta a ve - der che il li - ber - ti - no mi fa - rà pre - ci - pi - tar.
It's a ver - y pret - ty pick - le, And I can - not get a - way.

A.
ra - ta, ti sa - prò per - se - gui - tar, co - me fu - ria di - spe -
fu - ry You shall nev - er get a - way. From my un - re - lent - ing,
G.
fu - ria di - spe - ra - ta mi vuol far pre - ci - pi - tar, que - sta
un - re - lent - ing fu - ry I had bet - ter get a - way. From her
L.
Che tu - mul - to, oh ciel, che gri - di!
Mas - ter curs - ing, the la - dy scream - ing,
f
A.
ra - ta, di - spe - ra - ta, ti sa -
my a - veng - ing fu - ry You shall
G.
fu - ria di - spe - ra - ta mi vuol
un - re - lent - ing fu - ry I had
L.
Sta a veder che il li - ber - ti - no mi fa - rà pre - ci - pi -
Well, we're in a pret - ty pick - le; How am I to get a -
Ob. Fag. & Str.
p
A.
prò per - se - gui - tar.
nev - er get a - way.
G.
far pre - ci - pi - tar.
bet - ter get a - way.
L.
tar, sta a veder che il li - ber - ti - no mi fa - rà pre - ci - pi - tar, sta a veder che il li - ber -
way? Well, we're in a pret - ty pick - le; How am I to get a - way? Well, we're in a pret - ty

A.
ti sa - prò per - se - gui -
You shall nev - - - - er get a -
G.
mi vuol far pre - ci - pi -
I had bet - - - - ter get a -
L.
ti-no mi fa-rà pre-ci - pi-tar, sta a veder che il li - ber-ti-no mi fa-rà pre-ci - pi-
pick-le, How am I to get a-way? Well, we're in a pret-ty pickle; How am I to get a-
(Seeing the Commandant approach, she runs into the house.)
tar.
way.
(Don Giovanni haughtily confronts the Commandant.)
tar.
way.
(The Commandant enters hastily, a torch in his left hand, a sword in his right.)
tar.
way?
Tutti.
ff
ff
The Commandant. (with agitation, but energetically)
C.
Lascia-la in - de - gno, bat - ti - ti me - co!
Where is the vil-lain? Draw, sir, and fight me!
p
cresc.
Don Giovanni. (slightingly)
Va, non mi de - gno di pu - gnar te - co.
No! Pride for - bids me to draw on grey-beards.
Co - sì pre - ten - di
Faint-heart-ed cow - ard!
f
p
f

G.
C.
L.
Va, non mi de - gno, no!
No! Pride for-bids me, No!
da me fug-gir?
I chal - lenge you.
Leporello.
Co-sì pre-ten-di da
Faint-heart-ed cow-ard! I
(Po-tessi al-me - no di quà par-tir!
If I could on - ly get out of here!
mezza voce
più voce
(draws)
Mi - se-ro! Mi - se-ro! Mi-
Force me not! Force me not! Do -
me fug-gir? Bat-ti-ti!
chal - lenge you. Draw, I say!
po-tessi al-me - no di quà par-tir!)
If I could on - ly get out of here!
(He strikes the torch out of the Commandant's. hand.)
(First bout: the Commandant attacks.)
se - ro! at - ten-di se vuoi mo-rir!
tard, on guard, then! Your death is near.
(They fight.)
(2nd bout: Don G. attacks.)
(3rd bout.)
(The Commandant falls mortally wounded.)

(The moon rises slowly;

Andante. Don Giovanni. *sotto voce.*

G. Ah! già ca - de il scia - gu -
Ah, he's fall - en! — Ah, — he's —

The Commandant. (sinking slowly, leaning on his sword)

C. Ah! soc - cor - so! son tra - di - to! l'as - sas -
Ah, I'm wound-ed! Ah, I'm dy-ing! God, pro -

Leporello.

L. Qual mi - sfat - to!
Who has fall - en?

Andante.
Vls. Ob. & Cor.
pp

lights appear in the palace-windows: great excitement within: servants hasten with torches across the background behind the closed gate)

G. ra - to, af - fan - no - so e a - go - niz - zan - te già dal
dy-ing! Pay-ing dear - ly — for — his — fol - ly. On this

C. si - no m'ha fe - ri - to, e dal
tect my child from e - vil! From this

L. Qual ec - ces - so! En - tro il sen dal - lo spa -
Who is dy - ing? How I shiv - er, how I

G. se - no pal - pi - tan - te veg - go l'a - ni - ma par -
world of love and beau - ty He must close his a - ged

C. se - no pal - pi - tan - te
mor - tal scene of sor - row

L. ven - to pal - pi - tar il cor mi sen - to!
shud - der! Root - ed to the spot by ter - ror,

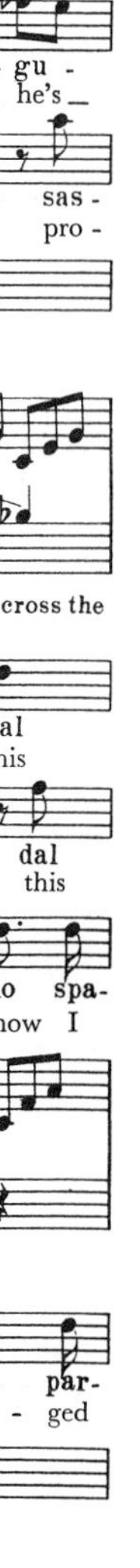

(Servants return with Don Octavio, and hasten with him from the street into the palace)
G.
tir, veg- -go l'a - ni - ma par - tir, già dal
eye, Now must close his a - ged eye. On this
C.
sen - to l'a - ni - ma par - tir,
My im - - mor - tal soul must fly,
L.
Io non sò che far, che dir, io non sò che far, che dir, en - tro il sen dal - lo spa-
I can nei-ther move nor cry, I can nei-ther move nor cry. How I shiv-er, how I
G.
se - no pal - pi - tan-te veg- -go l'a - ni - ma par-
world of love and beau-ty Now must close his a - ged
C.
sen- - to l'a- - ni- - ma par- -
My im - mor - tal soul must
L.
ven - to pal - pi - tar il cor mi sen - to, io non sò che far, che dir, io non sò che far, che
shud-der! Root-ed to the spot by ter-ror, I can nei-ther move nor cry, I can nei-ther move nor
G.
tir.
eye.
(Dies.)
C.
tir.
fly.
L.
dir!
cry.
Ob. Vln.
p
Fl. Fag.

Recit. *(Sotto voce,* **throughout this scene.)**

Don Giovanni. Le-po-rel-lo, o-ve se-i? **Leporello.** Son
Are you there, Le-po-rel-lo? I

(Don G. sheathes his sword and dons his cloak)

quì per mia di-sgra-zia; e vo-i? **Don Giovanni.** Son quì. **Leporello.** Chi è
on-ly wish I was-n't. Are *you* there? Of course. Are

mor-to, voi, o il vec-chio? **Don Giovanni.** Che do-man-da da be-stia! il vec-chio.
you a ghost? Is *he* one? What an im-bec-ile ques-tion! He's done for.

Leporello. Bra-vo! due im-pre-se leg-gia-dre! Sfor-zar la fi-glia, ed am-maz-zar il
Bra-vo! Pret-ty good for one eve-ning. To rape the daugh-ter and then skew-er the

pa-dre! **Don Giovanni.** L'ha vo-lu-to, suo dan-no! **Leporello.** Ma donn' An-na, - cosa ha vo-lu-to?
fa-ther! He com-pelled me; I had to. And Donn'An-na... al-so com-pelled you?

Don Giovanni. Ta-ci, non mi sec-car! Vien me-co, (Threatening to strike him.) se non vuoi qual-che co-sa an-cor tu.
Si-lence! No more from you. Re-mem-ber, you can join the old man if you wish.

Leporello. Non vo' nul-la, Si-gnor, non par-lo più. (Exeunt.)
From now on I'll be dumb as an-y fish.

No. 4, Catalogue Aria

L.

in Al - ma-gna due cen-to e trent' u - na,

Down for Eng-land, a hun - dred-e - lev - en;

p *f*

L.

cen - to in Francia in Turchia no-vant' u-na; ma, in I -

For San Ma-ri-no a mere nine-ty-sev-en; But prim and

p *fp*

L.

spa-gna, ma in I - spa-gna son già mille e tre! mil-le e tre!

prop-er Spain con - tri-butes a thou-sand-and-three! Can that be?

p *sfp* Vlns. Tutti *p*

L.

mil - le e tre! V'han fra que-ste con-ta - di - ne,

Yes, it's three. There are bar-maids, bas-ket-weav-ers,

L.

ca-me-rie - re, cit - ta-di - ne, V'han contesse, ba-ro-nes-se,

There are dair-y-maids and di-vas, Count-less count-ess-es, prin-cess-es,

marchesa - ne, prin-ci - pesse, e v'han don-ne d'o - gni gra-do, d'o-gni for-ma, d'ogni e-
In the ranks of his suc-cess-es, Ev-'ry pos - si - ble con - di-tion, Oc-cu-pa-tion, form and

cresc.

tà, d'o - gni for-ma, d'o-gni e-tà, In I - ta-li - a
age All a - rouse his gal - lant rage! In A - ra-bi-a,

f *p* Vla. Cello & Bass

sei cen-to e qua-ran - ta, in Al-ma-gna
ten doz-en were fool-ish; In Dal-ma-tia,

due cen - to e trent' u - na, cen - - to in Fran - cia, in Tur-
a hun-dred were wan-ton; Here's Hel - ve - tia— a

chia no - vant' u - na, ma, ma, ma in I - spa - gna! ma in I -
gross in each Can-ton; But, but, but o-ver-prud - ish Spain con-

L.
spagna son già mil-le e tre, mil-le e tre, mil-le e
tri-butes a thou-sand-and-three! You are one . . . of those
sfp
tre! V'han fra queste conta - di-ne, ca-me - rie - re, ci-ta-di-ne, v'han contesse, ba-ro -
three. Yes, with jealous-ly well-hid . Weeping wid-ows, mellow mid- And in-nu-mer - a-ble-
wives, -wives,
Vln.
Cl. Fag.
f sf p
nesse, marchesa - ne, prin-ci-pesse, e v'han donne d'o-gni gra-do, d'o-gni for-ma, d'ogni e-
nurs-es He has suf-fered no re-vers-es; Ev'ry pos-si - ble con-di-tion, Oc-cu-pa-tion, form and
Tutti.
cresc.
f
tà! d'o - - gni for - - ma, d'o - gni e - -
age— All a - rouse his gal - lant
f p
tà! d'o - gni for - ma, d'o - gni e - tà!
rage, All a - rouse his gal - lant rage!
cresc.

Andante con moto.
L.
Nel - la bionda e - gli ha l'u - san-za di lo - dar - la
All the prais-es with which he courts them Fol - low orders
Str.
p
Fl.
fp
la gen-ti - lez - za, nel - la bru - na la co -
where-by he sorts them: Blondes are mod-est, dark ones
Tutti
Cor.
f
stanza, nel - la bian - ca la dol - cez - za.
gra-cious, Red- heads can - did, white sa - ga- cious.
Fl.
Fag.
Vln.
Vuol d'in-ver - no la grassot - ta, vuol d'e-sta - te la ma-
Bulk at-tracts him dur-ing win - ter, Dur-ing sum - mer, more the
cresc.
grotta, e la gran - de ma - e -
splin-ter. He will woo them tall and

L.
sto - sa, e la gran - - de ma - - e -
flor - id, Sport - ing clouds a - bout the
f
p
cresc.
L.
sto - - - - - - sa. La pic - ci - na, la pic -
fore - - - - - - head; He will woo them Tee-ny-
Fl. Ob.
f
Bassi
p
Vln.
Fl. Ob.
Bassi
L.
ci - na, la pic - ci - na, la pic-ci - na, la pic-ci - na, la pic -
ti - ny, tee - ny- ti - ny, tee - ny- ti - ny, tee - ny- ti - ny, tee - ny-
Ob.
Vln.
Fag.
Fl.
Bassi
L.
ci-na, la pic-ci-na, la picci-na, la pic - ci - na è ognor vez - zo - sa, è ognor vez -
ti-ny, tee-ny- ti-ny, tee-ny- ti-ny, Tee-ny- ti - ny, of bare-ly bean- size And in all
Tutti
p
L.
zo - sa, è ognor vez - zo - sa; del - le vecchie fa con - qui - sta
man - ner of in - be - tween-size. Ripe du - en - nas he has con - tent - ed
p
fp

L.
pel pia - cer_ di por-le in li - sta, sua passion pre-do-mi-
That his _ list Might be some-what aug-ment-ed; But the most-of- all he

p

Fag.

L.
nan - te_ è la gio-vin prin-ci - pian-te;
sa - vors _ Un-in - i - ti - at - ed fa-vors.

Fl.
Fag.
Vln.

L.
non si pic - ca, se sia ric - ca, se sia brut - ta, se sia
Ill or health - y, Poor or wealth - y, Plain or pret - ty, Dull or

tr *tr* *tr* *tr*

cresc.

L.
bel - - la, se sia ric - ca, brut - ta, se sia bel - la, pur - chè_
wit - - ty, High- born, low - ly, Scrag-gy hags or beau-ties, Be they_

tr

Ob.
Vln.

p

L.
por - ti la_ gon - nel - la, voi sa - pe - te
fe - male, they're_ his du - ties— How he meets them,

L.
quel che fa, voi sa - pe - te quel che
this can show, How he greets them, this can
Fl.
Fag.
fa, pur che por - ti la gon - nel - la, voi sa - pe - te quel che
show. Be they fe - male, they're his du - ties In a serv - ice that you
Vln.
fa, voi sa - pe - te, voi sa - pe - te quel che fa,
know, In a serv - ice, In a serv - ice that you know.
Ob.
Vln.
Fl.
Fag.
mf
p
quel che fa, quel che fa, voi sa -
This can show That you know, In a
f
pe - te quel che fa.
serv - ice that you know.
(Exit hastily into villa.)

No. 7, Duet: *Là ci darem la mano*

Zerlina.
G.
Z.
sor — te! Pre - sto non son — più for - te, non son più for - te, non son — più —
long - er! Faint - ly I would that I were strong - er. that I — were — strong - -er. that I — were —
Tutti.
p
Cor.
p
(Donna Elvira appears on the verandah of the main building, and watches what is going on.)
Z.
for - te!
strong-er.
Vor -
I
Don Giovanni.
G.
Vie - ni! vie - ni! Là ci da-rem la ma-no,
Dear-est, gent - ly, Here with our hands en - twin-ing.
3
sfp
Z.
rei, e non vor - re - i,
fear you may de - ceive me
Mi trema un po - co il
I trem - ble to de -
G.
Là mi di-rai di sì,
Why not walk on with me?
p
Z.
cor;
part.
ma — può bur - lar - - mi an -
Should — I o - bey — my
G.
par - tiam, ben mio, da qui.
Let our de - signs a - gree:

(disengaging
Z.
cor. Mi fa- pie - tà- Ma - set - to; pre -
heart? Must poor- Ma - set - to- suf - fer? Dear -
(putting his arm around her.)
G.
Vie - ni, mio bel di - let - to! io can-gie - rò tua
Come to your no - ble lov - er! Peas - ant you'll be no
mf
p
mf
herself, and escaping to other side.)
- sto non son più for - te, non son più for - te, non son- più- for - te!
- - ly I hope I can be strong-er, I can- be- strong-er, I can- be- strong-er.
sor - te. An-
long-er. My
p
(throwing herself into his arms.)
Allegro.
An - diam! An - diam, an - diam, mio be - ne,- a
I will!- To - geth - er let us pure-ly- In -
(insistently)
diam! An - diam! An - diam, an - diam, mio be - ne,- a
love! Be mine! To - geth - er let us pure-ly- In -
Allegro.
ri - sto - rar le pe - ne- d'un' in - no - cen - te a - mor!
dulge a whim we sure-ly- Are fault - less- to ful - fill.
ri - sto - rar le pe - ne- d'un' in - no - cen - te a - mor!
dulge a whim we sure-ly- Are fault - less- to ful - fill.

Z.
G.
An - diam, an - diam, mio be - ne, — a ri - sto - rar le pe - ne — d'un'
For no - ble - man and peas - ant, — While do - ing what is pleas - ant — Can -
An - diam, an - diam, mio be - ne, a ri - sto - rar le pe - ne — d'un'
For no - ble - man and peas - ant, — While do - ing what is pleas - ant — Can -
in - no - cen - te a - mor!
not be — do - ing ill.
(Donna Elvira descends the steps, and
in - no - cen - te a - mor! An - diam!
not be — do - ing ill. Con - sent!
Fl.
tr
3
p
pizz.
posts herself at centre, back.)
An - diam! An - diam!
My love! Be true.
An -
I
tr
3
arco
An - diam, mio bene, an - diam, le pe - ne a ri - sto - rar d'un
We'll go with - out de - lay, And cheer - ful - ly at play Love
diam! An - diam, mio bene, an - diam, le pe - ne a ri - sto - rar, d'un
will! We'll go with - out de - lay, And cheer - ful - ly at play Love
3
tr

Z.
in - no - cen-te a - mor!
in - no - cent - ly still.
(Exeunt, arm in arm.)
G.
in - no - cen-te a - mor!
in - no - cent - ly still.
tr
f
p

35. MOZART, Symphony in G minor, K. 550 (1788)

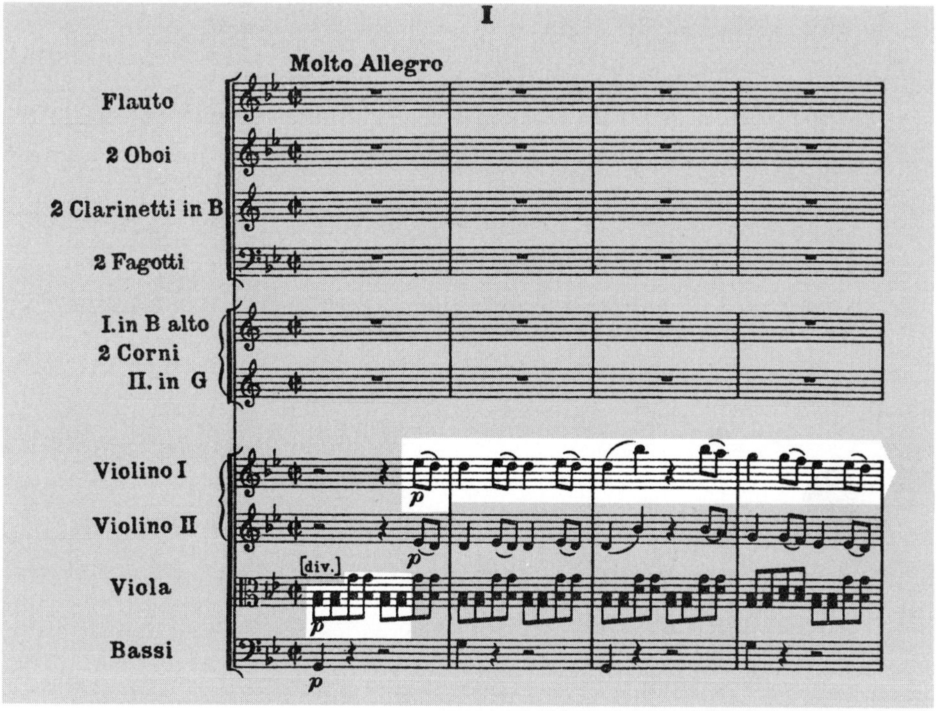

I
Molto Allegro
Flauto
2 Oboi
2 Clarinetti in B
2 Fagotti
I. in B alto
2 Corni
II. in G
Violino I
Violino II
Viola
Bassi
[div.]
p

Vl.
Vla.
Bi.

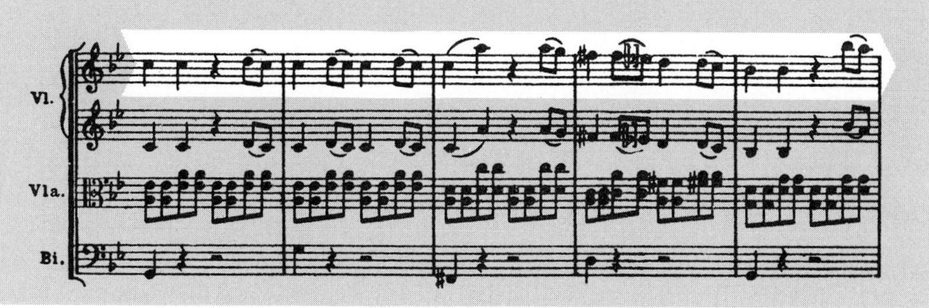

This edition presents the score of Mozart's second version, with clarinets.

10
Fl.
Cl.
(B)
Fg.
Vl.
Vla.
Bi.
p
1.

Ob.
Fg.
Vl.
Vla.
Bi.
p
[div.]

30
Fl.
Ob.
Cl. (B)
Fg.
Cor. (B)
Vl.
Vla.
Bi.
zu 2
1.
f

Fl.
Ob.
Cl. (B)
Fg.
zu 2
(B) Cor. (G)
Vl.
Vla.
Bi.
[sf]
40
Cor. (B)
1.
Solo

50
Fl.
1.
Cl. (B)
1.
Fg.
Solo
p
[p]
p
Vl.
Vla.
Bi.

Fl.
[p]
Cl. (B)
[p]
p
Fg.
[p]
Vl.
Vla.
Bi.

60
Fl.
Ob.
Cl. (B)
Fg.
(B) Cor. (G)
Vl.
Vla.
Bi.
cre - scen - do
[p]
zu 2
p
cresc.

Fl.
Ob.
Cl. (B)
Fg.
Cor. (B)
Vl.
Vla.
Bi.
tr
f
zu 2
1.
sf
[div.]

70
Fl.
Cl. (B)
Fg.
Vl.
Vla.
Bi.
p
1.
Fl.
Ob.
Cl. (B)
Fg.
(B) Cor. (G)
Vl.
Vla.
Bi.
80
f
ff
zu2

Fl.
Ob.
1.
Cl. (B)
1.
zu 2
Fg.
(B) Cor. (G)
Vl.
Vla.
Bi.
f

100
Fl.
Ob.
Cl. (B)
zu 2
Fg.
(B) Cor. (G)
Vl.
Vla.
Bi.

Fl.
Ob.
Cl. (B)
Fg.
(B) Cor. (G)
Vl.
Vla.
[div.]
Bi.

Fl.
Ob.
Cl. (B)
zu 2
Fg.
Cor. (G)
2.
Vl.
Vla.
Bi.
f

120

Fl.

Ob.

Cl. (B)

zu2

Fg.

(B) Cor. (G)

Vl.

Vla.

Bi.

Fl.

Ob.

Cl. (B)

zu2

Fg.

(B) Cor. (G)

Vl.

Vla.

Bi.

130
Fl.
Ob.
zu 2
Cl. (B)
zu 2
Fg.
zu 2
(B) Cor. (G)
Vl.
Vla.
Bi.

Fl.
p
Ob.
Cl. (B)
p
zu 2
Fg.
2.
Cor. (G)
Vl.
[div.]
p
Vla.
Bi.

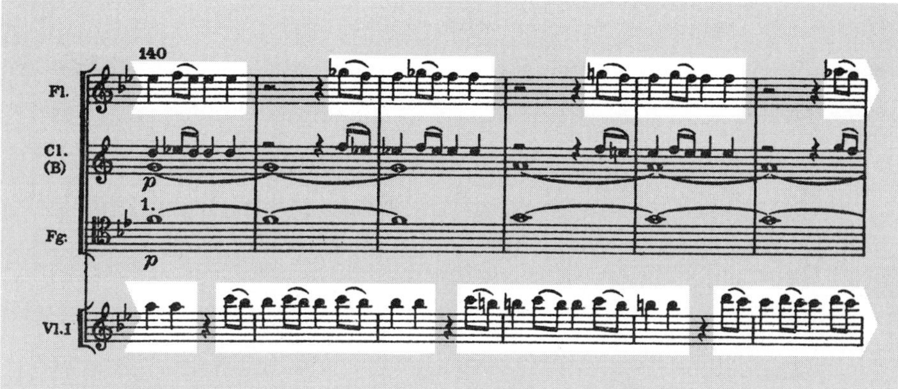
140
Fl.
Cl. (B)
p
1.
Fg.
p
Vl.I

150
Fl.
Cl. (B)
1.
Fg.
Vl.
p
Vla.
p
Vc.
p

Fl.
Ob.
Cl. (B)
Fg.
(B) Cor. (G)
Vl.
Vla.
Vc.
Cb.
Tutti Bassi
160
Bi.

Fl.
Cl. (B)
Fg.
1.
p
(B) Cor. (G)
p
p
Vl.
p
p
[div.]
Vla.
p
Bi.
p

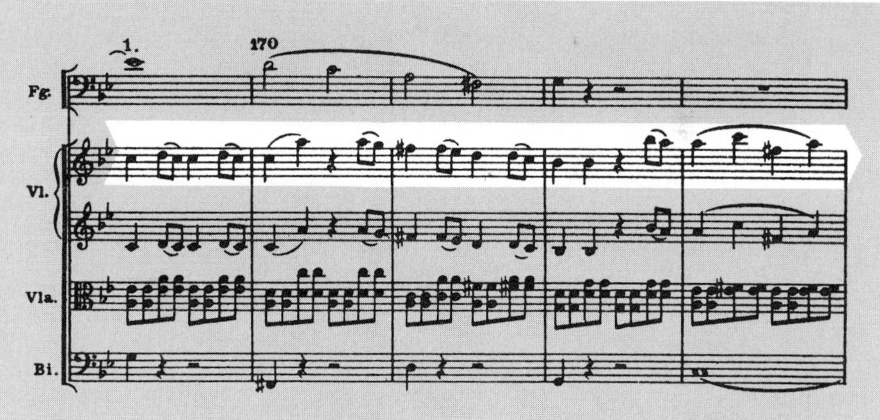

Fl.
Ob.
Cl. (B)
Fg.
(B) Cor. (G)
Vl.
Vla.
Bi.
1.
p
f
180
[div.]

190
Fl.
Ob.
Fg.
Vl.
Vla.
Bi.
p
1.

Fl.
Ob.
Cl.
(B)
Fg.
(B)
Cor.
(G)
Vl.
Vla.
Bi.
zu 2
f

200
Fl.
Ob.
Cl.
(B)
zu 2
Fg.
(B)
Cor.
(G)
Vl.
Vla.
Bi.

Fl.
Ob.
Cl.
(B)
zu 2
Fg.
(B)
Cor.
(G)
Vl.
Vla.
Bi.

210
Fl.
Ob.
Cl. (B)
zu 2
Fg.
(B) Cor. (G)
Vl.
Vla.
Bi.
220
Fl.
Ob.
Cl. (B)
zu 2
Fg.
(B) Cor. (G)
Vl.
Vla.
Bi.

Fl.
Ob.
Cl. (B)
zu 2
Fg.
(B) Cor. (G)
Vl.
Vla.
Bi.

240
Fl.
1.
Ob.
1.
Fg.
p
Vl.
Vla.
Bi.

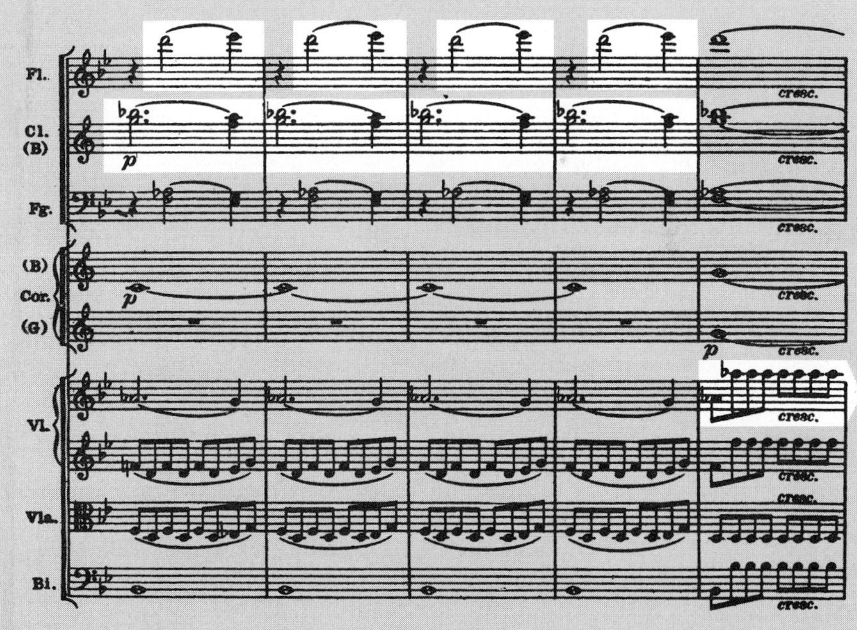
Fl.
cresc.
Cl.
(B)
p
cresc.
Fg.
cresc.
(B)
Cor.
(G)
p
cresc.
p
cresc.
Vl.
cresc.
cresc.
Vla.
cresc.
Bi.
cresc.

250
Fl.
Ob.
Cl. (B)
Fg.
(B) Cor. (G)
Vl.
Vla.
Bi.
a 2

280
Fl.
Ob.
Cl. (B)
zu 2
Fg.
1.
p
(B) Cor. (G)
Vl.
Vla.
Bi.

Fl.
Ob.
Cl. (B)
Fg.
1.
zu2
f
p
(B) Cor. (G)
Vl.
Vla.
Bi.

270
Fl.
Ob.
Cl.
(B)
Fg.
zu2
(B)
Cor.
(G)
Vl.
Vla.
Bi.
1.
p
f
zu 2

Fl.
Ob.
Cl. (B)
Fg.
(B) Cor. (G)
Vl.
Vla.
Bi.
zu2
280
sf
p

290
Fl.
Cl.
(B)
Fg.
(B)
Cor.
(G)
Vl.
Vla.
Bi.
1.
1.
p

Fl.
Ob.
Cl.
(B)
Fg.
(B)
Cor.
(G)
Vl.
Vla.
Bi.
f

II
Andante
Flauto
2 Oboi
2 Clarinetti in B
2 Fagotti
2 Corni in Es
Violino I
Violino II
Viola
Bassi
10
Cor. (Es)
Vl.
Vla.
Bi.
Cor. (Es)
Vl.
Vla.
Bi.

Fl.
Cl. (B)
Fg.
Cor. (Es)
Vl.
Vla.
Bi.

20
Fl.
Ob.
Cl. (B)
Vl.
Vla.
Bi.

Fl.
Cl. (B)
Vl.
Vla.
Bi.
Fl.
Cl. (B)
1.
Fg.
1.
Vl.
Vla.
Bi.
80
Fl.
Cl. (B)
1.
Fg.
1.
Vl.
Vla.
Bi.

Fl.
Ob.
Cl. (B)
Fg.
Cor. (Es)
Vl.
Vla.
Bi.
zu2
zu2
zu2
f
p
40
1.

Fl.
Ob.
Cl. (B)
Fg.
Cor. (Es)
Vl.
Vla.
Bi.
50
1.

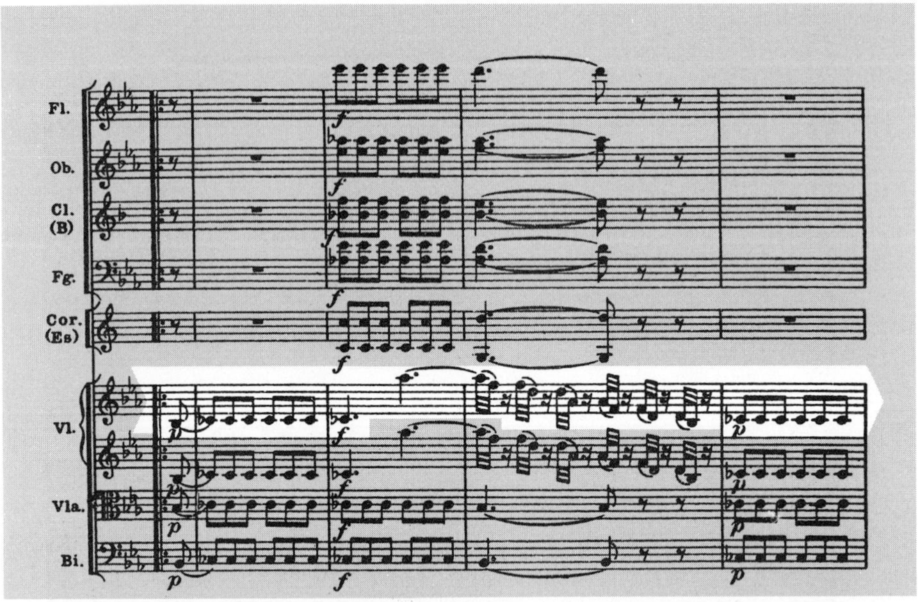

Fl.
Ob.
Cl. (B)
Fg.
Cor. (Es)
Vl.
Vla.
Bi.

60
Fl.
Ob.
zu2
Cl. (B)
Fg.
Cor. (Es)
Vl.
Vla.
Bi.
p

Fl.
Cl. (B)
Fg.
Cor. (Es)
Vl.
Vla.
Bi.

70
Fl.
Cl. (B)
Fg.
Cor. (Es)
Vl.
[div.]
Vla.
Bi.

Cor. (Es)
Vl.
Vla.
Bi.
80
sf
p
tr
Fl.
Ob.
Cl. (B)
Fg.
90
f

Fl.
Cl. (B)
Fg.
Cor. (Es)
Vl.
Vla.
Bi.
1.
1.

Fl.
Ob.
Cl. (B)
Fg.
Cor. (Es)
Vl.
Vla.
Bi.
1.
1.
sf
p
[p]

100
Fl.
1.
Cl. (B)
[p]
Fg.
1.
[p]
p
Vl.
Vla.
Bi.

Fl.
Ob.
1.
Cl. (B)
1.
Fg.
zu2
Cor. (Es)
Vl.
Vla.
Bi.
f

Fl.
Ob.
Cl. (B)
Fg.
Cor. (Es)
Vl.
p
p
Vla.
p
Bi.
p

Fl.
Ob.
Cl. (B)
Fg.
Cor. (Es)
Vl.
Vla.
Bi.
1.
1.
f
tr

120
Fl.
Ob.
Cl. (B)
Fg.
Cor. (Es)
Vl.
Vla.
Bi.
1.
1.
p
[p]

III

Menuetto. Allegretto

Flauto

2 Oboi

2 Clarinetti in B

2 Fagotti

2 Corni in G

Violino I

Violino II

Viola

Bassi

zu 2

zu2

zu2

10

Fl.

Ob.

Cl. (B)

Fg.

Cor. (G)

Vl.

Vla.

Bi.

zu 2

zu 2

zu 2

Fl.
Ob.
Cl.
(B♭)
Fg.
Cor.
(G)
Vl.
Vla.
Bi.
zu 2
20

Fl.
Ob.
Cl.
(B♭)
Fg.
Cor.
(G)
Vl.
Vla.
Bi.
zu 2

30
Fl.
Ob.
Cl. (B)
Fg.
Cor. (G)
Vl.
Vla.
Bi.

40
Fl.
Ob.
Cl. (B)
Fg.
Cor. (G)
Vl.
Vla.
Bi.
p
[Fine]

Trio
Ob.
Vl.
Vla.
Bi.
p

50
Fl.
Ob.
Fg.
p
cresc.
f
1.

60
Fl.
Ob.
Fg.
Vl.
Vla.
Bi.
p
1.

Fl.
Ob.
Fg.
Bi.
70
Cor. (G)
Vl.
Vla.
[div.]
cresc.
80
1.
D.C. Menuetto

IV
[Finale]. Allegro assai
Flauto
2 Oboi
2 Clarinetti in B
2 Fagotti
zu2
I. in B alto
2 Corni
II. in G
Violino I
Violino II
Viola
Bassi
Fl.
Ob.
Cl. (B)
Fg.
zu2
(B)
Cor.
(G)
Vl.
Vla.
Bi.
10

30
Fl.
Ob.
Cl. (B)
zu2
Fg.
p
f
(B) Cor. (G)
tr
Vl.
Vla.
Vc.
Cb.
40
zu2
zu2
Bi.

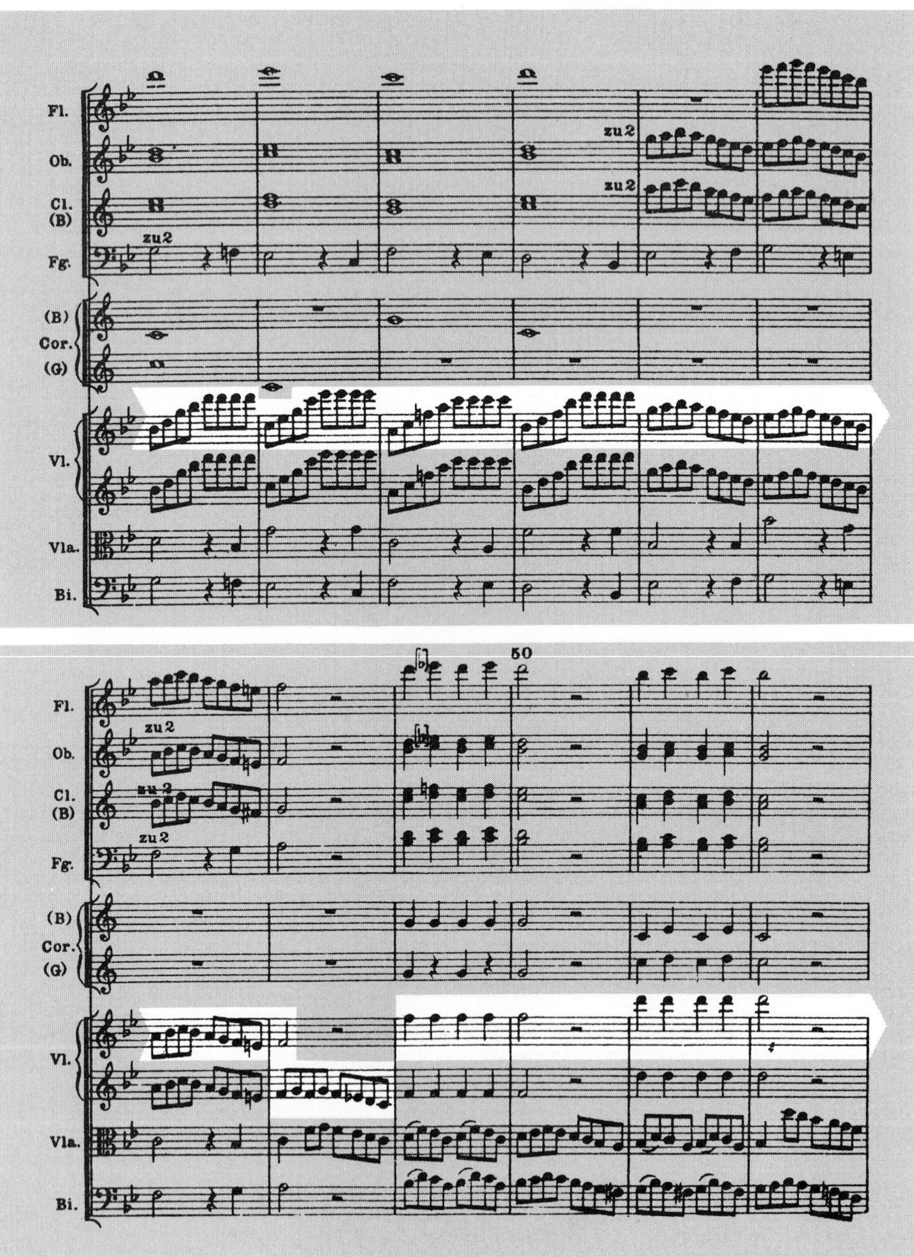
Fl.
Ob.
Cl. (B)
Fg.
(B) Cor. (G)
Vl.
Vla.
Bi.
zu 2
50

Fl.
Ob.
Cl.
(B)
Fg.
zu 2
(B)
Cor.
(G)
Vl.
Vla.
Bi.
60
zu 2
zu 2
zu 2

70
Fl.
Ob.
Cl.
(B)
zu 2
Fg.
1.
Cor.
(B)
Vl.
p
Vla.
Bi.

Vl.
mfp
p
mfp
Vla.
p
[mfp]

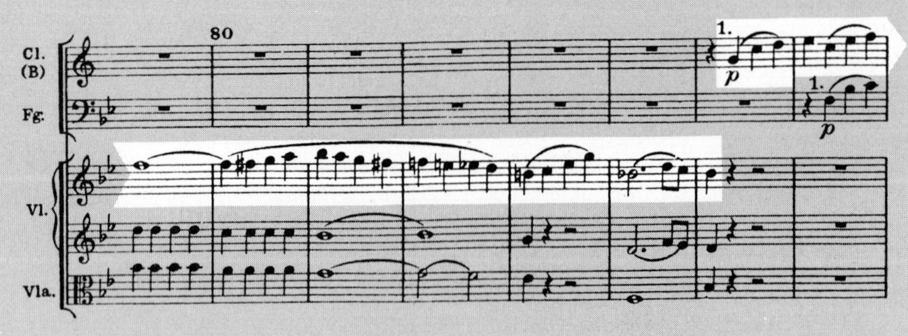
80
Cl.
(B)
1.
p
Fg.
1.
p
Vl.
Vla.

100

Fl.

Ob.

Cl.
(B)

Fg.

1.

Cor.
(B)

Vl.

Vla.

Bi.

p f [p]

Fl.
Ob.
Cl. (B)
Fg.
1.
Cor. (B)
f
Vl.
Vla.
Bi.

110
Fl.
Ob.
Cl. (B)
Fg.
1.
Cor. (B)
Vl.
p
Vla.
Bi.

Fl.
Ob.
Cl. (B)
Fg.
(B) Cor. (G)
Vl.
Vla.
Bi.
120

130
Fl.
Ob.
Cl. (B)
Fg.
Vl.
Vla.
Bi.
zu 2
f
f

Fl.
Ob.
Cl. (B)
Fg.
Vl.
Vla.
Bi.
p
[div.]

140
Ob.
Fg.
Cor. (B)
Vl.
Vla.
Bi.
1.
p
f

Cor. (B)
Vl.
Vla.
Bi.
1.
150
f

(B) Cor. (G)
Vl.
Vla.
Bi.
160
f

Fl.
Ob.
Cl.
(B)
Fg.
(B)
Cor.
(G)
Vl.
Vla.
Bi.

180
Fl.
Ob.
Cl. (B)
Fg.
Vl.
Vla.
Bi.

Fl.
Ob.
zu 2
Cl. (B)
zu 2
Fg.
Vl.
Vla.
Bi.

190
Fl.
Ob.
Cl.
(B)
Fg.
Vl.
Vla.
Vc.
Bi.
p
f
zu 2
f Tutti

200
Fl.
Ob.
Cl.
(B)
Fg.
(B)
Cor.
(G)
Vl.
Vla.
Bi.
zu 2
sf
f

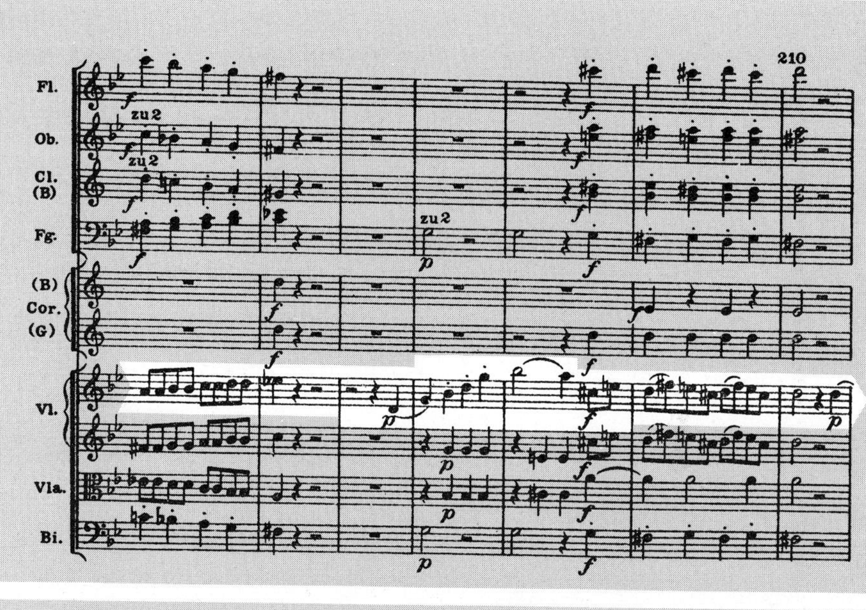
210
Fl.
Ob.
Cl. (B)
Fg.
(B) Cor. (G)
Vl.
Vla.
Bi.
zu 2
zu 2
zu 2

Fl.
Ob.
Cl. (B)
Fg.
(B) Cor. (G)
Vl.
Vla.
Vc.
Cb.
zu 2
tr

220

Fl.
Ob.
Cl. (B)
zu2
Fg.
p
f
(B) Cor. (G)
tr
Vl.
Vla.
Vc.
Cb.

Fl.
Ob.
Cl. (B)
zu2
Fg.
(B) Cor. (G)
Vl.
Vla.
Bi.

230
Fl.
Ob.
Cl.
(B)
zu2
Fg.
(B)
Cor.
(G)
Vl.
Vla.
Bi.

240
Fl.
zu2
Ob.
zu2
Cl.
(B)
zu2
Fg.
(B)
Cor.
(G)
Vl.
Vla.
Bi.

Fl.
Ob.
Cl. (B)
Fg.
(B) Cor. (G)
Vl.
Vla.
Bi.

Fl.
Cl. (B)
Fg.
Cor. (G)
Vl.
Vla.
Bi.
p
2.

270
Fl.
Cl. (B)
Fg.
Cor. (G)
Vl.
Vla.
Bi.
1.
2.
p

280
Fl.
Ob.
Cl. (B)
Fg.
(B) Cor. (G)
Vl.
Vla.
Bi.

290
Fl.
Ob.
Cl. (B)
Fg.
(B) Cor. (G)
Vl.
Vla.
Bi.
f
Fl.
Ob.
Cl. (B)
Fg.
(B) Cor. (G)
Vl.
Vla.
Bi.

300

Fl.
Ob.
Cl. (B)
Fg.
(B) Cor. (G)
Vl.
Vla.
Bi.

Fl.
Ob.
Cl. (B)
Fg.
(B) Cor. (G)
Vl.
Vla.
Bi.

36. LUDWIG VAN BEETHOVEN,
Piano Sonata in C minor, Opus 13 ("Pathétique") (1799)

Allegro di molto e con brio.
p
cresc.
[p]
cresc.
p
sf
sf
sf
sf
cresc.
sf
sf
sf
sf
sf
sf
p
sf
sf
sf
sf
sf
sf

rf
decresc.
pp
p
cresc.
f
p
cresc.
f
p
cresc.
f
f
f
f
f
ff
sf
ff

Tempo I.
fp
fp
fp
p
decresc.
pp
attacca subito Allegro molto e con brio.
Allegro molto e con brio.
p
cresc.
f
p
cresc.
f
p
cresc.
p
pp
cresc.

sf
pp
cresc.
sf
sf
sf
fp
p
sf
cresc.
p
sf
cresc.
p
cresc.
p
cresc.
p

decresc.
pp
p
cresc.
f
p

cresc.
f
[p]
cresc.
f
sf
f
ff
fff
Grave.
p
cresc.
sf
decresc.
pp
Allegro molto e con brio.
p
cresc.
ff
ff

Adagio cantabile.
p
cresc.

cresc.
p
pp
p
ppp
cresc.
sf
sf
[sf]
fp
decresc.
pp

cresc.
p
pp
rf
rf
rf
pp

RONDO.
Allegro.
p
tr.
f
fp
fp
dolce
p
sf
sf

p
cresc.
sf
p
sf
sf
cresc.
ff
5
sf
[p]

cresc.
f
p
p
cresc.
f
sf
cresc.
ff
sf
sf
sf

ff
sf
p
p
sf
p dolce
cresc.

p
ca - - - lan - - - - - - do.
p

cresc.
p
cresc.
sf
sf
ff
sf
sf
p
cresc.
f
sf
sf
sf
sf
sf
ff
sf
p
decresc.
pp
ff

37. BEETHOVEN, First movement from String Quartet in F major, Opus 18, No. 1 (1798-99)

Reprinted with permission of Ernst Eulenburg Ltd., London-Zürich, from the Eulenburg miniature score.

tr
40
pp
pp
pp
pp
cresc.
cresc.
cresc.
cresc.
sf
f
p
p
50
cresc.
ff

60
decresc.
p
p
p
70
cresc.
sf
cresc.
cresc.
p
p
p
p >
cresc.
cresc.
cresc
f
f
f
fp
fp
fp
cresc.
f

80
cresc.
cresc.
cresc.
cresc.
cresc.
f
f
f
f
tr
fp
fp
fp
p cresc.
p cresc.
p cresc.
p cresc.
90
fp
fp
fp
fp
fp
fp
fp
100
sf
ff
tr
p
p
p
p

110

cresc.

cresc.
cresc.
cresc.
cresc.
f
f
f
f

130

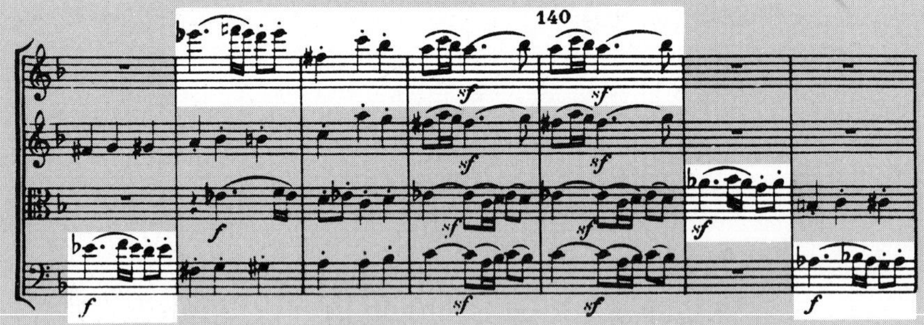
140

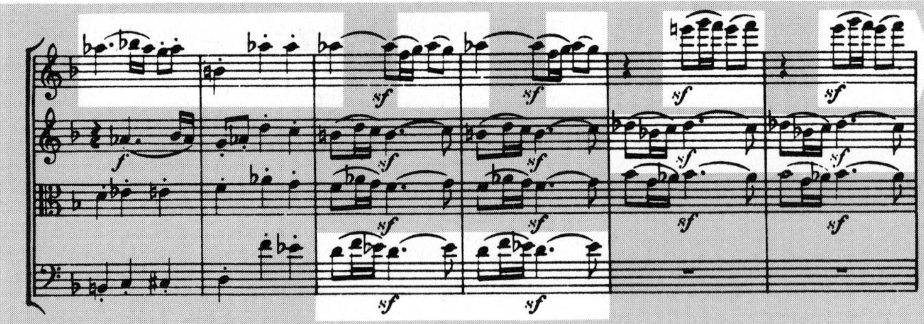

150

160
fp
fp
fp
fp
fp
fp
fp
fp
fp
fp
fp
fp
sf
sf
sf
sf
170
sf
sf
sf
sf
sf
sf
sf
sf
sf
sf
sf
sf
sf
sf
sf
sf
sf
sf
sf
sf

180
sf
sf
sf
cresc.
ff
cresc.
ff
sf
cresc.
ff
sf
cresc.
ff
p
p
p
p
p
p
190
cresc.
cresc.
p
cresc.
cresc.
200
tr
tr
tr
p
p
p
p

210
cresc.
f
p
cresc.
f
p
cresc.
f
p
cresc.
f
cresc.
p
cresc.
cresc.
cresc.
220
ff
decresc.
ff
ff
ff
p
p
p

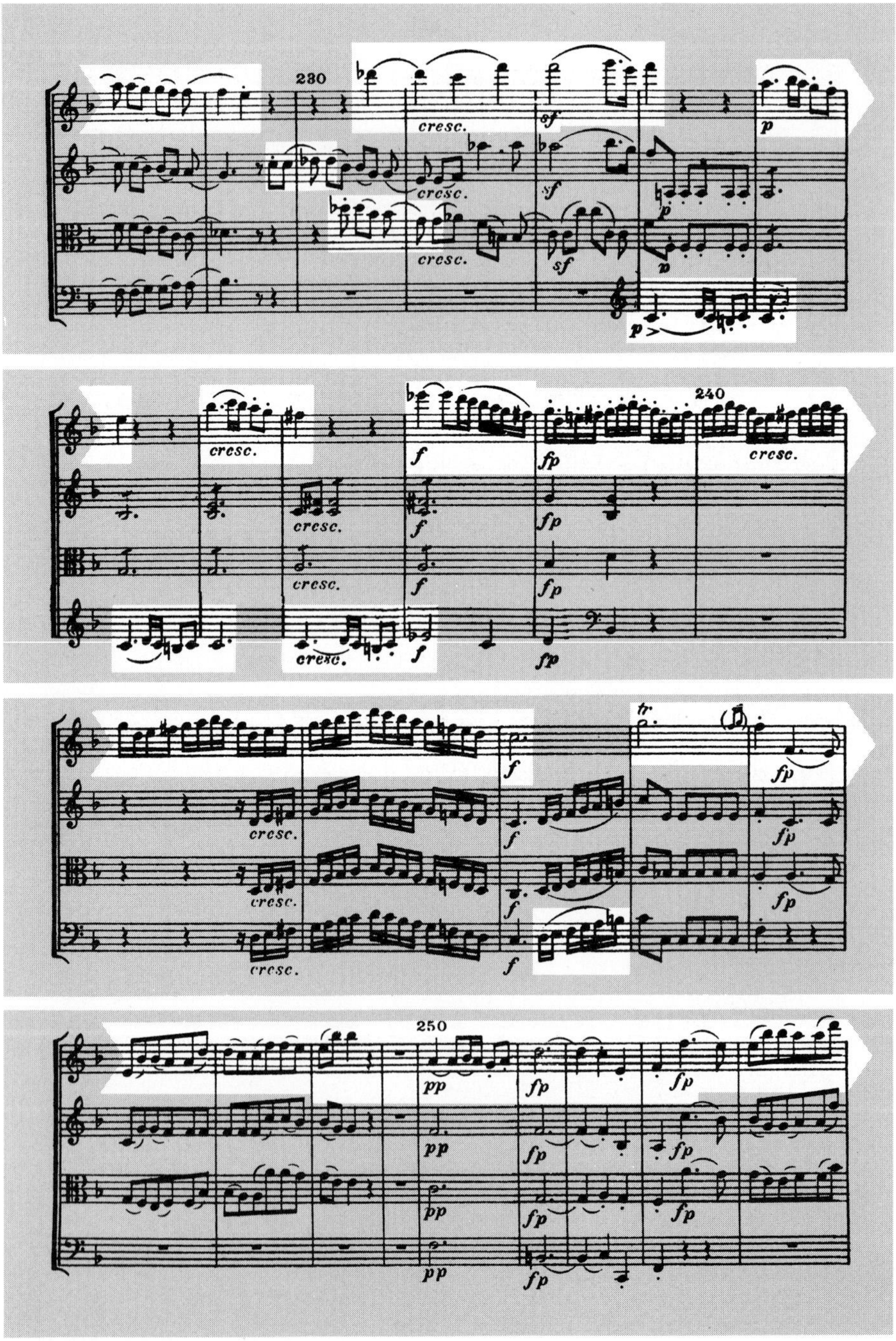
230
cresc.
sf
p
240
f
fp
250
pp
tr

280
ff
sf
ff
sf

pp
290
cresc.
sf
800
f

38. BEETHOVEN, Symphony No. 5 in C minor (1807)

20
Fl.
Ob.
Cl.
Fg.
Cor. (Es)
Tr. (C)
Tp.
Vl.
Vla.
Vc.
Cb.
p cresc.
cresc.
zu 2
f
30
zu 2
ff
1.
p

40
50
Fl.
Ob.
Cl.
Fg.
Cor. (Es)
Tr. (C)
Timp.
Vl.
Vla.
Vc. Cb.
cresc.

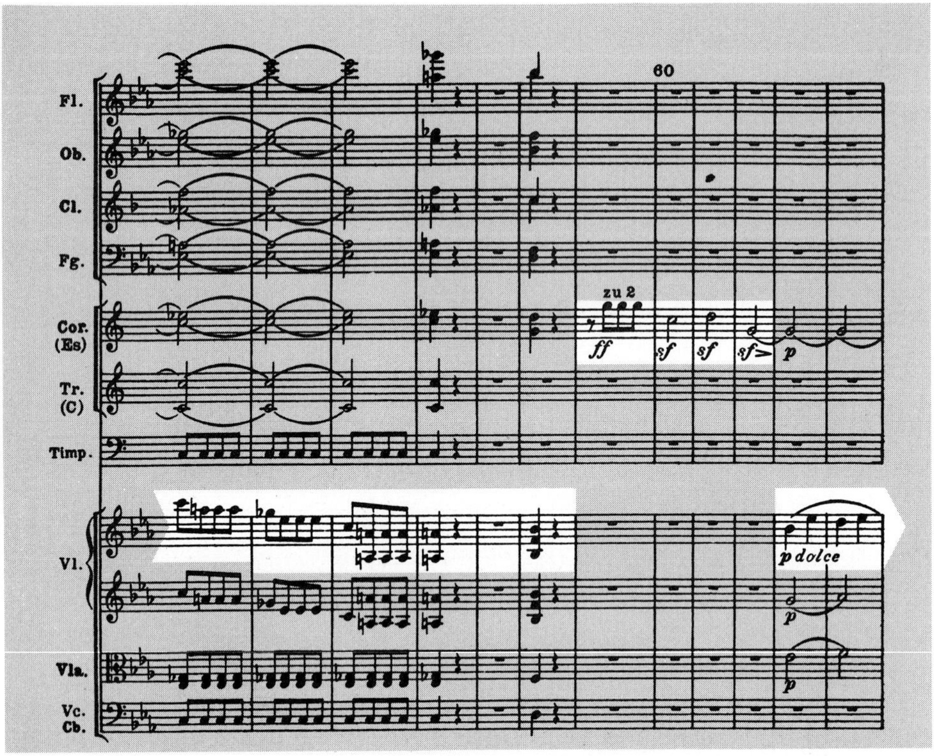

60
Fl.
Ob.
Cl.
Fg.
Cor. (Es)
zu 2
ff sf sf sf> p
Tr. (C)
Timp.
Vl.
p dolce
p
Vla.
p
Vc. Cb.

90
1.
Fl.
Ob.
Cl.
Fg.
Cor.
(Es)
Tr.
(C)
Vl.
Vla
Vc.
Cb.
cresc.
ff
zu 2

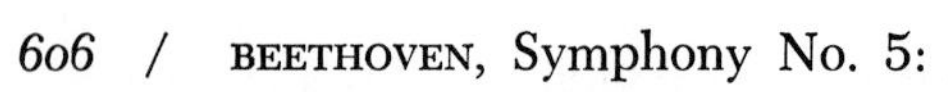

100

Fl.
Ob.
Cl.
Fg.
Cor. (Es)
Tr. (C)
Timp.
Vl.
Vla.
Vc. Cb.

ff f

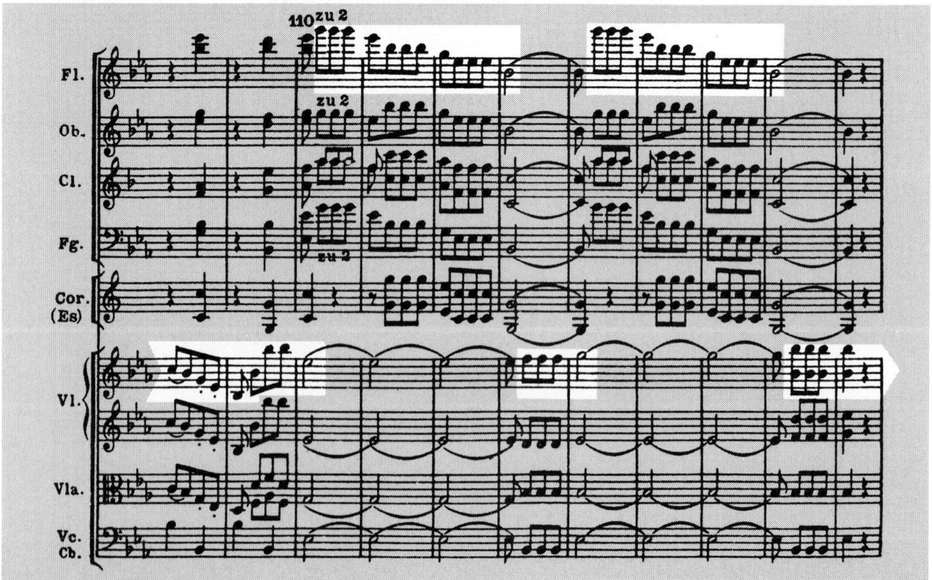

110 zu 2

zu 2

zu 2

Fl.
Ob.
Cl.
Fg.
Cor. (Es)
Vl.
Vla.
Vc. Cb.

120
130
Fl.
Ob.
Cl.
zu 2
ff
p
Fg.
zu 2
ff
p
Cor. (Es)
zu 2
ff
Vl.
ff
ff
p
Vla.
ff
Vc.
ff
Cb.
ff
140
Cl.
Fg.
Vl.
p
Vla.
Vc.

150
Cl.
Fg.
Cor. (Es)
Vl.
Vla.
Vc.
Cb.
cresc.
p
pizz.
Fl.
Ob
Tr. (C)
Timp.
zu 2
1.
pp
arco

160
Fl.
Ob.
Cl.
Fg.
Cor. (Es)
Tr. (C)
Timp.
Vl.
Vla.
Vc.
Cb.
cresc.
f

170
180
Fl.
Ob.
Cl.
Fg.
Cor. (Es)
Tr. (C)
Timp.
Vl.
Vla.
Vc.
b.
più f
ff
sf

190
Fl.
Ob.
Cl.
Fg.
Cor. (Es)
zu 2
Tr. (C)
zu 2
Timp.
Vl.
Vla.
Vc.
Cb.
sf

Fl.
Ob.
Cl.
Fg.
Cor. (Es)
Tr. (C)
Timp.
Vl.
Vla.
Vc. Cb.
zu 2
ff
200
zu 2
210
1.
dimin.
p
sempre più p
pp
220

230
1.
Fl.
Ob.
Cl.
Fg.
Cor. (Es)
Tr. (C)
Vl.
Vla.
Vc. Cb.
zu 2
ff
pp
240
Fl.
Ob.
Cl.
Fg.
Cor. (Es)
Vl.
Vla.
Vc.
Cb.
f

250
Fl.
Ob.
Cl
Fg.
Cor. (Es)
Tr. (C)
Timp.
Vl.
Vla.
Vc.
Cb.
ff
ten.
1.
p
pizz.
260
zu 2
cresc.
arco

Adagio.
270
280
1.
Fl.
Ob.
Cl.
Fg.
Cor. (Es)
Tr. (C)
Timp
Vl.
Vla.
Vc. Cb.
cresc.
arco
p cresc.

290
Fl.
Ob.
Cl.
Fg.
Cor. (Es)
Tr. (C)
Timp
Vl.
Vla.
Vc. Cb.
300
zu 2
pdolce

310
320
330
Fl.
Ob.
Fg.
Cor. (Es)
Timp
Vl.
Vla.
Vc. Cb.
Cl.
Vc.
Cb.
1.
p
cresc.

840
Fl.
Cl.
Fg.
Cor (Es)
Vl.
Vla.
Vc.
Cb.
cresc.
cresc
zu 2
cresc.
350
Fl.
Ob.
Cl.
Fg.
Cor. (Es)
Tr. (C)
Timp.
Vl.
Vla.
Vc. Cb.
ff

360
zu 2
Fl.
Ob.
Cl.
Fg.
Cor. (Es)
Tr. (C)
Timp.
Vl.
Vla.
Vc. Cb.
370
sf
f

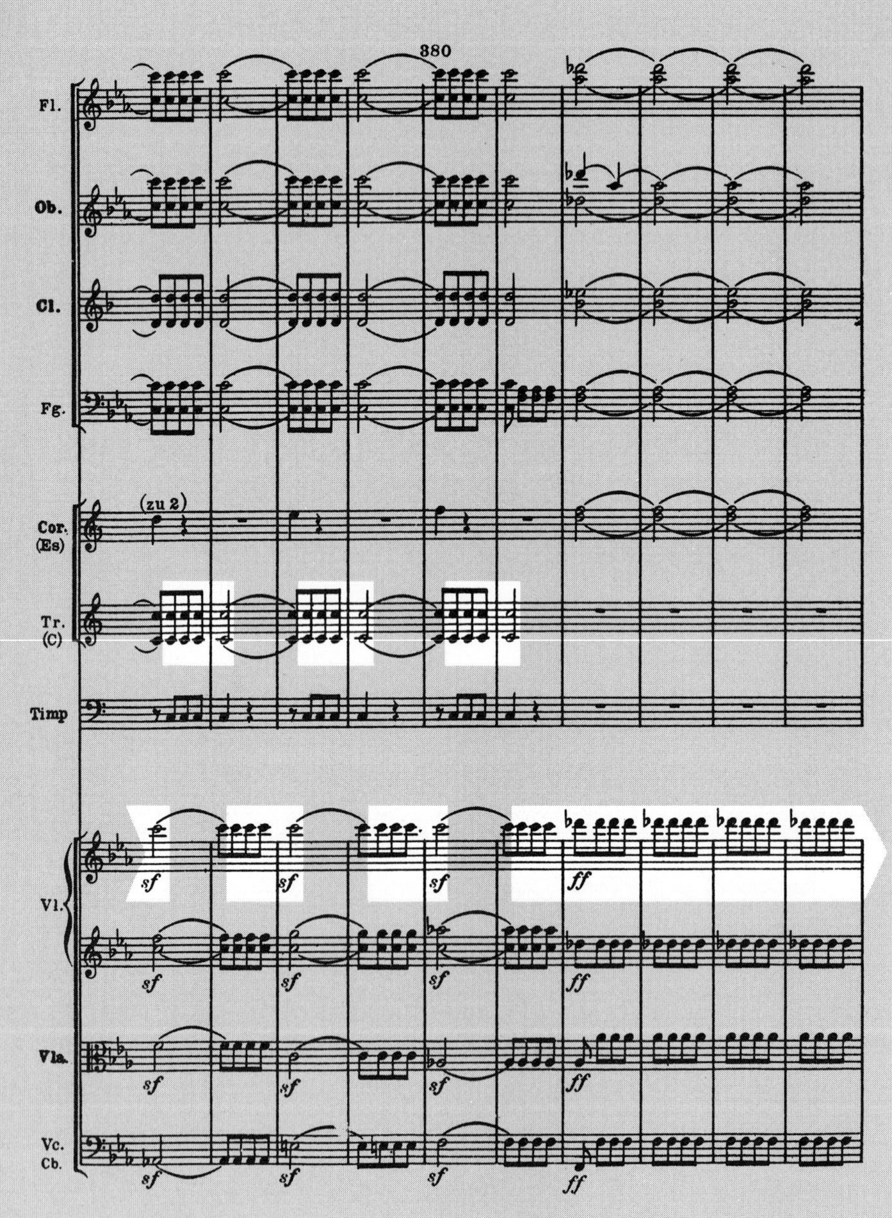
380
Fl.
Ob.
Cl.
Fg.
(zu 2)
Cor. (Es)
Tr. (C)
Timp
Vl.
Vla.
Vc. Cb.
sf
ff

390
Fl.
Ob.
Cl.
Fg.
Cor. (Es)
Tr. (C)
Timp.
Vl.
Vla.
Vc. Cb.
zu 2
p
ff

400
Fl.
Ob
Cl.
Fg.
Cor.
(Es)
Tr.
(C)
Timp.
Vl.
Vla.
Vc.
Cb.

1.
410
Fl.
Ob.
zu 2
Cl.
zu 2
Fg.
Cor. (Es)
zu 2.
Tr. (C)
Timp.
Vl.
Vla.
Vc.
Cb.

420
Fl.
Ob.
Cl.
Fg.
Cor. (Es)
Tr. (C)
Timp.
Vl.
Vla.
Vc. Cb.
sf

430
440
zu 2
Fl.
ff
Ob.
ff
Cl.
zu 2
ff
Fg.
ff
Cor. (Es)
Tr. (C)
Timp.
Vl.
Vla.
Vc. Cb.

450
Fl.
Ob.
Cl.
Fg.
Cor. (Es)
Tr. (C)
Timp.
Vl.
Vla.
Vc.
Cb.

460
Fl.
Ob.
Cl.
Fg.
Cor. (Es)
Tr. (C)
Timp.
Vl.
Vla.
Vc. Cb.
sf

470
Fl.
Ob.
zu 2
Cl.
Fg.
Cor. (Es)
zu 2
Tr. (C)
Timp.
Vl.
Vla.
Vc. Cb.
ff

480
490
Fl.
Ob.
1.
p
Cl.
Fg.
Cor
(Es)
Tr.
(C)
Timp.
Vl.
pp
Vla.
Vc.
Cb.

500
Fl.
Ob.
Cl
Fg.
Cor. (Es)
Tr. (C)
Timp.
Vl.
Vla.
Vc.
Cb.
ff

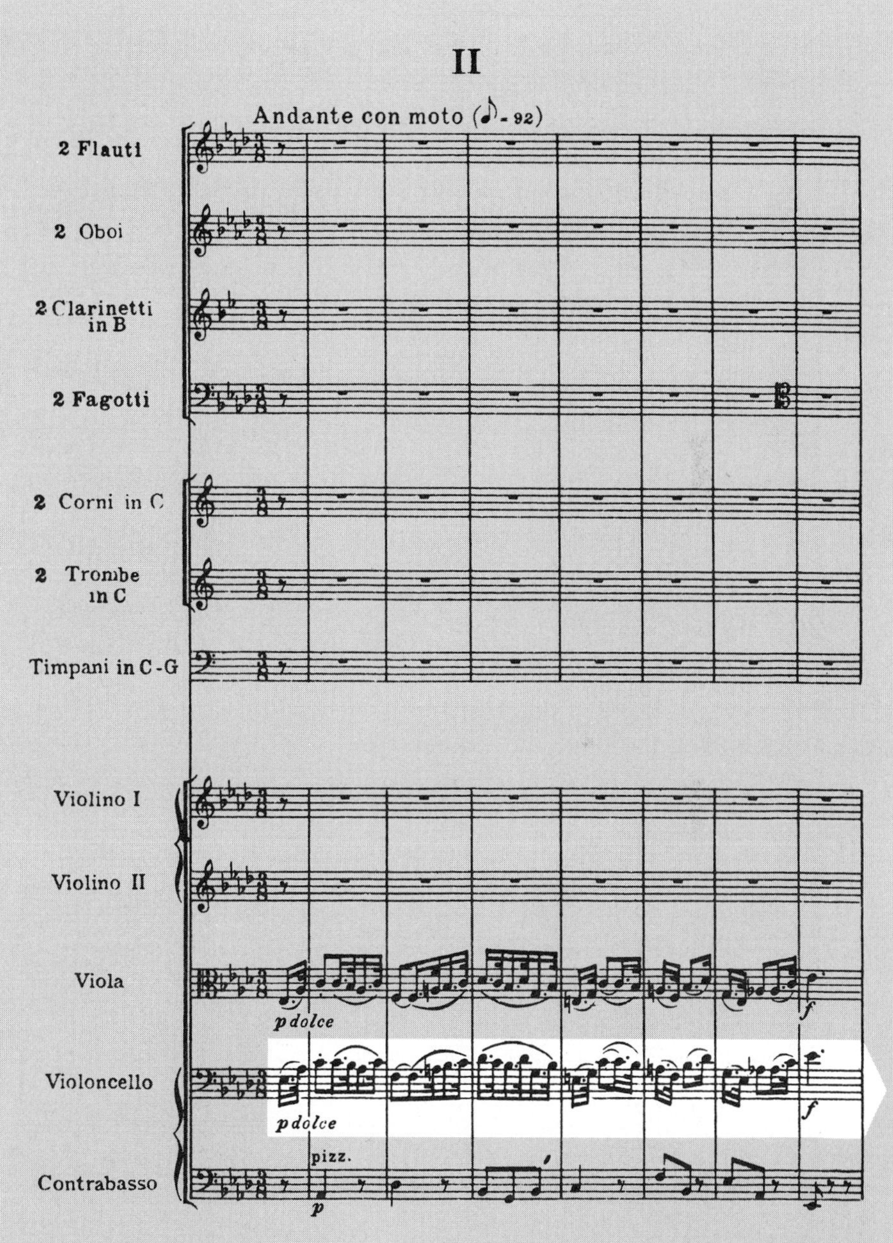
II
Andante con moto (♪ = 92)
2 Flauti
2 Oboi
2 Clarinetti in B
2 Fagotti
2 Corni in C
2 Trombe in C
Timpani in C-G
Violino I
Violino II
Viola
p dolce
f
Violoncello
p dolce
f
Contrabasso
pizz.
p

20
Fl.
Ob.
Cl.
Fg.
Vl.
Vla.
Vc.
Cb.
dolce
p dolce
pizz.

Fl.
Ob.
Cl.
Fg.
Cor. (C)
Tr. (C)
Timp.
Vl.
Vla.
Vc.
Cb.
30
pp
ff
arco

40
Ob.
Cl.
Fg.
Cor. (C)
Tr. (C)
Vl.
Vla.
Vc.
Cb.
pp
sempre pp
cresc.
pizz.
50
dolce

70
Fl.
Ob.
Cl.
Fg.
Vl.
Vla.
Vc.
Cb.
cresc.
dolce
pizz.

Fl.
Ob.
Cl.
Fg.
Vl.
Vla.
Vc.
Cb.
1.
pp
80
ff
Cor. (C)
Tr. (C)
Timp
tr
arco
Vc.
Cb

Ob.
Cor. (C)
Tr. (C)
Timp.
Vl.
Vla.
Vc. Cb.
sf
tr
f
Ob.
Fg.
Cor. (C)
Tr. (C)
Timp.
Vl.
Vla.
Vc.
Cb.
90
f dim.
p
pp
sempre pp

Fl.
Ob.
Cl.
Fg.
Vl.
Vla.
Vc.
Cb.
1.
zu 2
zu 2
cresc.
ff
f
100
pizz.
p dolce

Fl.
Ob.
Fg.
Vl.
Vla
Vc.
Cb.
pp
Cl.
1.
p
arco
dolce
sempre pp
pizz.
Vla.

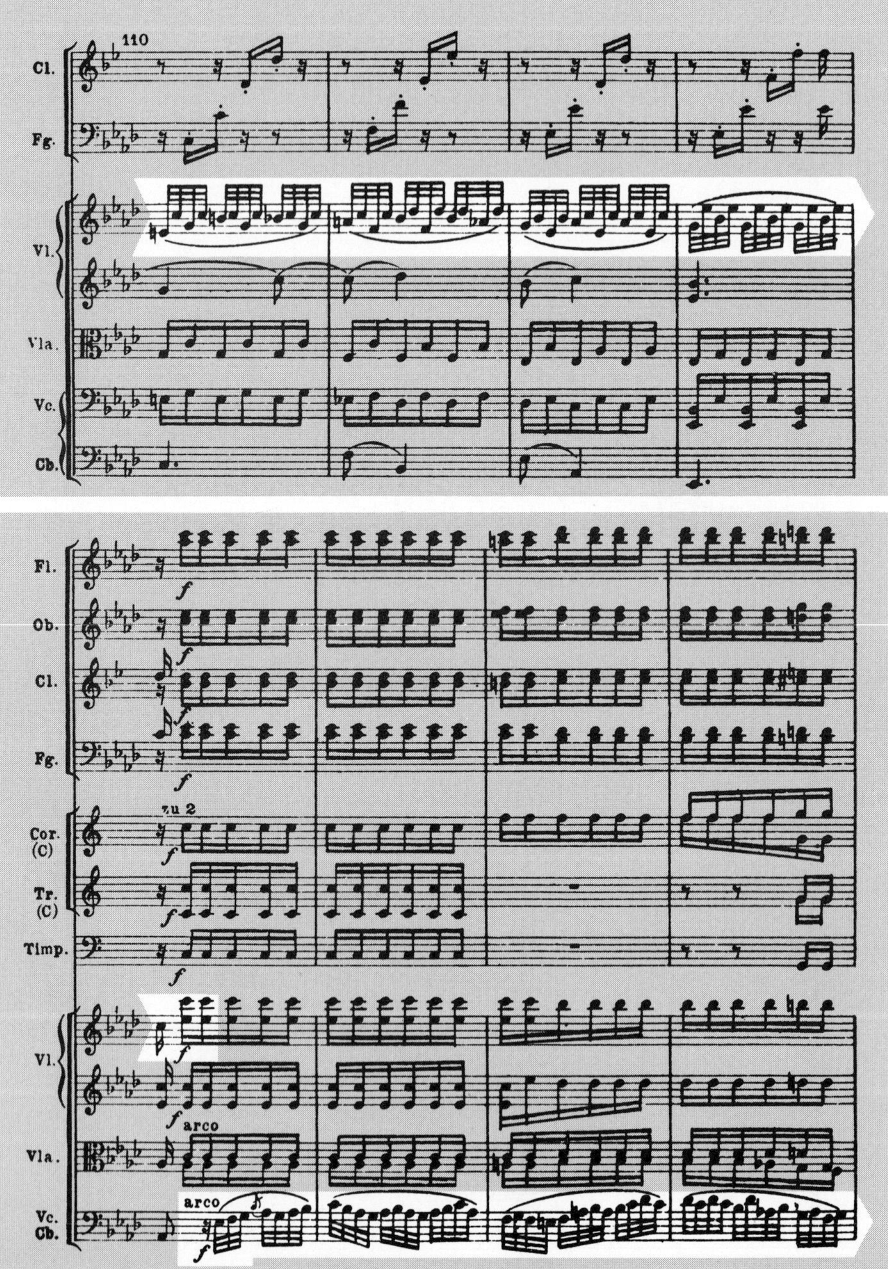
110
Cl.
Fg.
Vl.
Vla.
Vc.
Cb.
Fl.
Ob.
Cl.
Fg.
zu 2
Cor. (C)
Tr. (C)
Timp.
Vl.
arco
Vla.
arco
Vc. Cb.

120
Fl.
Ob.
zu 2
Cl.
zu 2
Fg.
zu 2
zu 2
Cor. (C)
Tr. (C)
Timp.
Vl.
Vla.
Vc. Cb.
130
1.
dolce
1.
dolce
1.
dolce
1.
dolce
pp
sempre pp
f

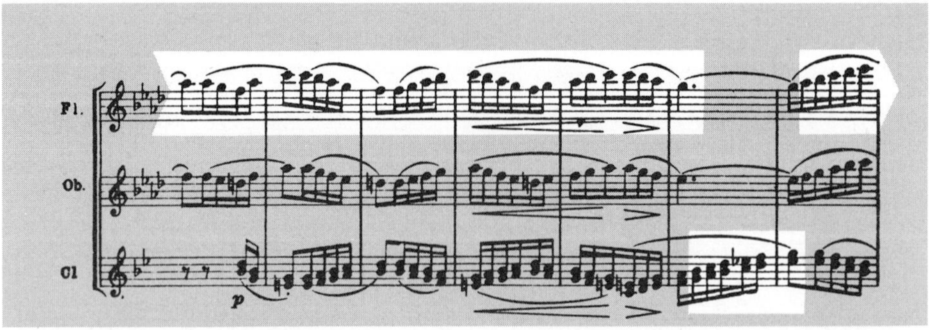

Fl.
Ob.
Cl
p

140
Fl.
cresc.
ff
Ob.
cresc.
ff
Cl.
cresc.
Fg.
ff
Cor.
(C)
f
ff
Tr.
(C)
ff
Timp.
ff
Vl.
p
ff
p
ff
Vla.
p
ff
Vc.
Cb.
p
ff

150
Fl.
dimin. p
Ob.
dimin. p
Cl.
ff
Fg.
dimin. p
Cor. (C)
dimin. p
Tr. (C)
dimin. p
Timp.
tr
dimin. p
Vl.
p
pizz.
p
Vla.
p
Vc. Cb.
pizz.
dimin. p

Fl.
Ob.
Cl.
Fg.
Vl.
Vla
Vc.
Cb.
1.
p
pp
pizz.
170
Vla.
Vc.
Cb.

cresc.
p dolce
Fl.
Ob.
f sf
f
cresc.
Cl.
Fg.
cresc.
Vl.
cresc.
Vla.
Vc.
Cb.
180
1.
p dolce
arco
cresc.
pp

zu 2
Fl.
cresc.
ff
Ob.
cresc.
ff
zu 2
Cl.
cresc.
ff
zu 2
1.
Fg.
cresc.
ff
Cor. (C)
ff
Tr. (C)
ff
Timp
ff
Vl.
cresc.
ff
ff
Vla
ff
Vc. Cb.
ff

190
Fl.
Ob.
Cl.
Fg.
Cor.
(C)
Tr.
(C)
Timp.
Vl.
Vla
Vc.
Cb.

Fl.
Ob.
Cl.
Fg.
Cor. (C)
Tr. (C)
Timp.
Vl.
Vla.
Vc. Cb.
zu 2
sf
p dolce
200
p
Vla

Piu mosso. (♪ = 116.)
Fl.
Cl.
Fg.
dolce
1.
pp
Vl.
Vla.
Vc.
Cb.
210
Fl.
Ob.
Cl.
Fg.
Cor. (C)
zu 2
Vl.
Vla.
Vc.
Cb.
p
f
cresc.

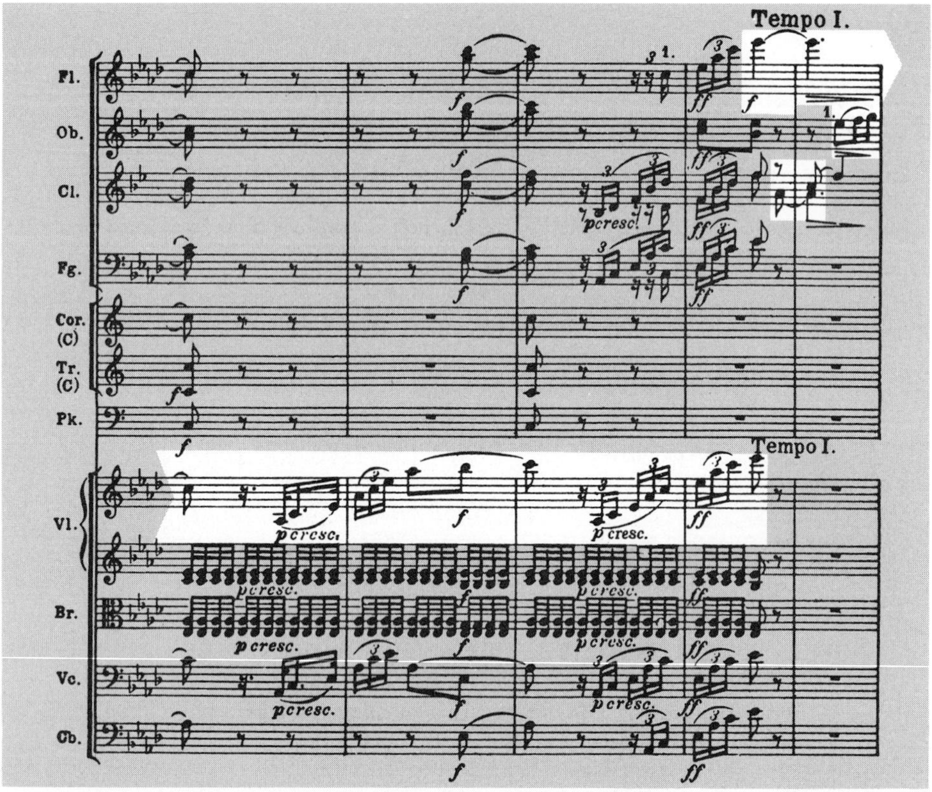

Tempo I.

Fl.
Ob.
Cl.
Fg.
Cor. (C)
Tr. (C)
Pk.

Tempo I.

Vl.
Br.
Vc.
Cb.

p cresc.
f
ff

280
Cl.
Fg.
Vl.
Vla.
Vc.
Cb.
cresc.
f

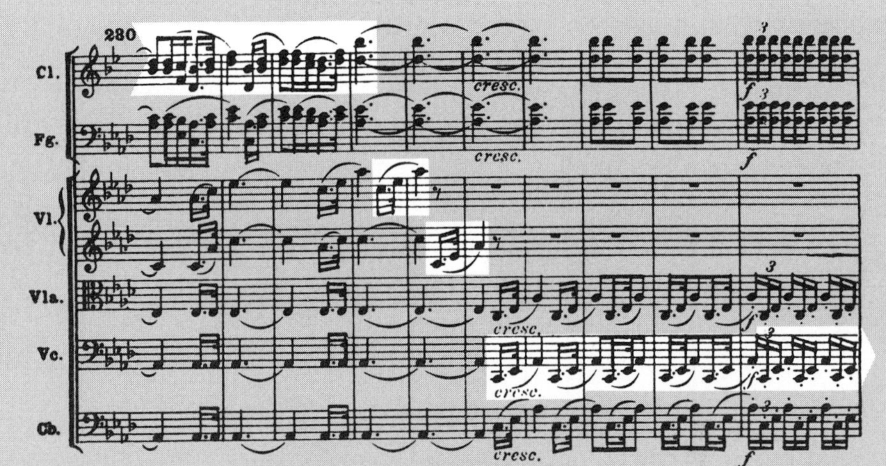

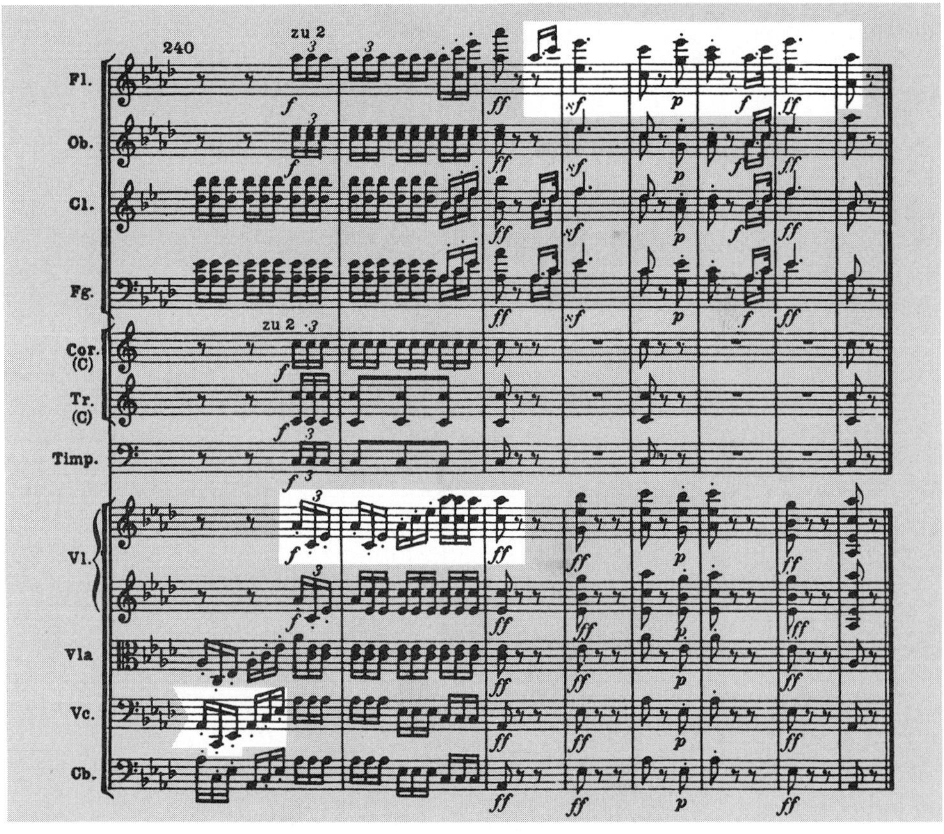

240
zu 2
Fl.
Ob.
Cl.
Fg.
Cor. (C)
Tr. (C)
Timp.
Vl.
Vla
Vc.
Cb.
f
ff
sf
p

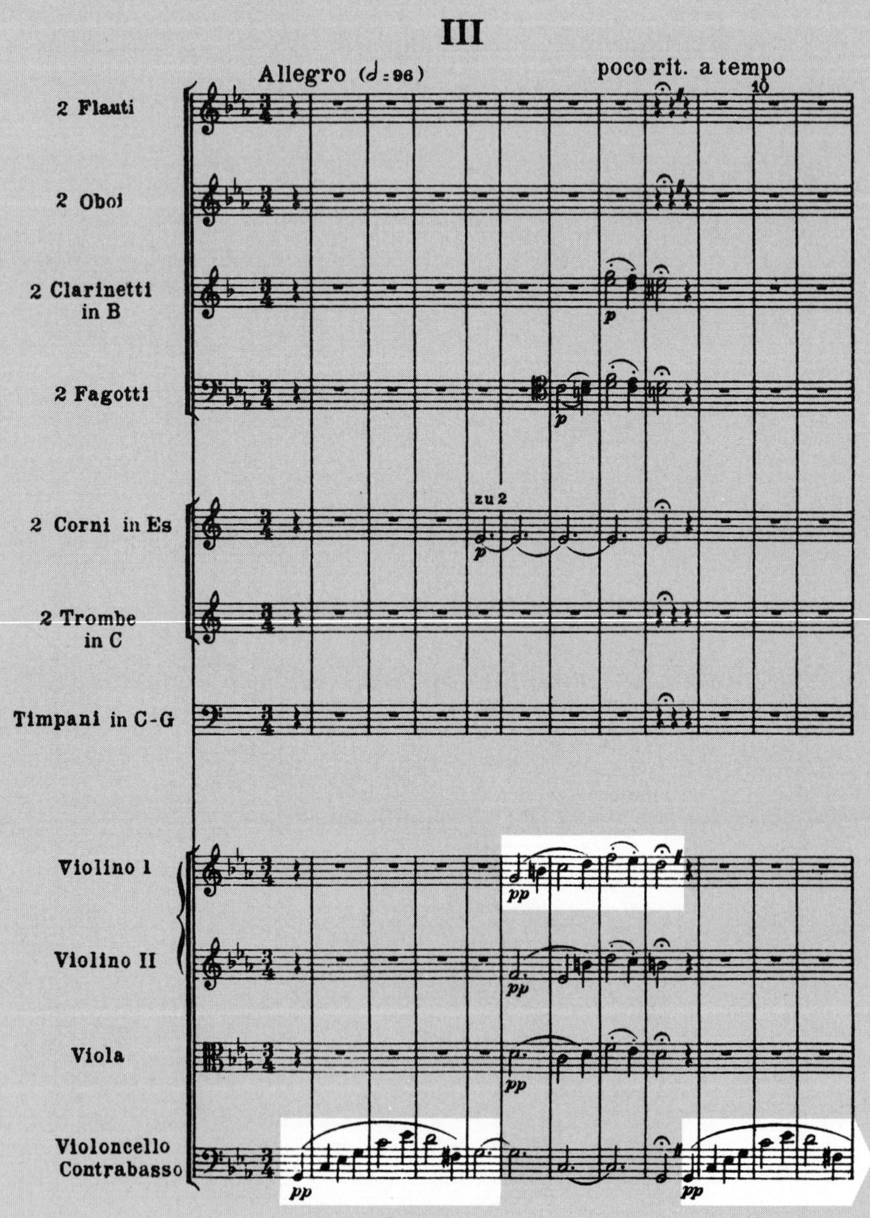
III
Allegro (𝅗𝅥 = 96)
poco rit. a tempo
10
2 Flauti
2 Oboi
2 Clarinetti in B
2 Fagotti
zu 2
2 Corni in Es
2 Trombe in C
Timpani in C-G
Violino I
Violino II
Viola
Violoncello Contrabasso
p
pp

poco rit.
1.
a tempo
20
Fl.
p
Cl.
1.
p
Fg.
1.
p
Cor.
(Es)
zu 2
ff
Vl.
pp
f
pp
f
Vla
pp
f
Vc.
Cb.
fp
f
zu 2
30
Fl.
f
Ob
f
Cl.
f
zu 2
Fg.
f
Cor.
(Es)
zu 2
Vl.
f
f
Vla.
f
Vc.
Cb.
f

40
Fl.
Ob.
Cl.
Fg.
Cor. (Es)
Vl.
Vla
Vc. Cb.
zu 2
zu 2
2.
sf
dimin. pp
p
pp

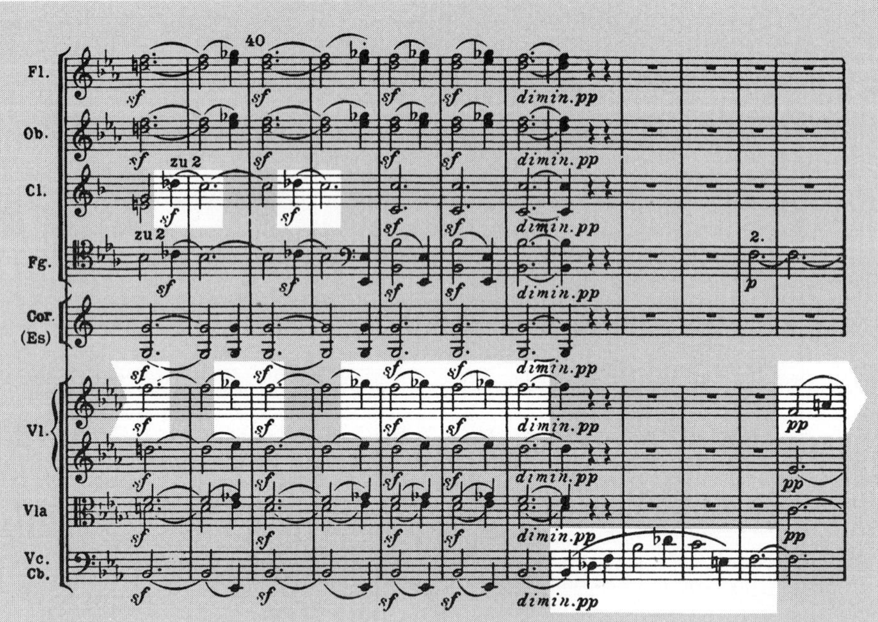

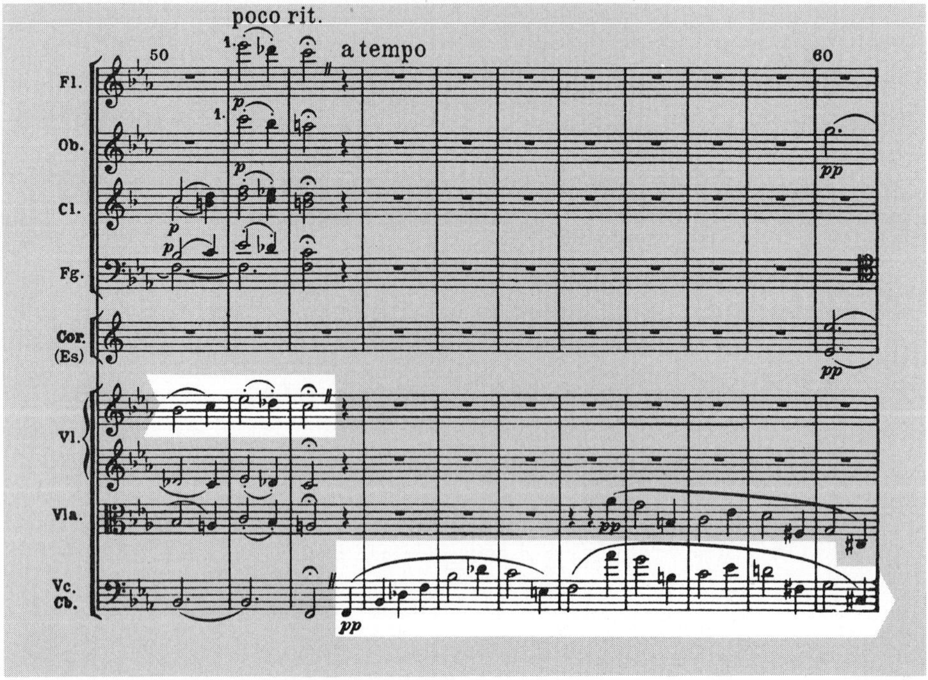

poco rit.
a tempo
50
60
Fl.
Ob.
Cl.
Fg.
Cor. (Es)
Vl.
Vla.
Vc. Cb.
1.
1.
p
pp

70
Ob.
Cl.
Cor. (Es)
Vl.
Vla.
Vc. Cb.
pp
cresc.
1.
zu 2
80
Fl.
Ob.
Cl.
Fg.
Cor. (Es)
Tr. (C)
Timp.
Vl.
Vla.
Vc. Cb.
f
ff

90
Fl.
Ob.
zu 2
Cl.
Fg.
Cor. (Es)
Tr. (C)
Timp.
Vl.
Vla.
Vc. Cb.
ff
sf

100
1.
Fl.
sf
sf
dimin. pp
p
Ob.
Cl.
Fg.
Cor. (Es)
zu 2
Tr. (C)
p dimin. pp
Timp.
Vl.
Vla.
Vc.
Cb.

110
Fl.
Ob.
Cl.
Fg.
Cor. (Es)
Timp.
Vl.
Vla.
Vc.
Cb.
zu 2
p
arco
pizz.
f>p
120
pp
sempre p
cresc.

130
Fl.
Ob.
Cl.
Fg.
Cor. (Es)
Tr. (C)
Timp.
Vl.
Vla.
Vc.
Cb.
p
cresc.
f
arco

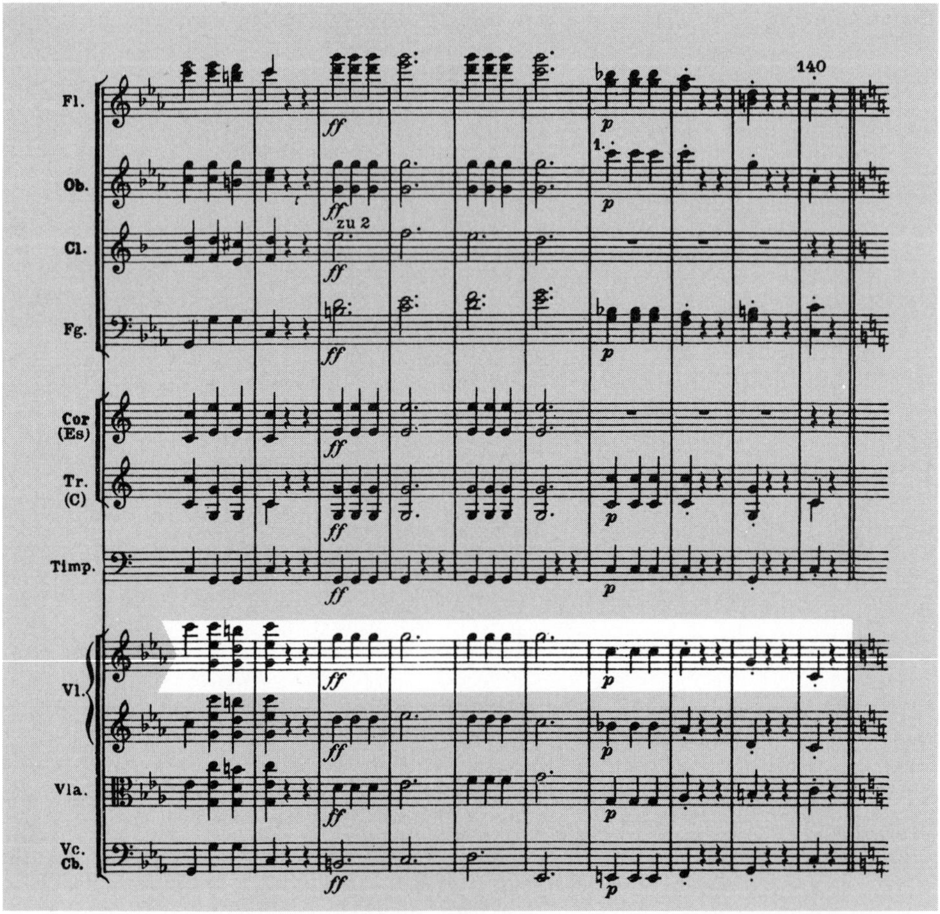

140

Fl.

Ob.

Cl.

Fg.

Cor (Es)

Tr. (C)

Timp.

Vl.

Vla.

Vc. Cb.

ff

p

1.

zu 2

150

Fl.

1.

f

Ob.

f

Fg.

f

Cor. (Es)

f

Timp.

f

Vl.

f

f

Vla.

f

Vc. Cb.

180
Fl.
Ob.
f
Cl.
f
Fg.
Cor.
(Es)
f
Tr.
(C)
f
Timp.
f
Vl.
f
f
Vla.
Vc.
Cb.

Fl.
Ob.
Cl.
Fg.
zu 2
Cor. (Es)
Tr. (C)
Timp.
Vl.
Vla.
Vc.
Cb.
sf

190
zu 2
Fl.
Ob.
Cl.
Fg.
Cor.
(Es)
Tr.
(C)
Timp.
Vl.
ff
Vla
ff
Vc.
Cb.

Cl.
1.
210
p
sempre più p
Vla.
p
sempre più p
Vc.
Cb.
sempre più p
Fl.
1.
pp
sempre pp
220
Ob.
1.
pp
pp
sempre pp
Cl.
pp
pp
sempre pp
Fg.
pp
sempre pp
Vl.
pp
pp
Vla.
Vc.
Cb.
Fl.
230
Ob.
1.
Cl.
1.
pp
Fg.
1.
pp

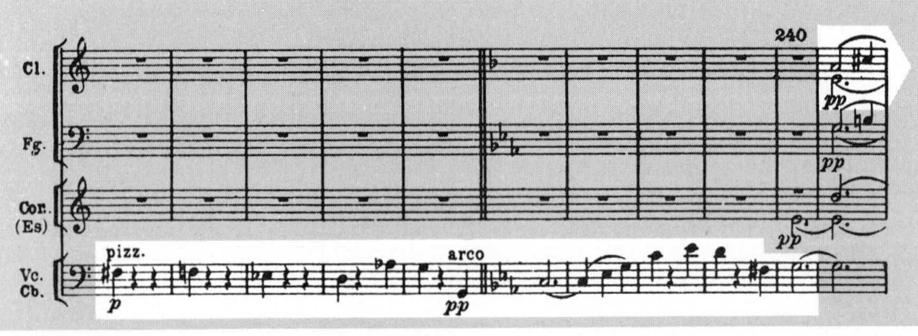
240
Cl.
Fg.
Cor. (Es)
Vc. Cb.
pizz.
arco
p
pp

poco ritard. a tempo
250
Cl.
Fg.
zu 2
Cor. (Es)
Vl.
Vla.
Vc.
Cb.
pizz.
p

poco ritard. a tempo
260
Cl.
zu 2
pp
Fg.
Vl.
arco
sempre pp
pizz.
Vla.
Vc.

1.
270
Ob.
pp
Fg.
pp
sempre pp
pizz.
Vl.
pp
sempre pp
sempre pp
pizz.
arco
Vla.
sempre pp
Vc.
sempre pp
280
Fg.
Vl.
Vla.
Vc.
290
Ob.
p
p
Fg.
pp
1.
Cor.
(Es)
p
Vl.
sempre pp
sempre pp
Vla.
pp
sempre pp
Vc.
sempre pp

Fg.
Cor. (Es)
Vl.
Vla.
Vc.
1.
300
p
310
320
pp
pizz.
arco
Ve

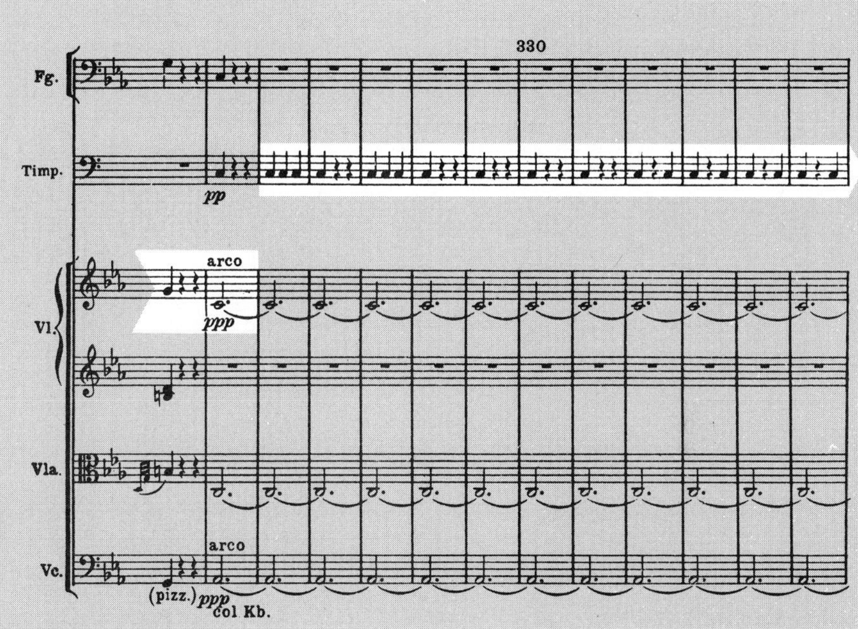
330
Fg.
Timp.
pp
arco
ppp
Vl.
Vla.
arco
Vc.
(pizz.) ppp
col Kb.

340
Timp.
sempre pp
Vl.
sempre pp
arco
sempre pp
Vla.
sempre pp
Vc
Cb.
sempre pp

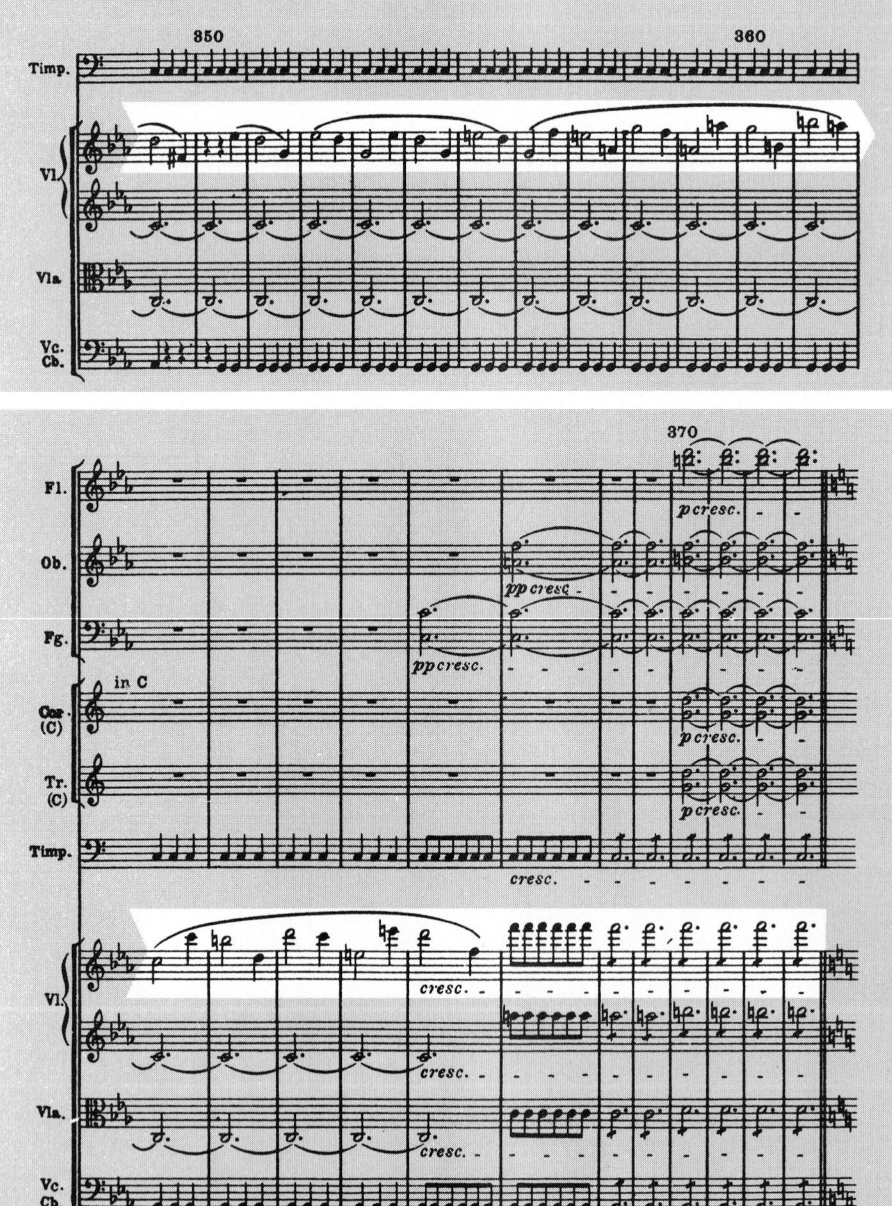
350
360
Timp.
Vl.
Vla.
Vc.
Cb.
370
Fl.
p cresc.
Ob.
pp cresc.
Fg.
pp cresc.
in C
Cor.
(C)
p cresc.
Tr.
(C)
p cresc.
Timp.
cresc.
Vl.
cresc.
cresc.
Vla.
cresc.
Vc.
Cb.
cresc.
Attacca:

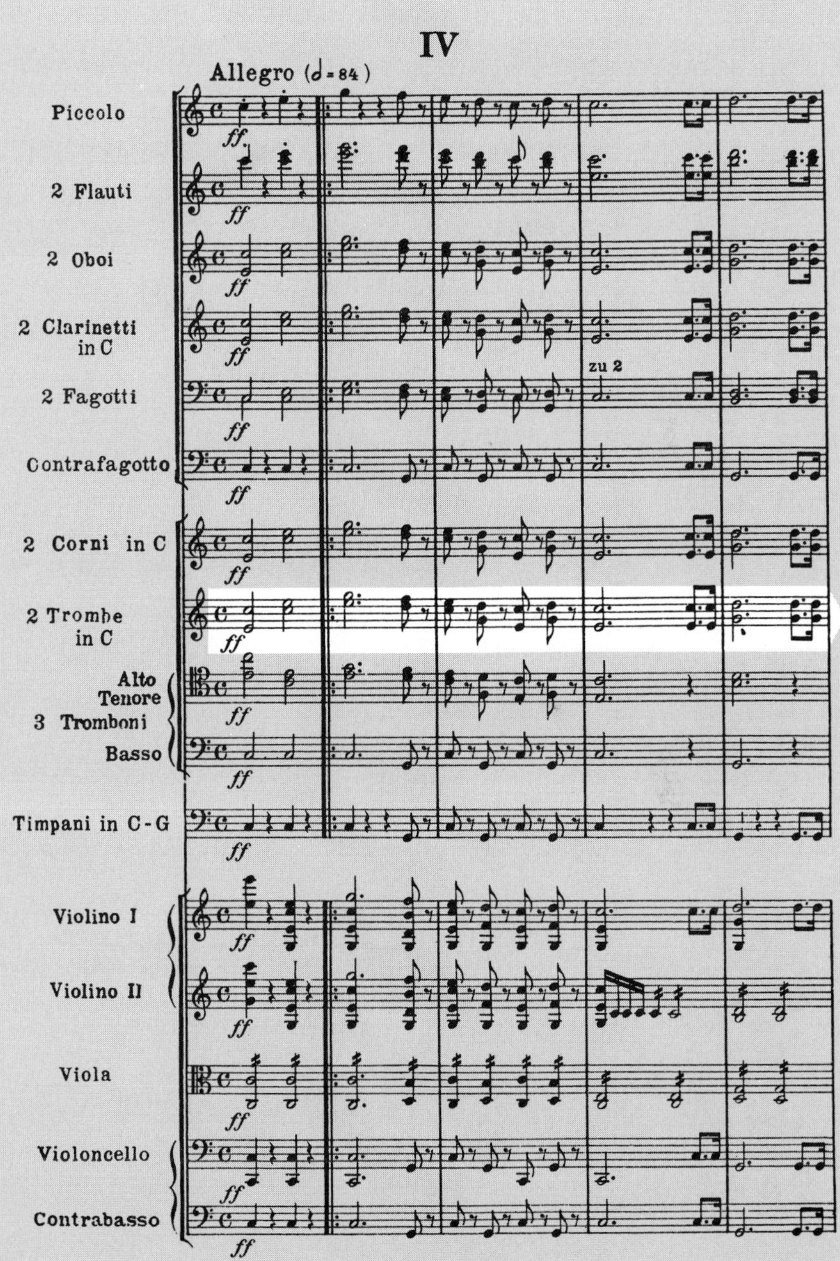
IV
Allegro (𝅗𝅥 = 84)
Piccolo
2 Flauti
2 Oboi
2 Clarinetti in C
2 Fagotti
zu 2
Contrafagotto
2 Corni in C
2 Trombe in C
Alto
Tenore
3 Tromboni
Basso
Timpani in C-G
Violino I
Violino II
Viola
Violoncello
Contrabasso
ff

10
Picc.
Fl.
zu 2
Ob.
zu 2
Cl.
Fg.
Cfg.
Cor. (C)
Tr. (C)
Tbni.
Timp.
Vl.
Vla.
Vc. Cb.

Picc.
Fl.
Ob.
Cl.
Fg.
Cfg.
Cor.
(C)
Tr.
(C)
Tbni.
Timp.
Vl.
Vla.
Vc.
Cb.

20
Picc.
Fl.
zu 2
Ob.
Cl.
Fg.
Cfg.
Cor. (C)
Tr. (C)
Toni.
Timp.
Vl.
Vla.
Vc. Cb.

Picc.
Fl.
Ob.
zu 2
Cl.
zu 2
Fg.
Cfg.
Cor.
(C)
Tr.
(C)
Tbni.
Timp.
Vl.
Vla.
Vc.
Cb.

30
Picc.
Fl.
Ob.
Cl.
Fg.
Cfg.
Cor. (C)
Tr. (C)
Tbni
Timp.
Vl.
Vla.
Vc.
Cb.

Fl.
Ob.
Cl.
Fg.
Cfg.
Cor. (C)
zu 2
Tr. (C)
zu 2
Tbni.
Timp.
Vl.
Vla.
Vc. Cb.

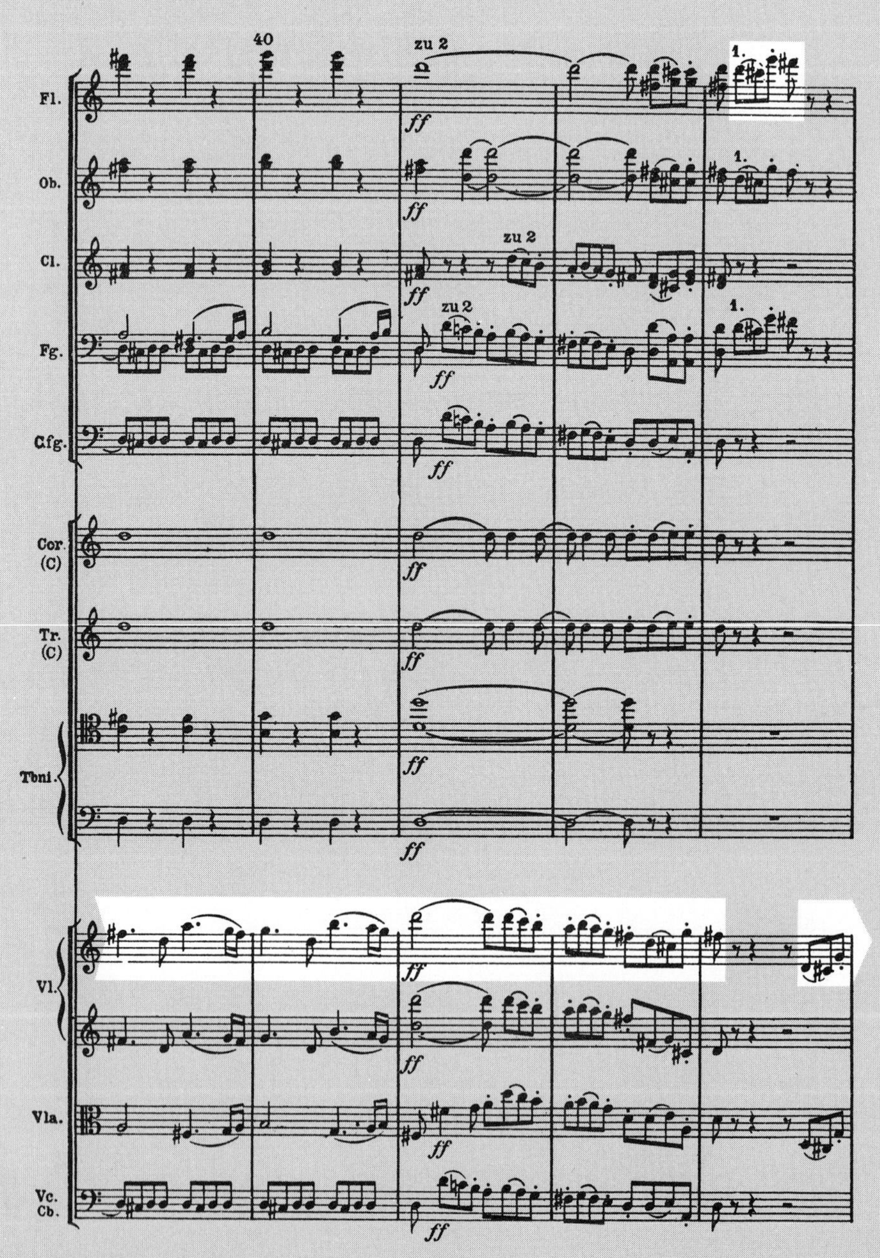
40
zu 2
Fl.
ff
1.
Ob.
ff
1.
Cl.
zu 2
ff
Fg.
zu 2
ff
1.
Cfg.
ff
Cor. (C)
ff
Tr. (C)
ff
Tbni.
ff
ff
Vl.
ff
ff
Vla.
ff
Vc. Cb.
ff

Picc.
Fl.
Ob.
Cl.
Fg.
Cfg.
Cor. (C)
Tr. (C)
Timp.
Vl.
Vla.
Vc.
Cb.
zu 2
cresc.
f
p

50
Picc
Fl.
Ob.
Cl.
Fg.
Cfg.
Cor. (C)
Tr. (C)
Tbni.
Timp.
Vl.
Vla.
Vc.
Cb.

Fl.
Ob.
Cl.
Fg.
Cfg.
Cor. (C)
Tr. (C)
Tbni.
Timp.
Vl.
Vla
Vc.
Cb.
pp
cresc.
ff
zu 2
f
dolce

60
Fl.
Ob.
zu 2
Cl.
Fg.
Cfg.
Cor
(C)
Tr.
(C)
Tbni.
Timp.
Vl.
Vla.
Vc.
Cb.

Fl.
Ob.
Cl.
Fg.
Cfg.
Cor. (C)
Tr. (C)
Tbni.
Timp.
Vl.
Vla
Vc.
Cb.

70
Picc.
Fl.
Ob.
Cl.
Fg.
Cfg.
Cor. (C)
Tr. (C)
Tbni.
Timp.
Vl.
Vla.
Vc.
Cb.
zu 2
1.
p dolce
f
p

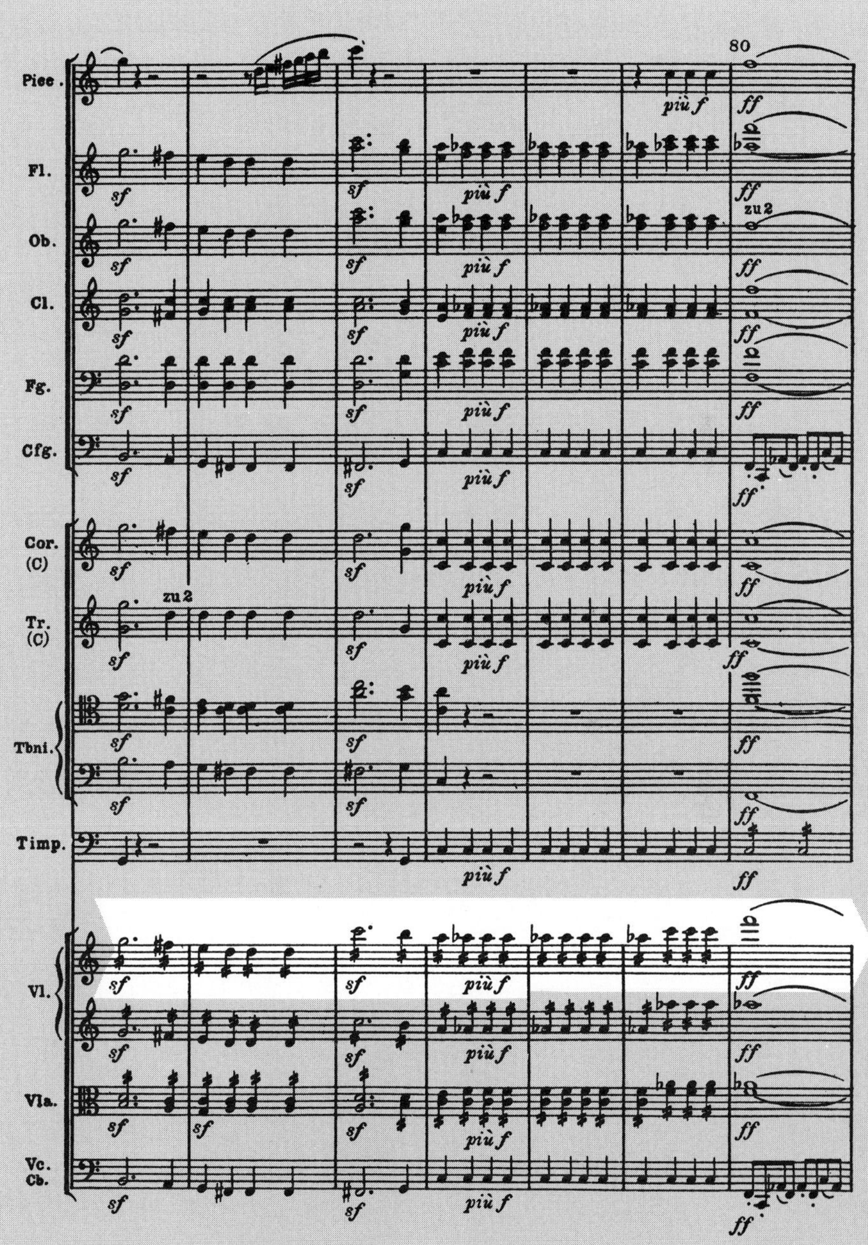
80
Picc.
Fl.
Ob.
Cl.
Fg.
Cfg.
Cor. (C)
Tr. (C)
Tbni.
Timp.
Vl.
Vla.
Vc. Cb.
zu 2
sf
più f
ff

1.
Picc.
Fl.
Ob.
zu 2
Cl.
Fg.
zu 2
Cfg.
Cor. (C)
Tr. (C)
Tbni.
Timp.
Vl.
Vla.
Vc.
Cb.

2.
Picc.
zu 2
Fl.
zu 2
Ob.
Cl.
zu 2
Fg.
Cfg.
Cor. (C)
Tr. (C)
Tbni.
Timp.
Vl.
Vla.
Vc. Cb.

90
Picc.
Fl.
Ob.
Cl.
Fg.
Cfg.
Cor. (C)
Tr. (C)
Tbni.
Vl.
Vla.
Vc.
Cb.
zu 2
p

Fl.
Ob.
Cl.
Fg.
Cor.
(C)
Vl.
Vla.
Vc.
100
dolce
1.
p
zu 2

Fl.
Ob.
Cl.
Fg.
Cfg.
Vl.
Vla.
Vc.
Kb.
p
f
110
Fl.
Ob.
Cl.
Fg.
Cfg.
Vl.
Vla.
Vc.
Cb.

Fl.
Ob.
Cl.
Fg.
zu 2
ff
C fg.
Cor. (C)
f
Tr. (C)
Tbni.
Timp.
tr
Vl.
Vla.
Vc.
Cb.

zu 2
120
Fl.
zu 2
Ob.
Cl.
zu 2
Fg.
Cfg.
Cor. (C)
zu 2
Tr. (C).
Trbni
Timp.
Vl.
Vla.
Vc.
Cb.

Fl.
Ob.
Cl.
Fg.
Cfg.
Cor. (C)
Tr. (C)
Tbni.
Timp.
Vl.
Vla.
Vc.
Cb.
più f
zu 2

130

Fl.

1.

Ob.

Cl.

Fg.

Cfg.

zu 2

Cor. (C)

zu 2

Tr. (C)

Tbni.

Timp.

Vl.

Vla.

Vc. Cb.

Picc.
Fl.
Ob.
Cl.
zu 2
Fg.
Cfg.
Cor. (C)
Tr. (C)
Tbni
Timp.
Vl.
Vla.
Vc. Cb.
ff
3

Picc.
Fl.
Ob.
Cl.
Fg.
Cfg.
Cor. (C)
Tr. (C)
Tbni.
Timp.
Vl.
Vla.
Vc.
Cb.

140
Picc.
Fl.
Ob.
Cl.
Fg.
Cfg.
Cor. (C)
Tr. (C)
Tbni.
Timp.
Vl.
Vla.
Vc.
Cb.
sempre ff
sf
tr

Picc.
Fl.
Ob.
Cl.
Fg.
Cfg.
Cor. (C)
Tr. (C)
Tbni.
Timp.
Vl.
Vla.
Vc. Cb.

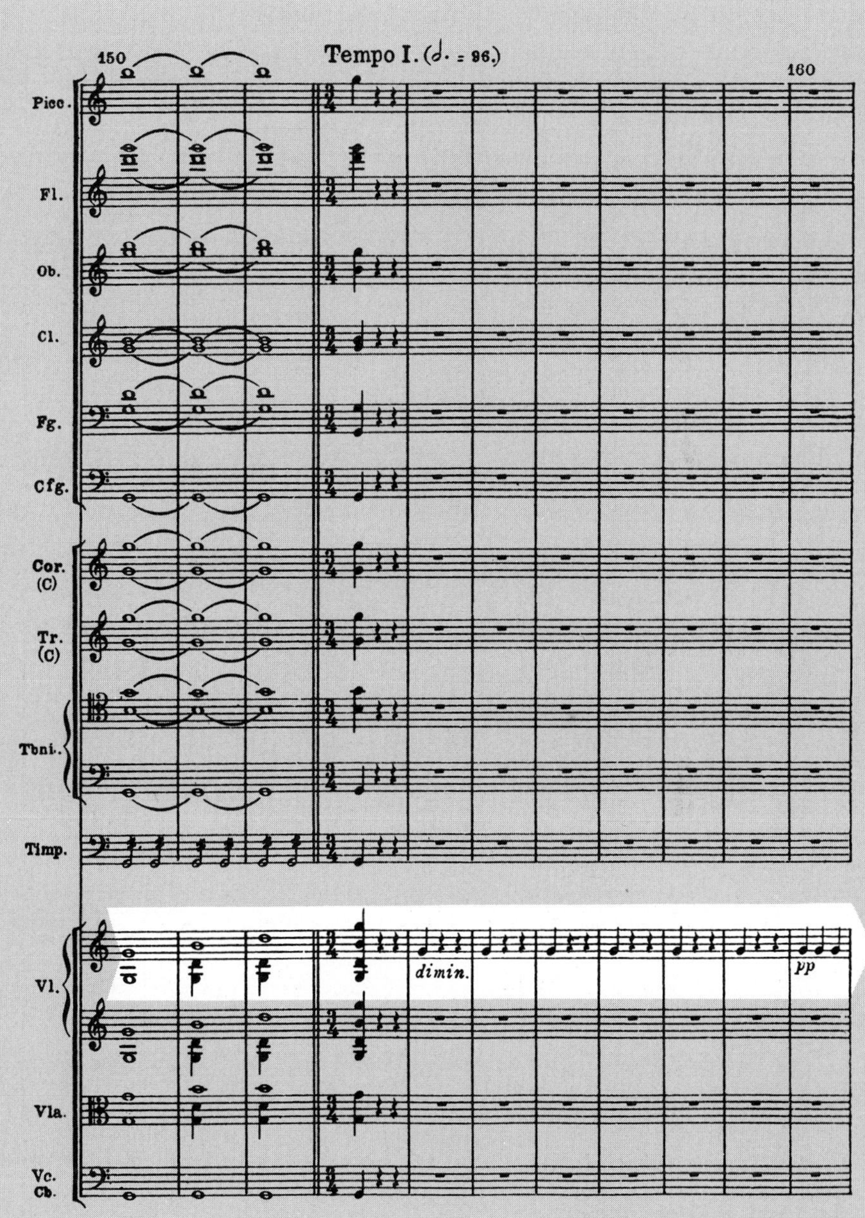
150
Tempo I. (𝅗𝅥. = 96.)
160
Picc.
Fl.
Ob.
Cl.
Fg.
Cfg.
Cor. (C)
Tr. (C)
Tbni.
Timp.
Vl.
dimin.
pp
Vla.
Vc. Cb.

170
1
Ob.
Cl.
p
p
pizz.
arco
pizz.
Vl.
pizz.
pp
pizz.
Vla
pp
Vc.
pp

180
Ob
Cl.
Cor.
(C)
pp
pp
Vl.
arco
Vla.
Vc.

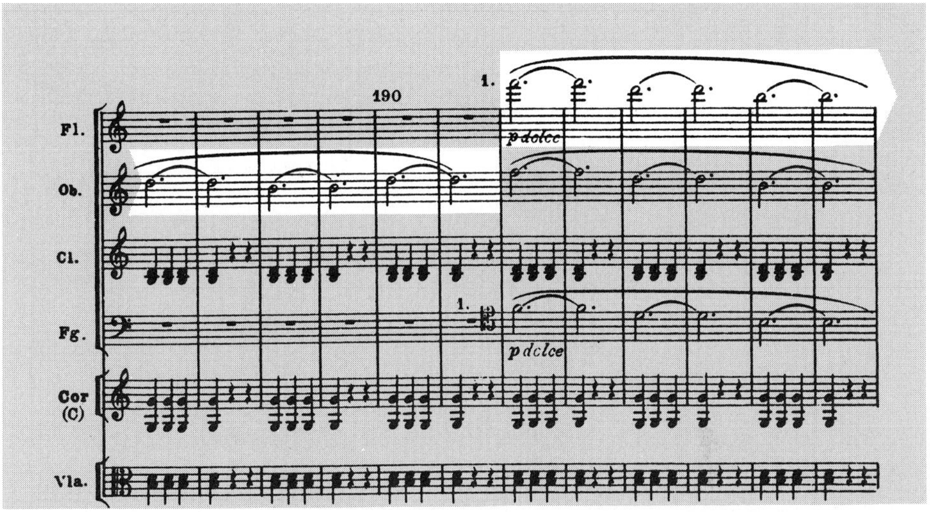

190

Fl. 1. *p dolce*

Ob.

Cl.

Fg. 1. *p dolce*

Cor. (C)

Vla.

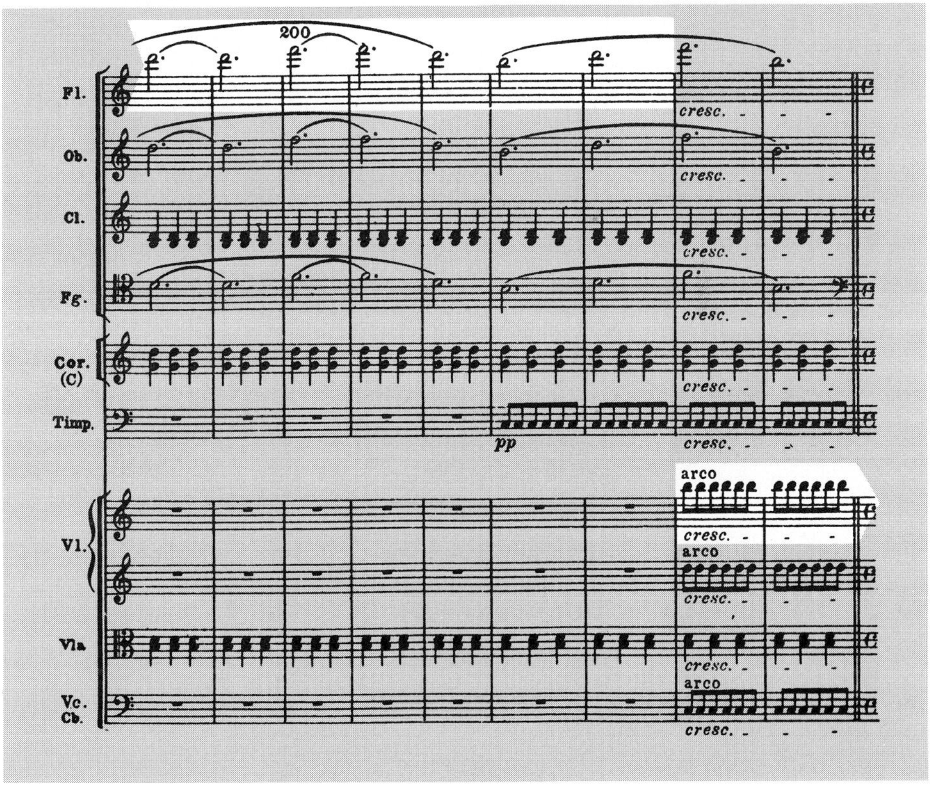

200

Fl. *cresc.*

Ob. *cresc.*

Cl. *cresc.*

Fg. *cresc.*

Cor. (C) *cresc.*

Timp. *pp* *cresc.*

Vl. arco *cresc.* arco *cresc.*

Vla *cresc.*

Vc. Cb. arco *cresc.*

Allegro. (𝅗𝅥 = 84)
210
Picc.
Fl.
Ob.
Cl.
Fg.
Cfg.
Cor. (C)
Tr. (C)
Tbni.
Timp.
Vl.
Vla.
Vc.
Cb.
ff
zu 2

Picc.
Fl.
Ob.
Cl.
Fg.
Cfg.
Cor. (C)
Tr. (C)
Tbni.
Timp.
Vl.
Vla.
Vc. Cb.

220
Picc.
Fl.
Ob.
Cl.
Fg.
Cfg.
Cor
(C)
Tr.
(C)
Tbni.
Timp.
Vl.
Vla.
Vc.
Cb.

Picc.
Fl.
zu 2
Ob.
Cl.
Fg.
Cfg.
Cor.
(C)
Tr.
(C)
Tbni.
Timp.
Vl.
Vla.
Vc.
Cb

230
Ficc.
Fl.
Ob.
Cl.
Fg.
Cfg.
Cor. (C)
Tr. (C)
Tbni.
Timp.
Vl.
Vla.
Vc.
Cb.
zu 2
zu 2

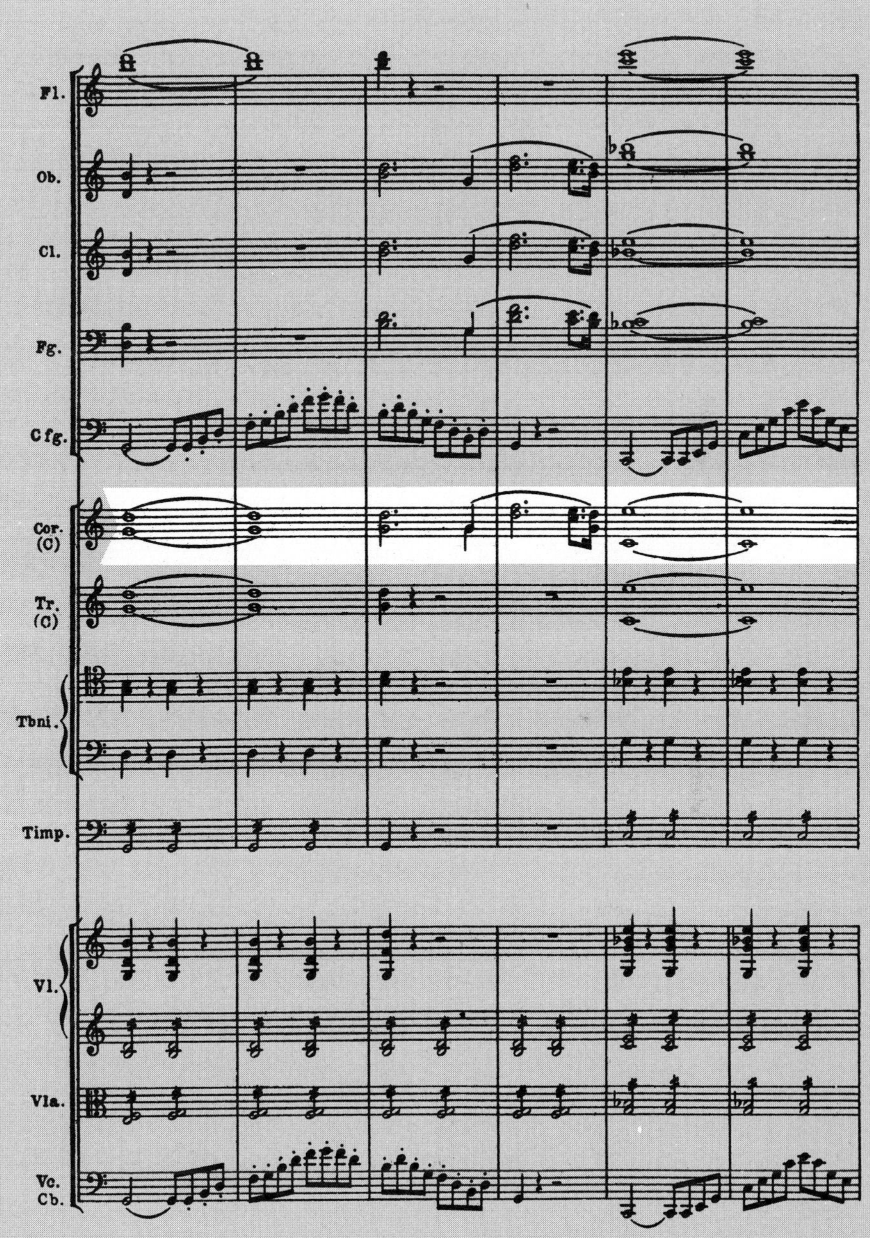
Fl.
Ob.
Cl.
Fg.
Cfg.
Cor. (C)
Tr. (C)
Tbni.
Timp.
Vl.
Vla.
Vc. Cb.

240
Picc.
Fl.
zu 2
Ob.
zu 2
Cl.
Fg.
zu 2
Cfg.
Cor. (C)
Tr. (C)
Tbni.
Timp.
Vl.
Vls.
Vc. Cb.

250
Picc.
Fl.
Ob.
Cl.
zu 2
Fg.
Cfg.
Cor. (C)
Tr. (C)
Tbni.
Timp.
Vl.
Vla.
Vc. Cb.

Fl.
Ob.
Cl.
Fg.
Cfg.
Cor. (C)
Tr. (C)
Tbni.
Timp.
Vl.
Vla.
Vc.
Cb.

p

260
Picc.
Fl.
Ob.
Cl.
Fg.
Cfg.
Cor. (C)
Tr. (C)
Tbni.
Timp.
Vl.
Vla.
Vc.
Cb.
cresc.
f
p
1.
p dolce

Fl.
Ob.
Cl.
Fg.
Cfg.
Cor (C)
Tr. (C)
Tbni.
Timp.
Vl.
Vla.
Vc.
Cb.
1.
pp
p dolce
cresc.
ff
f

270
Picc.
Fl.
zu 2
Ob.
zu 2
Cl.
zu 2
Fg.
Cfg.
Cor. (C)
Tr. (C)
Tbni.
Timp.
Vl.
Vla.
Vc. Cb

Picc.
Fl.
1.
p dolce
Ob.
1.
fp dolce
fp
fp
Cl.
fp dolce
fp
Fg.
fp dolce
fp
fp
Cfg.
Cor.
(C)
p dolce
fp
Tr.
(C)
Timp.
Vl.
p
p
f
p
fp
fp
Vla.
f
fp
fp
Vc.
Cb.

280
zu 2
Fl.
Ob.
Cl.
Fg.
Cfg.
Cor. (C)
Tr. (C)
Tbni.
Timp.
Vl.
Vla.
Vc. Cb.

290
Fl.
Ob.
Cl.
Fg.
Cfg.
Cor (C)
Tr. (C)
Tbni.
Timp.
Vl.
Vla.
Vc. Cb.
sf
più f
ff
tr

Fl.
Ob.
Cl.
Fg.
C.fg.
Cor (C)
Tr. (C)
Tbni.
Timp.
Vl.
Vla.
Vc.
Cb.
sf
f
1.

300
Fl.
Ob.
Cl.
Fg.
Cfg.
Cor. (C)
Tr. (C)
Tbni.
Timp
Vl.
Vla.
Vc.
Cb.
più f
sf

Fl.
Ob.
Cl.
zu 2
Fg.
Cfg.
Cor. (C)
Tr. (C)
Tbni.
Timp.
Vl.
Vla.
Vc. Cb.
ff
sf

310
Fl.
Ob.
Cl.
Fg.
C fg.
Cor.
(C)
Tr.
(C)
Tbni.
Timp.
Vl.
Vla.
Vc.
Cb.
sf

320
Fl.
1.
p dolce cresc. poco a poco
Ob.
Cl.
1.
p cresc. poco a poco
Fg.
zu 2
ff
1.
p
cresc.
Cfg.
Cor. (C)
zu 2
p dolce
cresc. poco a poco
Tr. (C)
Tbni.
Timp.
Vl.
p cresc. poco a poco
Vla.
p cresc. poco a poco
Vc. Cb.

Picc.
p cresc.
f
Fl.
f
Ob.
1.
p cresc.
f
Cl.
f
Fg.
f
C.fg.
f
Cor. (C)
f
Tr. (C)
p cresc.
f
Tbni.
f
f
Timp.
tr
p cresc.
f
Vl.
f
p cresc.
f
Vla.
f
Vc.
p cresc. poco a poco
f
Cb.
cresc.
f

330
Picc.
Fl.
Ob.
Cl.
Fg.
Cfg.
Cor. (C)
Tr. (C)
Tbni.
Timp.
Vl.
Vla.
Vc. Cb.
p
f

340
Picc.
p dolce
cresc. poco a poco
Fl.
1.
p cresc. poco a poco
p cresc.
Ob.
1.
p dolce
p cresc. poco a poco
Fg.
p cresc.
Cfg.
zu 2
Cor. (C)
p dolce
cresc. poco a poco
Vl.
p cresc. poco a poco
p cresc. poco a poco
Vla.
p cresc. poco a poco
Vc.
p cresc. poco a poco
Cb.
p cresc.

tr
Picc.
Fl.
zu 2
Ob.
Cl.
cresc.
Fg.
Cfg.
Cor. (C)
Tr. (C)
p cresc.
Tbni.
Timp.
p cresc.
Vl.
Vla
Vc.
Cb.

350
Sempre
Picc
Fl.
Ob.
Cl.
Fg.
Cfg.
Cor. (C)
Tr. (C)
Tbni.
Timp.
Vl.
Vla.
Vc. Cb.
1.
zu 2
zu 2
p
cresc. poco a poco

più allegro
360
Presto (o = 112.)
Picc.
Fl.
Ob.
Cl.
Fg.
zu 2
Cfg.
p
cresc.
fp
Cor. (C)
zu 2
Tr. (C)
zu 2
p
cresc.
Timp.
p
cresc.
f
Vl.
fp
Vla.
fp
Vc. Cb
fp

370
Fl.
1.
fp
Ob.
1.
fp
Cl.
fp
Fg.
1.
fp
Cfg.
fp
Cor.
(C)
f
Tr.
(C)
f
Timp.
f
Vl.
fp
Vla
fp
Vc.
Cb.
fp

380
Fl.
Ob.
Cl.
Fg.
Cfg.
Cor. (C)
Tr. (C)
Timp.
Vl.
Vla.
Vc. Cb.
fp
f
cresc.
p cresc.

390
Picc.
cresc.
f
ff
Fl.
zu 2
Ob.
Cl.
Fg.
Cfg.
Cor. (C)
Tr. (C)
Tbni.
Timp.
Vl.
Vla.
Vc. Cb.

Picc.
Fl.
Ob.
Cl.
Fg.
zu 2
C fg.
Cor. (C)
zu 2
Tr. (C)
zu 2
Timp.
Vl.
Vla.
Vc. Cb.

400
Picc.
Fl.
Ob.
zu 2
Cl.
zu 2
Fg.
Cfg.
Cor (C)
Tr. (C)
Timp.
tr
Vl.
Vla.
Vc. Cb.

410
Picc.
Fl.
Ob.
Cl.
Fg.
C fg.
Cor. (C)
Tr. (C)
Tbni.
Timp.
Vl.
Vla.
Vc. Cb.
sempre ff

420
Picc
Fl.
zu 2
Ob.
zu 2
Cl.
Fg.
zu 2
Cfg.
Cor. (C)
Tr. (C)
zu 2
Tbni.
Timp.
Vl.
Vla.
Vc. Cb.

430
Picc.
Fl.
Ob.
Cl.
Fg.
Cfg.
Cor. (C)
Tr. (C)
Tbni.
Timp.
Vl.
Vla.
Vc. Cb.

440
Picc.
Fl.
Ob.
Cl.
Fg.
zu 2
Cfg.
Cor. (C)
Tr. (C)
Tbni.
Timp.
tr
Vl.
Vla.
Vc. Cb.

Appendix A

Reading an Orchestral Score

CLEFS

The music for some instruments is written in clefs other than the familiar treble and bass. In the following example, middle C is shown in the four clefs used in orchestral scores:

The *alto clef* is primarily used in viola parts. The *tenor clef* is employed for cello, bassoon, and trombone parts when these instruments play in a high register.

TRANSPOSING INSTRUMENTS

The music for some instruments is customarily written at a pitch level different from their actual sound. The following list, with examples, shows the transposing instruments in these scores and the degree of transposition.

Instrument	*Transposition*	*Written Note*	*Actual Sound*
Piccolo	sound an octave higher than written	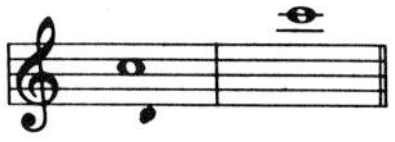	
Trumpet in F	sound a fourth higher than written	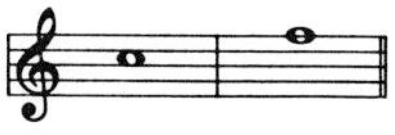	
Trumpet in D	sound a major second higher than written	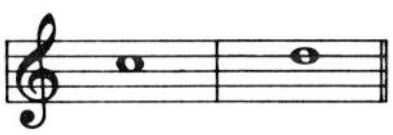	

Instrument	*Transposition*	*Written Note*	*Actual Sound*
Clarinet in B♭ Horn in B♭ alto	sound a major second lower than written		
Horn in G	sound a fourth lower than written		
Horn in F	sound a fifth lower than written		
Horn in E♭	sound a major sixth lower than written		
Contrabassoon Horn in C Double bass	sound an octave lower than written		

Appendix B

Instrumental Names and Abbreviations

The following tables set forth the English, Italian, German, and French names used for the various musical instruments in these scores, and their respective abbreviations. A brief note explains the special terminology used in the scores for the Baroque works, and a table of the foreign-language names for scale degrees and modes is also provided.

Woodwinds

English	*Italian*	*German*	*French*
Piccolo (Picc.)	Flauto piccolo (Fl. Picc.)	Kleine Flöte (Kl. Fl.)	Petite flûte
Flute (Fl.)	Flauto (Fl.); Flauto grande (Fl. gr.)	Grosse Flöte (Fl. gr.)	Flûte (Fl.)
Oboe (Ob.)	Oboe (Ob.)	Hoboe (Hb.); Oboe (Ob.)	Hautbois (Hb.)
English horn (E. H.)	Corno inglese (C. ingl.)	Englisches Horn (E. H.)	Cor anglais (C. A.)
Clarinet (C., Cl., Clt.)	Clarinetto (Cl.)	Klarinette (Kl.)	Clarinette (Cl.)
Bass clarinet (B. Cl.)	Clarinetto basso (Cl. b., Cl. basso, Clar. basso)	Bass Klarinette (Bkl.)	Clarinette basse (Cl. bs.)
Bassoon (Bsn., Bssn.)	Fagotto (Fag., Fg.)	Fagott (Fag.)	Basson (Bssn.)
Contrabassoon (C. Bsn.)	Contrafagotto (Cfg., Cont. F.)	Kontrafagott (Kfg.)	Contrebasson (C. bssn.)

Brass

English	*Italian*	*German*	*French*
French horn (Hr., Hn.)	Corno (Cor.)	Horn (Hr.) [*pl.* Hörner]	Cor; Cor à pistons
Trumpet (Tpt., Trp., Tr.)	Tromba (Tr.)	Trompete (Tr.)	Trompette (Tr.)
Cornet	Cornetto	Kornett	Cornet à pistons (C. à p., Pist.)
Trombone (Tr., Tbe., Trb., Trbe.)	Trombone [*pl.* Tromboni (Tbni., Trni.)]	Posaune (Ps.)	Trombone (Tr.)
Tuba (Tb.)	Tuba (Tb.)	Tuba (Tb.) [*also* Basstuba (Btb.)]	Tuba (Tb.)

Percussion

English	*Italian*	*German*	*French*
Percussion (Perc.)			Batterie (Batt.)
Kettledrums (K. D.)	Timpani (Timp., Tp.)	Pauken (Pk.)	
Snare drum (S. D.)	Tamburo militare (Tamb. milit.)		Tambour militaire (Tamb. milit.); Caisse claire (C. cl.)
Bass drum	Gran cassa (Gr. Cassa, Gr. C., G. C.)		Grosse caisse (Gr. c.)
Glockenspiel	Campanelli (Cmp.)		
Chimes	Campane (Cmp.)		
Cymbals (Cym., Cymb.)	Piatti (Piat.)		
Antique cymbals			Cymbales antiques
Tambourine (Tamb.)	Tamburino (Tamb.)		Tambour de Basque (T. de B., Tamb. de Basque)
Triangle (Trgl.)	Triangolo (Trgl.)		
Tam-Tam (Tam-T.)			

Strings

English	*Italian*	*German*	*French*
Violin (V., Vl., Vln.)	Violino (V., Vl., Vln.)	Violine (V., Vl., Vln.)	Violon (V., Vl., Vln.)
Viola (Va., Vl., Vas.)	Viola (Va.) [*pl.* Viole (Vle.)]	Bratsche (Br.)	Alto (A.)
Cello (Vc.)	Violoncello (Vc., Vlc.)	Violoncell (Vc.)	Violoncelle (Vc.)
Double bass (D. Bs.)	Contrabasso (Cb., C. B.) [*pl.* Contra-bassi or Bassi (C. Bassi, Bi.)]	Kontrabass (Kb.)	Contre basse (C. B.)

Other Instruments

English	*Italian*	*German*	*French*
Harp (Hp.)	Arpa	Harfe	Harpe (Hp.)
Piano	Pianoforte (P.-f.)	Klavier	Piano
Harpsichord	Cembalo		Clavecin
Organ (Org.)	Organo		

Note on Baroque Instruments

In the Baroque works, certain older instruments, not used in the modern orchestra, were required by the composers; the following list defines these terms.

Continuo (*Con.*) A method of indicating an accompanying part by the bass notes only, together with figures designating the chords to be played above them. In general practice, the chords are played on a harpsichord or organ, while a viola da gamba or cello doubles the bass notes.

and a bass lute (as continuo instruments).

Corno. Although this term usually designates the French horn, in the Bach Cantata No. 140 it refers to the *cornett,* or *zink*—a wooden trumpet without valves.

Taille (Tail.). In the Bach Cantata No. 140, this term indicates a tenor oboe or English horn.

Violino piccolo. A small violin, tuned a fourth higher than the standard violin.

Violone (V.). A string instrument intermediate in size between the cello and the double bass. (In modern performances, the double bass is commonly substituted.)

Names of Scale Degrees and Modes

Scale Degrees

English	*Italian*	*German*	*French*
C	do	C	ut
C-sharp	do diesis	Cis	ut dièse
D-flat	re bemolle	Des	ré bémol
D	re	D	ré
D-sharp	re diesis	Dis	ré dièse
E-flat	mi bemolle	Es	mi bémol
E	mi	E	mi
E-sharp	mi diesis	Eis	mi dièse
F-flat	fa bemolle	Fes	fa bémol
F	fa	F	fa
F-sharp	fa diesis	Fis	fa dièse
G-flat	sol bemolle	Ges	sol bémol
G	sol	G	sol
G-sharp	sol diesis	Gis	sol dièse
A-flat	la bemolle	As	la bémol
A	la	A	la
A-sharp	la diesis	Ais	la dièse
B-flat	si bemolle	B	si bémol
B	si	H	si
B-sharp	si diesis	His	si dièse
C-flat	do bemolle	Ces	ut bémol

Modes

major	maggiore	dur	majeur
minor	minore	moll	mineur

Appendix C

Glossary of Musical Terms Used in the Scores

The following glossary is not intended to be a complete dictionary of musical terms, nor is knowledge of all these terms necessary to follow the scores in this book. However, as the listener gains experience in following scores, he will find it useful and interesting to understand the composer's directions with regard to tempo, dynamics, and methods of performance.

In most cases, compound terms have been broken down in the glossary and defined separately, as they often recur in varying combinations. A few common foreign-language particles are included in addition to the musical terms. Note that names and abbreviations for instruments and for scale degrees will be found in Appendix B.

a. The phrases *a 2, a 3* (etc.) indicate that the part is to be played in unison by 2, 3 (etc.) players; when a simple number (1., 2., etc.) is placed over a part, it indicates that only the first (second, etc.) player in that group should play.

accompagnato (accomp.). In a continuo part, this indicates that the chord-playing instrument resumes (cf. *tasto solo*).

accordez. Tune the instrument as specified.

accelerando. Growing faster.

adagio. Slow, leisurely.

ad libitum (ad lib.). An indication giving the performer liberty to: (1) vary from strict tempo; (2) include or omit the part of some voice or instrument; (3) include a cadenza of his own invention.

affettuoso. With emotion.

affrettando (affrett.). Hastening a little.

agitato. Agitated, excited.

agitazione. Agitation.

allargando (allarg.). Growing broader.

allegretto. A moderately fast tempo (between allegro and andante).

allegro. A rapid tempo (between allegretto and presto).

allmählich. Gradually.

alto, altus (A.). The deeper of the two main divisions of women's (or boys') voices.

andante. A moderately slow tempo (between adagio and allegretto).

andantino. A moderately slow tempo.

an dem Griffbrett (a.d.G.). Played on the fingerboard.

anima. Spirit, animation.

animando. With increasing animation.

animato, animé. Animated.

a piacere. The execution of the passage is left to the performer's discretion.

appassionato. Impassioned.
arco. Played with the bow.
armonioso. Harmoniously.
arpeggiando (arpeg.). Played in harp style, i.e. the notes of the chord played in quick succession rather than simultaneously.
assai. Very.
a tempo. At the (basic) tempo.
attacca. Begin what follows without pausing.
auf dem. On the (as in *auf dem G*, on the G string).

bacchetto di tamburo militare (bacch. di tamb. milit.). Snare-drum sticks.
baguettes d'éponge. Sponge-headed drumsticks.
bass, basso, bassus (B.). The lowest male voice.
belebend. With increasing animation.
belebt. Animated.
ben. Very.
bestimmt. Energetic.
bewegt. Agitated.
bewegter. More agitated.
bien. Very.
Bogen (Bog.). Played with the bow.
bouché. Muted.
bravura. Boldness.
breit. Broadly.
brio. Spirit, vivacity.

cadenza. An extended passage for solo instrument in free, improvisatory style.
calma, calmo. Calm, calmly.
cantabile (cant.). In a singing style.
canto. Voice (as in *col canto*, a direction for the accompaniment to follow the solo part in tempo and expression).
cantus. An older designation for the highest part in a vocal work.
changez. Change (usually an instruction to re-tune a string or an instrument).
circa (ca.). About, approximately.
col, coll'. With the.
come prima. As at first; as previously.
con. With.
contratenor (CT.). In medieval polyphonic music, a voice part in the same range as the tenor.
corda. String; for example, *seconda (2a) corda* is the second string (the A string on the violin).
coro. Chorus.
coulisse. Wings (of a theater).
court. Short, staccato.
crescendo (cresc.). An increase in volume.
cuivré. Played with a harsh, blaring tone.
cupo. Dark, veiled.

da capo (D.C.). Repeat from the beginning.
dal segno. Repeat from the sign.
dans. In.
début. Beginning.
decrescendo (decresc., decr.). A decreasing of volume.
détaché. With a broad, vigorous bow stroke, each note bowed singly.
diminuendo (dim., dimin.). A decreasing of volume.
distinto. Distinct, clear.
divisés, divisi (div.). Divided; indicates that the instrumental group should be divided into two parts to play the passage in question.
dolce. Sweetly and softly.
dolcemente. Sweetly.
dolcissimo (dolciss.). Very sweetly.
doux. Sweetly.

e. And.
en animant. Becoming more animated.
enchainez. Continue to the next material without pause.

en dehors. With emphasis.
espansione. Expansion, broadening.
espressione intensa. Intense expression.
espressivo (espress., espr.). Expressively.
et. And.
etwas. Somewhat, rather.
expressif. Expressively.

fiero. Fiercely.
fine. End, close.
flutter-tongue. A special tonguing technique for wind instruments, producing a rapid trill-like sound.
forte (f). Loud.
fortissimo (ff). Very loud (*fff* indicates a still louder dynamic).
forza. Force.
fuga. Fugue.
fuoco. Fire, spirit.

geteilt (get.). Divided; indicates that the instrumental group should be divided into two parts to play the passage in question.
giusto. Moderately.
gli altri. The others.
glissando (gliss.). Rapid scales produced by running the fingers over all the strings.
gradamente. Gradually.
grande. Large, great.
grande taille. Large size.
grave. Slow, solemn.
gut gehalten. Well sustained.

harmonic (harm.). A flute-like sound (produced on a string instrument by lightly touching the string with the finger instead of pressing it down).

jeté. With a bouncing motion of the bow.
jusqu'à la fin. To the end.

langsam. Slow.
langsamer. Slower.
langueur. Languor.
largamente. Broadly.
larghetto. Slightly faster than largo.
largo. A very slow tempo.
languente. Languishing.
lebhaft. Lively.
legatissimo. A more forceful indication of *legato.*
legato. Performed without any perceptible interruption between notes.
légèrement. Lightly.
leggiero (legg.). Light and graceful.
legno. The wood of the bow (*col legno tratto,* bowed with the wood; *col legno battuto,* tapped with the wood).
lent. Slowly.
lentamente. Slowly.
lento. A slow tempo (between andante and largo).
l.h. Abbreviation for "left hand."
lieblich. Lovely, sweetly.
loco. Indicates a return to the written pitch, following a passage played an octave higher or lower than written.
lontano. Far away, from a distance.
lunga. Long, sustained.
lungo silenzio. A long pause.

ma. But.
mässig. Moderate.
maestoso. Majestic.
manual. A keyboard played with the hands (as distinct from the pedal keyboard on an organ).
marcatissimo. With very marked emphasis.
marcato (marc.). Marked, with emphasis.
marcia. March.
marqué. Marked, with emphasis.
même. Same.
meno. Less.
mezza voce. With half the voice power.
mezzo forte (mf). Moderately loud.

mezzo piano (mp). Moderately soft.
minore. In the minor mode.
M. M. Metronome; followed by an indication of the setting for the correct tempo.
modéré. At a moderate tempo.
modo ordinario (ordin.). In the usual way (usually cancelling an instruction to play using some special technique).
molto. Very, much.
morendo. Dying away.
mormorato. Murmured.
mosso. Rapid.
motetus. In medieval polyphonic music, a voice part above the tenor; generally, the first additional part to be composed.
moto. Motion.
mouvement (mouvt.). Tempo.
muta. Change the tuning of the instrument as specified.

nachgebend. Becoming slower.
nach und nach. More and more.
naturalezza. A natural, unaffected manner.
naturel. In the usual way, (generally cancelling an instruction to play using some special technique).
non. Not.

octava (8va). Octave; if not otherwise qualified, means the notes marked should be played an octave higher than written.
octava bassa (8va. bassa). Play an octave lower than written.
open. (1) In brass instruments, the opposite of muted; (2) in string instruments, refers to the unstopped string (i.e. sounding at its full length).
ordinario (ordin.) In the usual way (generally cancelling an instruction to play using some special technique).
ossia. An alternative (usually easier) version of a passage.
ôtez vite les sourdines, Remove the mutes quickly.

P In the Schoenberg Concerto, principal parts are marked at their beginning with a "P," and at the end with a right-angled bracket.
parlante. Sung in a manner resembling speech.
Paukenschlägel. Timpani stick.
pedal (ped., P.) (1) In piano music, indicates that the damper pedal should be depressed; an asterisk indicates the point of release (brackets below the music are also used to indicate pedalling) (2) On an organ, the pedals are a keyboard played with the feet.
perdendosi. Gradually dying away.
pesante. Heavily.
peu. Little, a little.
pianissimo (pp). Very soft (*ppp* indicates a still softer dynamic).
piano (p). Soft.
più. More.
pizzicato (pizz.). The string plucked with the finger.
plus. More.
pochissimo (pochiss.). Very little, a very little.
poco. Little, a little.
poco a poco. Little by little.
ponticello (pont.). The bridge (of a string instrument).
portando la voce. With a smooth sliding of the voice from one tone to the next.
position naturel (pos. nat.). In the normal position (usually cancelling an instruction to play using some special technique).
praeludium. Prelude.
premier mouvement (1er mouvt.). At the original tempo.
préparez le ton. Prepare the instrument

to play in the key named.
presto. A very quick tempo (faster than allegro).
principale (pr.) Principal, solo.
punta d'arco. Played with the top of the bow.

quasi niente. Almost nothing, i.e. as softly as possible.
quasi trill (tr.). In the manner of a trill.
quintus. An older designation for the fifth part in a vocal work.

rallentando (rall., rallent.). Growing slower.
recitative (recit.). A vocal style designed to imitate and emphasize the natural inflections of speech.
retenu. Held back.
rigore di tempo. Strictness of tempo.
ritardando (rit., ritard.) Gradually slackening in speed.
ritenuto. Immediate reduction of speed.
rubato. A certain elasticity and flexibility of tempo, consisting of slight accelerandos and ritardandos according to the requirements of the musical expression.
ruhig. Quietly.
rullante. Rolling.

S In the Schoenberg Concerto subordinate parts (less important than principal parts, but more important than the accompaniment) are marked at their beginning with an "S," and at the end with a right-angled bracket.
sans timbre. Without snares.
scena vuota. Empty stage.
scherzando (scherz.). Playful.
schmachtend. Languishing.
schnell. Fast.
schneller. Faster.
secco. Dry, simple.
seconda volta. The second time.
segue. (1) Continue to the next movement without pausing; (2) continue in the same manner.
sehr. Very.
semplicità. Simplicity.
sempre. Always, continually.
senza. Without.
sforzando, sforzato (sfz, sf). With sudden emphasis.
sfumato. Diminishing and fading away.
simile. In a similar manner.
sino al. Up to the . . . (usually followed by a new tempo marking, or by a dotted line indicating a terminal point).
smorzando (smorz.). Dying away.
solo (s.). Executed by one performer.
sonator. Player (*uno sonator*, one player; *due sonatori*, two players).
soprano (s.). The voice classification with the highest range.
sordino (sord.). Mute.
sostenendo, sostenuto. Sustained.
sotto voce. In an undertone, subdued, under the breath.
sourdine. Mute.
soutenu. Sustained.
spiccato. With a light bouncing motion of the bow.
staccatissimo. Very staccato.
staccato (stacc.) Detached, separated, abruptly disconnected.
stentando, stentato (stent.). Delaying, retarding.
stesso movimento. The same basic pace.
stretto. In a non-fugal composition, indicates a concluding section at an increased speed.
stringendo. Quickening.
subito (sub.). Suddenly, immediately.
sul. On the (as in *sul G*, on the G string).
suono. Sound, tone.
sur. On.

tacet. The instrument or vocal part so marked is silent.

tasto solo. In a continuo part, this indicates that only the string instrument plays; the chord-playing instrument is silent.

tempo primo (tempo I). At the original tempo.

tenor, tenore (T.). (1) The highest male voice; (2) in medieval polyphonic music, the voice part (generally a pre-existent melody) around which the piece was composed.

tenuto (ten.). Held, sustained.

tornando al tempo primo. Returning to the original tempo.

touch. Fingerboard (of a string instrument).

toujours. Always, continually.

tranquillo. Quietly, calmly.

tre corda (t.c.) Release the soft (or *una corda*) pedal of the piano.

tremolo (trem). On string instruments, a quick reiteration of the same tone, produced by a rapid up-and-down movement of the bow; also a rapid alternation between two different notes.

très. Very.

trill (tr.) The rapid alternation of a given note with the diatonic second above it. In a drum part it indicates rapid alternating strokes with two drumsticks.

triplum. In medieval polyphonic music, a voice part above the tenor; generally composed after the motetus.

troppo. Too much.

tutti. Literally, "all"; usually means all the instruments in a given category as distinct from a solo part.

una corda (u.c.). With the "soft" pedal of the piano depressed.

unison (unis.). The same notes or melody played by several instruments at the same pitch. Often used to emphasize that a phrase is not to be divided among several players.

vivace. Quick, lively.

vivo. Lively.

voce. Voice (as in *colla voce,* a direction for the accompaniment to follow the solo part in tempo and expression).

wie oben. As above, as before.

wüthend. Furiously.

zart. Tenderly, delicately.

Zeitmass. Tempo.

zu. The phrases *zu 2, zu 3* (etc.) indicate that the part is to be played in unison by 2, 3 (etc.) players.

zurückhaltend. Slackening in speed.

Index of Forms and Genres

A roman numeral following a title indicates a movement within the work named.